Maple 7
Programming Guide

M. B. Monagan K. O. Geddes K. M. Heal
G. Labahn S. M. Vorkoetter J. McCarron
P. DeMarco

D1361521

Waterloo Maple Inc.
57 Erb Street West
Waterloo, ON N2L 6C2
Canada

ISBN 1-894511-14-X

Contents

1   Introduction

As a Maple user, you may fall into any number of categories. You may have used Maple only interactively. You may already have written many of your own programs. Even more fundamentally, you may or may not have programmed in another computer language before attempting your first Maple program. Indeed, you may have used Maple for some time without realizing that the same powerful language you regularly use to enter commands is itself a complete programming language.

Writing a Maple program can be very simple. It may only involve putting a `proc()` and an **end proc** around a sequence of commands that you use every day. On the other hand, the limits for writing Maple procedures with various levels of complexity depend only on you. Ninety to ninety-five percent of the thousands of commands in the Maple language are themselves Maple programs. You are free to examine these programs and modify them to suit your needs, or extend them so that Maple can tackle new types of problems. You should be able to write useful Maple programs in a few hours, rather than the few days or weeks that it often takes with other languages. This efficiency is partly due to the fact that Maple is *interactive*; this interaction makes it easier to test and correct programs.

Coding in Maple does not require expert programming skills. Unlike traditional programming languages, the Maple language contains many powerful commands which allow you to perform complicated tasks with a single command instead of pages of code. For example, the **solve** command computes the solution to a system of equations. Maple comes with a large library of routines, including graphical display primitives, so putting useful programs together from its powerful building blocks is easy.

The aim of this chapter is to provide basic knowledge for proficiently writing Maple code. To learn quickly, read until you encounter some example programs and then write your own variations. This chapter includes many examples along with exercises for you to try. Some of them highlight

1

important differences between Maple and traditional computer languages, which lack symbolic computation capability. Thus, this chapter is also important for those who have written programs in other languages.

This chapter informally presents the most essential elements of the Maple language. You can study the details, exceptions, and options in the other chapters, as the need arises. The examples of basic programming tasks for you to do come with pointers to other chapters and help pages that give further details.

1.1   Getting Started

Maple runs on many different platforms. You can use it through a specialized worksheet interface, or directly through interactive commands typed at a plain terminal. In either case, when you start a Maple session, you will see a Maple prompt character.

>

The prompt character > indicates that Maple is waiting for input.

Throughout this book, the command-line (or one-dimensional) input format is used. For information on how to toggle between *Maple notation* and *standard math notation*, please refer to the first chapter of the *Getting Started Guide*.

Your input can be as simple as a single expression. A command is followed immediately by its result.

> 103993/33102;

$$\frac{103993}{33102}$$

Ordinarily, you complete the command with a semicolon, then press ENTER. Maple echoes the result—in this case an exact rational number—to the worksheet or to the terminal and the particular interface in use, displaying the result as closely to standard mathematical notation as possible.[1]

You may enter commands entirely on one line (as in the previous example) or stretch them across several lines.

---

[1] section 10.6 discusses specific commands to control printing.

```
> 103993
> / 33102
> ;
```

$$\frac{103993}{33102}$$

You can even put the terminating semicolon on a separate line. Nothing evaluates until you complete the command. Maple may, however, parse the command for errors at this stage.

Associate names with results by using the assignment statement, :=.

```
> a := 103993/33102;
```

$$a := \frac{103993}{33102}$$

Once assigned a value in this manner, you can use the name **a** as if it were the value 103993/33102. For example, you can use Maple's `evalf` command to compute an approximation to 103993/33102 divided by 2.

```
> evalf(a/2);
```

$$1.570796326$$

A Maple *program* is essentially just a prearranged group of commands that Maple always carries out together. The simplest way of creating such a Maple program (or procedure) is to encapsulate the sequence of commands that you would have used to carry out the computation interactively. The following is a program corresponding to the above statement.

```
> half := proc(x)
>     evalf(x/2);
> end proc;
```

$$half := \mathbf{proc}(x)\, \mathrm{evalf}(1/2 * x)\, \mathbf{end\ proc}$$

The program takes the input, called **x** within the procedure, and approximates the value of **x** divided by two. Since this is the last calculation done within the procedure, the **half** procedure returns this approximation. Give the name **half** to the procedure using the := notation, just as you would assign a name to any other object. Once you have defined a new procedure, you can use it as a command.

> `half(2/3);`

$$.3333333333$$

> `half(a);`

$$1.570796326$$

> `half(1) + half(2);`

$$1.500000000$$

Merely enclosing the command `evalf(x/2);` between a `proc(...)` and the words **end proc** turns it into a procedure.

Create another program corresponding to the following two statements.

> `a := 103993/33102;`

> `evalf(a/2);`

The procedure needs no input.

```
> f := proc() local a;
>      a := 103993/33102;
>      evalf(a/2);
> end proc;
```

$$f := \mathbf{proc}()$$
$$\mathbf{local}\, a;$$
$$a := 103993/33102\,;\ \mathrm{evalf}(1/2 * a)$$
$$\mathbf{end\ proc}$$

Maple's interpretation of this procedure definition appears immediately after the command lines that created it. Examine it carefully and note the following:

- The *name* of this program (procedure) is **f**.

- The procedure *definition* starts with **proc()**. The empty parenthesis indicate that this procedure does not require any *input data*.

- Semicolons separate the individual commands that make up the procedure. Another semicolon after the words **end proc** signals the end of the procedure definition.

- You see a display of the procedure definition (just as for any other Maple command) only after you complete it with an **end proc** and a semicolon. Even the individual commands that make up the procedure do not display until you complete the entire procedure and enter the last semicolon.

- The *procedure definition* that echoes as the value of the name **f** is equivalent to but not identical to the procedure definition that you entered.

- The **local a;** statement declares **a** as a *local* variable. This means that the variable **a** within the procedure is not the same as the variable **a** outside the procedure. Thus, it does not matter if you use that name for something else. Section 1.1 discusses these further.

Execute the procedure **f**—that is, cause the statements forming the procedure to execute in sequence—by typing its name followed by parentheses. Enclose any input to the procedure, in this case none, between the parentheses.

```
> f();
```

$$1.570796326$$

The execution of a procedure is also referred to as an *invocation* or a procedure *call*.

When you invoke a procedure, Maple executes the statements forming *the procedure body* one at a time. The procedure *returns* the result of the last computed statement as the *value* of the procedure call.

As with ordinary Maple expressions, you can enter procedure definitions with a large degree of flexibility. Individual statements may appear on different lines, or span several lines. You may also place more than one statement on one line, though that can affect readability of your code. You may even put extra semicolons between statements without causing problems. In some instances, you may omit semicolons.[2]

---

[2]For example, the semicolon in the definition of a procedure between the last command and the **end proc** is optional.

Sometimes you may not want Maple to display the result of constructing a complicated procedure definition. To suppress the display, use a colon (:) instead of a semicolon (;) at the end of the definition.

```
> g := proc() local a;
>     a := 103993/33102;
>     evalf(a/2);
> end proc:
```

Sometimes you may find it necessary to examine the body of a procedure long after constructing it. For ordinary named objects in Maple, such as e, defined below, you can obtain the actual value of the name simply by referring to it by name.

```
> e := 3;
```

$$e := 3$$

```
> e;
```

$$3$$

If you try this with the procedure g, Maple displays only the name g instead of its true value. Both procedures and tables potentially contain many subobjects. This model of evaluation, referred to as *last name evaluation*, hides the detail. To obtain the true value of the name g, use the `eval` command, which forces *full evaluation*.

```
> g;
```

$$g$$

```
> eval(g);
```

$$\textbf{proc}()$$
$$\textbf{local } a;$$
$$a := 103993/33102 \, ; \ evalf(1/2 * a)$$
$$\textbf{end proc}$$

To print the body of a Maple library procedure, set the `interface` variable `verboseproc` to 2. See `?interface` for details on `interface` variables.

Locals and Globals

Variables that you use at the interactive level in Maple, that is, not within a procedure body, are called *global variables*.

Variables that can be accessed only from the procedures in which they are declared are called *local variables*. While Maple executes a procedure, a global variable by the same name remains unchanged, no matter what value the local variables assume. This allows you to make temporary assignments inside a procedure without affecting anything else in your session.

The *scope of a variable* refers to the collection of procedures and statements which have access to the value of the variable. With simple (that is, non-nested) procedures in Maple, only two possibilities exist. Either the value of a name is available everywhere (that is, *global*) or only to the statements that form the particular procedure definition (that is, *local*). The more involved rules that apply for nested procedures are outlined in Section 2.2.

To demonstrate the distinction between local and global names, first assign a value to the global (that is, top-level) name b.

```
> b := 2;
```

$$b := 2$$

Next, define two nearly identical procedures: g, explicitly using b as a local variable and h, explicitly using b as a global variable.

```
> g := proc()
>      local b;
>      b := 103993/33102;
>      evalf(b/2);
> end proc:
```

and

```
> h := proc()
>      global b;
>      b := 103993/33102;
>      evalf(b/2);
> end proc:
```

Defining the procedures has no effect on the global value of b. In fact, you can even execute the procedure g (which uses local variables) without affecting the value of b.

```
> g();
```

$$1.570796326$$

Therefore, the value of the global variable **b** is still 2. The procedure **g** made an assignment to the local variable **b** which is different from the global variable of the same name.

```
> b;
```

$$2$$

The effect of using the procedure **h** (which uses *global* variables) is very different.

```
> h();
```

$$1.570796326$$

h changes the global variable **b**, so it is no longer 2. When you invoke **h**, the global variable **b** changes as a *side effect*.

```
> b;
```

$$\frac{103993}{33102}$$

If you do not indicate whether a variable used inside a procedure is local or global, Maple decides on its own and warns you of this. You can always use the `local` or `global` statements to override Maple's choice. However, it is good programming style to declare all variables either local or global.

Inputs, Parameters, Arguments

An important class of variables that you can use in procedure definitions are neither local nor global. These represent the *inputs* to the procedure. *Parameters* or *arguments* are other names for this class.

Procedure arguments are placeholders for the actual values of data that you supply when you invoke the procedure, which may have more than one argument. The following procedure **h** accepts *two* quantities, p and q, and constructs the expression p/q.

```
> k := proc(p,q)
>    p/q;
> end proc:
```

The *arguments* to this procedure are **p** and **q**. That is, **p** and **q** are place-holders for the actual *inputs* to the procedure.

```
> k(103993,33102);
```

$$\frac{103993}{33102}$$

Maple considers floating-point values to be approximations, rather than exact expressions. Floating-point expressions compute immediately.

```
> k( 23, 0.56);
```

$$41.07142857$$

In addition to support for exact and floating-point approximate numbers and symbols, Maple provides direct support for *complex* numbers. By default, Maple uses the capital letter I to represent the imaginary unit, $\sqrt{-1}$.

```
> (2 + 3*I)^2;
```

$$-5 + 12\,I$$

```
> k(2 + 3*I, %);
```

$$\frac{2}{13} - \frac{3}{13}\,I$$

```
> k(1.362, 5*I);
```

$$-.2724000000\,I$$

Suppose you want to write a procedure which calculates the norm, $\sqrt{a^2 + b^2}$, of a complex number $z = a + bi$. You can make such a procedure in several ways. The procedure **abnorm** takes the real and imaginary parts, a and b, as separate parameters.

```
> abnorm := proc(a,b)
>    sqrt(a^2+b^2);
> end proc;
```

$$abnorm := \mathbf{proc}(a,\, b)\, \mathrm{sqrt}(a^2 + b^2)\, \mathbf{end\ proc}$$

Now **abnorm** can calculate the norm of $2 + 3i$.

```
> abnorm(2, 3);
```

$$\sqrt{13}$$

You could instead use the **Re** and **Im** commands to pick out the *real* and *imaginary* parts, respectively, of a complex number. Hence, you can also calculate the norm of a complex number in the following manner.

```
> znorm := proc(z)
>    sqrt( Re(z)^2 + Im(z)^2 );
> end proc;
```

$$znorm := \mathbf{proc}(z)\, \mathrm{sqrt}(\Re(z)^2 + \Im(z)^2)\, \mathbf{end\ proc}$$

The norm of $2 + 3i$ is still $\sqrt{13}$.

```
> znorm( 2+3*I );
```

$$\sqrt{13}$$

Finally, you can also compute the norm by re-using the **abnorm** procedure. The **abznorm** procedure below uses **Re** and **Im** to pass information to **abnorm** in the form it expects.

```
> abznorm := proc(z)
>    local r, i;
>    r := Re(z);
>    i := Im(z);
>    abnorm(r, i);
> end proc;
```

$$abznorm := \mathbf{proc}(z)$$
$$\mathbf{local}\, r,\, i;$$
$$r := \Re(z)\,;\, i := \Im(z)\,;\, \mathrm{abnorm}(r,\, i)$$
$$\mathbf{end\ proc}$$

Use **abznorm** to calculate the norm of $2 + 3i$.

```
> abznorm( 2+3*I );
```

$$\sqrt{13}$$

If you do not specify enough information for Maple to calculate the norm, **abznorm** returns a symbolic formula. Here Maple treats x and y

as complex numbers. If they were real numbers, then $\Re(x + i\,y)$ would simplify to x.

```
> abznorm( x+y*I );
```

$$\sqrt{\Re(x + I\,y)^2 + \Im(x + I\,y)^2}$$

Many Maple commands return unevaluated in such cases. Thus, you might alter `abznorm` to return `abznorm(x+y*I)` in the above example. Later examples in this book show how to give your own procedures this behavior.

1.2   Basic Programming Constructs

This section describes the programming constructs you require to get started with real programming tasks. It covers assignment statements, `for` loops and `while` loops, conditional statements (`if` statements), and the use of local and global variables.

The Assignment Statement

Use assignment statements to associate names with computed values. They have the following form.

```
variable := value ;
```

This syntax assigns the name on the left-hand side of `:=` to the computed value on the right-hand side. You have seen this statement used in many of the earlier examples.

The use of `:=` here is similar to the assignment statement in programming languages, such as Pascal. Other programming languages, such as C and Fortran, use `=` for assignments. Maple does not use `=` for assignments, since it is such a natural choice for representing mathematical equations.

If you want to write a procedure called `plotdiff` which plots an expression $f(x)$ together with its derivative $f'(x)$ on the interval $[a, b]$, you can accomplish this task by computing the derivative of $f(x)$ with the `diff` command and then plotting both $f(x)$ and $f'(x)$ on the same interval with the `plot` command.

```
> y := x^3 - 2*x + 1;
```

$$y := x^3 - 2x + 1$$

Find the derivative of y with respect to x.

```
> yp := diff(y, x);
```

$$yp := 3x^2 - 2$$

Plot y and yp together.

```
> plot( [y, yp], x=-1..1 );
```

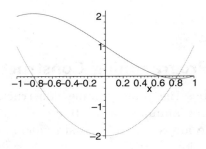

The following procedure combines this sequence of steps.

```
> plotdiff := proc(y,x,a,b)
>      local yp;
>      yp := diff(y,x);
>      plot( [y, yp], x=a..b );
> end proc;
```

$$plotdiff := \mathbf{proc}(y, x, a, b)$$
$$\mathbf{local}\ yp;$$
$$yp := \mathrm{diff}(y, x)\,; \mathrm{plot}([y, yp], x = a..b)$$
$$\mathbf{end\ proc}$$

The procedure name is `plotdiff`. It has four parameters: y, the expression it differentiates; x, the name of the variable it uses to define the expression; and a and b, the beginning and the end of the interval over which it generates the plot. The procedure returns a Maple plot object which you can either display, or use in further plotting routines.

By specifying that yp is a local variable, you ensure that its usage in the procedure does not clash with any other usage of the variable that you may have made elsewhere in the current session.

To use the procedure, simply invoke it with appropriate arguments. Plot $\cos(t)$ and its derivative, for t running from 0 to 2π.

```
> plotdiff( cos(t), t, 0, 2*Pi );
```

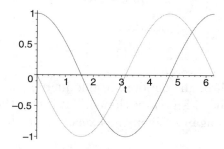

The for Loop

Use looping constructs, such as the **for** loop, to repeat similar actions a number of times. For example, you can calculate the sum of the first five natural numbers in the following way.

```
> total := 0;
```

```
> total := total + 1;
```

```
> total := total + 2;
```

```
> total := total + 3;
```

```
> total := total + 4;
```

```
> total := total + 5;
```

You may instead perform the same calculations by using a **for** loop.

```
> total := 0:
> for i from 1 to 5 do
>     total := total + i;
> end do;
```

$$total := 1$$

$$total := 3$$

$$total := 6$$

$$total := 10$$

$$total := 15$$

For each cycle through the loop, Maple increments the value of i by one and checks whether i is greater than 5. If it is not, then Maple executes the body of the loop again. When the execution of the loop finishes, the value of **total** is 15.

```
> total;
```

15

The following procedure uses a **for** loop to calculate the sum of the first n natural numbers.

```
> SUM := proc(n)
>      local i, total;
>      total := 0;
>      for i from 1 to n do
>          total := total+i;
>      end do;
>      total;
> end proc:
```

The purpose of the **total** statement at the end of **SUM** is to ensure that **SUM** returns the value **total**. Calculate the sum of the first 100 numbers.

```
> SUM(100);
```

5050

The **for** statement is an important part of the Maple language, but the language also provides many more succinct and efficient looping constructs. For example, the command **add**.

```
> add(n, n=1..100);
```

5050

The Conditional Statement

The loop is one of the two most basic constructs in programming. The other basic construct is the **if** or *conditional statement*. It arises in many contexts. For example, you can use the **if** statement to implement an absolute value function.

$$|x| = \begin{cases} x & \text{if } x \geq 0 \\ -x & \text{if } x < 0. \end{cases}$$

Below is a first implementation of **ABS**. Maple executes the **if** statement as follows: If $x < 0$, then Maple calculates $-x$; otherwise it calculates x. In either case, the absolute value of x is the last result that Maple computes and so is the value that **ABS** returns.

The closing words **end if** completes the **if** statement.

```
> ABS := proc(x)
>     if x<0 then
>         -x;
>     else
>         x;
>     end if;
> end proc;
```

$$ABS := \mathbf{proc}(x)\,\mathbf{if}\,x < 0 \ \mathbf{then}\ -x\,\mathbf{else}\,x\,\mathbf{end\ if\ end\ proc}$$

```
> ABS(3); ABS(-2.3);
```

$$3$$

$$2.3$$

Returning Unevaluated   The **ABS** procedure above cannot handle nonnumeric input.

```
> ABS( a );
```

```
Error, (in ABS) cannot evaluate boolean: a < 0
```

The problem is that since Maple knows nothing about **a**, it cannot determine whether **a** is less than zero. In such cases, your procedure should *return unevaluated*; that is, **ABS** should return **ABS(a)**. To achieve this result, consider the following example.

```
> 'ABS'(a);
```

$$\mathrm{ABS}(a)$$

The single quotes tell Maple not to evaluate **ABS**. You can modify the **ABS** procedure by using the `type(..., numeric)` command to test whether x is a number.

```
> ABS := proc(x)
>    if type(x,numeric) then
>          if x<0 then -x else x end if;
>    else
>          'ABS'(x);
>    end if;
> end proc:
```

The above **ABS** procedure contains an example of a *nested* **if** statement, that is, one **if** statement appearing within another. You need an even more complicated nested **if** statement to implement the function

$$\text{hat}(x) = \begin{cases} 0 & \text{if } x \le 0 \\ x & \text{if } 0 < x \le 1 \\ 2 - x & \text{if } 1 < x \le 2 \\ 0 & \text{if } x > 2. \end{cases}$$

Here is a first version of **HAT**.

```
> HAT := proc(x)
>    if type(x, numeric) then
>       if x<=0 then
>          0;
>       else
>          if x<=1 then
>             x;
>          else
>             if x<=2 then
>                2-x;
>             else
>                0;
>             end if;
>          end if;
>       end if;
>    else
>       'HAT'(x);
>    end if;
> end proc:
```

The indentations make it easier to identify which statements belong to which **if** conditions.

A better implementation uses the optional **elif** clause (else if) in the second-level **if** statement.

```
> HAT := proc(x)
>    if type(x, numeric) then
>       if x<=0 then 0;
>       elif x<=1 then x;
>       elif x<=2 then 2-x;
```

```
>        else 0;
>          end if;
>     else
>        'HAT'(x);
>     end if;
> end proc:
```

You may use as many `elif` branches as you need.

Symbolic Transformations   You can improve the ABS procedure from the last section even further. Consider the product ab. Since ab is an unknown, ABS returns unevaluated.

```
> ABS( a*b );
```

$$\text{ABS}(a\,b)$$

However, the absolute value of a product is the product of the absolute values.

$$|ab| \rightarrow |a||b|$$

That is, ABS should map over products.

```
> map( ABS, a*b );
```

$$\text{ABS}(a)\,\text{ABS}(b)$$

You can use the `type(..., '*')` command to test whether an expression is a product and use the **map** command to apply ABS to each operand of the product.

```
> ABS := proc(x)
>     if type(x, numeric) then
>        if x<0 then -x else x end if;
>     elif type(x, '*') then
>        map(ABS, x);
>     else
>        'ABS'(x);
>     end if;
> end proc:
> ABS( a*b );
```

$$\text{ABS}(a)\,\text{ABS}(b)$$

This feature is especially useful if some of the factors are numbers.

```
> ABS( -2*a );
```

$$2\,\mathrm{ABS}(a)$$

You may want to improve **ABS** further so that it can calculate the absolute value of a complex number.

Parameter Type Checking   Sometimes when you write a procedure, you intend it to handle only a certain type of input. Calling the procedure with a different type of input may not make any sense. You can use type checking to verify that the inputs to your procedure are of the correct type. Type checking is especially important for complicated procedures as it helps you to identify mistakes early .

Consider the original implementation of SUM.

```
> SUM := proc(n)
>     local i, total;
>     total := 0;
>     for i from 1 to n do
>         total := total+i;
>     end do;
>     total;
> end proc:
```

Clearly, n should be an integer. If you try to use the procedure on symbolic data, it breaks.

```
> SUM("hello world");
```

```
Error, (in SUM) final value in for loop must be numeric
or character
```

The error message indicates what went wrong inside the **for** statement while trying to execute the procedure. The test in the **for** loop failed because "hello world" is a string, not a number, and Maple could not determine whether to execute the loop. The following implementation of SUM provides a much more informative error message. The type(...,integer) command determines whether n is an integer.

```
> SUM := proc(n)
>     local i,total;
>     if not type(n, integer) then
>         error("input must be an integer");
>     end if;
>     total := 0;
>     for i from 1 to n do  total := total+i  end do;
>     total;
> end proc:
```

Now the error message is more helpful.

```
> SUM("hello world");
```

```
Error, (in SUM) input must be an integer
```

Using **type** to check inputs is such a common task that Maple provides a simple means of declaring the type of an argument to a procedure. For example, you can rewrite the SUM procedure in the following manner. An informative error message helps you to find and correct a mistake quickly.

```
> SUM := proc(n::integer)
>    local i, total;
>    total := 0;
>    for i from 1 to n do  total := total+i  end do;
>    total;
> end proc:
```

```
> SUM("hello world");
```

```
Error, invalid input: SUM expects its 1st argument, n,
to be of type integer, but received hello world
```

Maple understands a large number of types. In addition, you can combine existing types algebraically to form new types, or you can define entirely new types. See **?type**.

The while Loop

The **while** loop is an important type of structure. It has the following structure.

```
while condition do commands end do;
```

Maple tests the *condition* and executes the *commands* inside the loop over and over again until the *condition* fails.

You can use the **while** loop to write a procedure that divides an integer n by two as many times as is possible. The **iquo** and **irem** commands calculate the quotient and remainder, respectively, using integer division.

```
> iquo( 7, 3 );
```

$$2$$

```
> irem( 7, 3 );
```

1

Thus, you can write a `divideby2` procedure in the following manner.

```
> divideby2 := proc(n::posint)
>     local q;
>     q := n;
>     while irem(q, 2) = 0 do
>         q := iquo(q, 2);
>     end do;
>     q;
> end proc:
```

Apply `divideby2` to 32 and 48.

```
> divideby2(32);
```

1

```
> divideby2(48);
```

3

The **while** and **for** loops are both special cases of a more general repetition statement; see section 4.3.

Modularization

When you write procedures, identifying subtasks and writing these as separate procedures is a good idea. Doing so makes your procedures easier to read, and you may be able to reuse some of the subtask procedures in another application.

Consider the following mathematical problem. Suppose you have a positive integer, in this case, forty.

```
> 40;
```

40

Divide the integer by two, as many times as possible; the `divideby2` procedure above does just that for you.

```
> divideby2( % );
```

5

Multiply the result by three and add one.

```
> 3*% + 1;
```

$$16$$

Again, divide by two.

```
> divideby2( % );
```

$$1$$

Multiply by three and add one.

```
> 3*% + 1;
```

$$4$$

Divide.

```
> divideby2( % );
```

$$1$$

The result is 1 again, so from now on you will get 4, 1, 4, 1, ... Mathematicians have conjectured that you always reach the number 1 in this way, no matter with which positive integer you begin. You can study this conjecture, known as *the $3n + 1$ conjecture*, by writing a procedure which calculates how many iterations you need to get to the number 1. The following procedure makes a single iteration.

```
> iteration := proc(n::posint)
>     local a;
>     a := 3*n + 1;
>     divideby2( a );
> end proc:
```

The **checkconjecture** procedure counts the number of iterations.

```
> checkconjecture := proc(x::posint)
>     local count, n;
>     count := 0;
>     n := divideby2(x);
>     while n>1 do
>         n := iteration(n);
>         count := count + 1;
>     end do;
>     count;
```

```
> end proc:
```
You can now check the conjecture for different values of x.

```
> checkconjecture( 40 );
```

$$1$$

```
> checkconjecture( 4387 );
```

$$49$$

You could write **checkconjecture** as one self-contained procedure without references to **iteration** or **divideby2**. But then, you would have to use nested **while** statements, thus making the procedure much harder to read.

Recursive Procedures

Just as you can write procedures that call other procedures, you can also write a procedure that calls itself. This is called *recursive programming*. As an example, consider the Fibonacci numbers, which are defined in the following procedure.

$$f_n = f_{n-1} + f_{n-2} \qquad \text{for } n \geq 2,$$

where $f_0 = 0$, and $f_1 = 1$. The following procedure calculates f_n for any n.

```
> Fibonacci := proc(n::nonnegint)
>     if n<2 then
>         n;
>     else
>         Fibonacci(n-1)+Fibonacci(n-2);
>     end if;
> end proc:
```
Here is a sequence of the first sixteen Fibonacci numbers.

```
> seq( Fibonacci(i), i=0..15 );
```

$$0, 1, 1, 2, 3, 5, 8, 13, 21, 34, 55, 89, 144, 233, 377, 610$$

The **time** command tells you the number of seconds a procedure takes to execute. **Fibonacci** is not very efficient.

```
> time( Fibonacci(20) );
```

$$.450$$

The reason is that **Fibonacci** recalculates the same results over and over again. To find f_{20}, it must find f_{19} and f_{18}; to find f_{19}, it must find f_{18} again and f_{17}; and so on. One solution to this efficiency problem is to tell **Fibonacci** to remember its results. That way, **Fibonacci** only has to calculate f_{18} once. The **remember** option makes a procedure store its results in a *remember table*. Section 2.5 further discusses remember tables.

```
> Fibonacci := proc(n::nonnegint)
>     option remember;
>     if n<2 then
>         n;
>     else
>         Fibonacci(n-1)+Fibonacci(n-2);
>     end if;
> end proc:
```

This version of **Fibonacci** is much faster.

```
> time( Fibonacci(20) );
```

$$0.$$

```
> time( Fibonacci(2000) );
```

$$.133$$

If you use remember tables indiscriminately, Maple may run out of memory. You can often rewrite recursive procedures by using a loop, but recursive procedures are often easier to read. On the other hand, iterative procedures are more efficient. The procedure below is a loop version of **Fibonacci**.

```
> Fibonacci := proc(n::nonnegint)
>     local temp, fnew, fold, i;
>     if n<2 then
>         n;
>     else
>         fold := 0;
>         fnew := 1;
>         for i from 2 to n do
>             temp := fnew + fold;
>             fold := fnew;
>             fnew := temp;
>         end do;
```

```
>        fnew;
>      end if;
> end proc:


> time( Fibonacci(2000) );
```

$$.133$$

When you write recursive procedures, you must weigh the benefits of remember tables against their use of memory. Also, you must make sure that your recursion stops.

The return Statement   A Maple procedure by default returns the result of the last computation within the procedure. You can use the **return** statement to override this behavior. In the version of **Fibonacci** below, if $n < 2$ then the procedure returns n and Maple does not execute the rest of the procedure.

```
> Fibonacci := proc(n::nonnegint)
>      option remember;
>      if n<2 then
>          return n;
>      end if;
>      Fibonacci(n-1)+Fibonacci(n-2);
> end proc:
```

Using the **return** statement can make your recursive procedures easier to read; the usually complicated code that handles the general step of the recursion does not end up inside a nested **if** statement.

Exercise

1. The Fibonacci numbers satisfy the following recurrence.

$$F(2n) = 2F(n-1)F(n) + F(n)^2 \quad \text{where } n > 1$$

and

$$F(2n+1) = F(n+1)^2 + F(n)^2 \quad \text{where } n > 1$$

Use these new relations to write a recursive Maple procedure which computes the Fibonacci numbers. How much recomputation does this procedure do?

1.3   Basic Data Structures

The programs developed so far in this chapter have operated primarily on a single number or a single formula. More advanced programs often manipulate more complicated collections of data. A *data structure* is a systematic way of organizing data. The organization you choose for your data can directly affect the style of your programs and how fast they execute.

Maple has a rich set of built-in data structures. This section will address the basic structure of *sequences*, *lists*, and *sets*.

Many Maple commands take sequences, lists, and sets as inputs, and produce sequences, lists, and sets as outputs. The following problem illustrates how such data structures are useful in solving problems.

> **Problem:** Write a Maple procedure which given $n > 0$ data values $x_1, x_2, \ldots, x_n$ computes their average, where the following equation gives the average of n numbers.

$$\mu = \frac{1}{n} \sum_{i=1}^{n} x_i.$$

You can easily represent the data for this problem as a list. **nops** gives the total number of entries in a list **X**, while the ith entry of the list is denoted **X[i]**.

```
> X := [1.3, 5.3, 11.2, 2.1, 2.1];
```

$$X := [1.3, 5.3, 11.2, 2.1, 2.1]$$

```
> nops(X);
```

$$5$$

```
> X[2];
```

$$5.3$$

You can add the numbers in a list by using the **add** command.

```
> add( i, i=X );
```

$$22.0$$

The procedure **average** below computes the average of the entries in a list. It handles empty lists as a special case.

```
> average := proc(X::list)
>     local n, i, total;
>     n := nops(X);
>     if n=0 then error "empty list" end if;
>     total := add(i, i=X);
>     total / n;
> end proc:
```

Using this procedure you can find the average of the list X.

```
> average(X);
```

$$4.400000000$$

The procedure still works if the list has symbolic entries.

```
> average( [ a , b , c ] );
```

$$\frac{1}{3}a + \frac{1}{3}b + \frac{1}{3}c$$

Exercise

1. Write a Maple procedure called **sigma** which, given $n > 1$ data values, $x_1, x_2, \ldots, x_n$, computes their standard deviation. The following equation gives the standard deviation of $n > 1$ numbers,

$$\sigma = \sqrt{\frac{1}{n} \sum_{i=1}^{n} (x_i - \mu)^2}$$

where μ is the average of the data values.

You create lists and many other objects in Maple out of more primitive data structures called *sequences*. The list X defined previously contains the following sequence.

```
> Y := X[];
```

$$Y := 1.3, 5.3, 11.2, 2.1, 2.1$$

You can select elements from a sequence in the same way you select elements from a list.

```
> Y[3];
```

$$11.2$$

```
> Y[2..4];
```

$$5.3, \ 11.2, \ 2.1$$

```
> Y[2..-2];
```

$$5.3, \ 11.2, \ 2.1$$

The important difference between sequences and lists is that Maple flattens a sequence of sequences into a single sequence.

```
> W := a,b,c;
```

$$W := a, \ b, \ c$$

```
> Y, W, Y;
```

$$1.3, \ 5.3, \ 11.2, \ 2.1, \ 2.1, \ a, \ b, \ c, \ 1.3, \ 5.3, \ 11.2, \ 2.1, \ 2.1$$

In contrast, a list of lists remains just that, a list of lists.

```
> [ X, [a,b,c], X ];
```

$$[[1.3, \ 5.3, \ 11.2, \ 2.1, \ 2.1], \ [a, \ b, \ c], \ [1.3, \ 5.3, \ 11.2, \ 2.1, \ 2.1]]$$

If you enclose a sequence in a pair of braces, you get a *set*.

```
> Z := { Y };
```

$$Z := \{1.3, \ 5.3, \ 11.2, \ 2.1\}$$

As in mathematics, a set is an *unordered* collection of distinct objects, unlike a list which is an ordered sequence of objects. Hence, Z has only four elements as the **nops** command demonstrates.

```
> nops(Z);
```

4

You can select elements from a set in the same way you select elements from a list or a sequence, but the order of the elements in a set is session dependent. Do not make any assumptions about this order.

You may also use the **seq** command to build sequences.

```
> seq( i^2, i=1..5 );
```

$$1, 4, 9, 16, 25$$

```
> seq( f(i), i=X );
```

$$f(1.3), f(5.3), f(11.2), f(2.1), f(2.1)$$

You can create lists or sets by enclosing a sequence in square brackets or braces, respectively. The following command creates a list of sets.

```
> [ seq( { seq( i^j, j=1..3) }, i=-2..2 ) ];
```

$$[\{-8, -2, 4\}, \{-1, 1\}, \{0\}, \{1\}, \{2, 4, 8\}]$$

Exercise

1. Write a Maple procedure which, given a list of lists of numerical data, computes the means of each column of the data.

A MEMBER Procedure

You may want to write a procedure that determines whether a certain object is an element of a list or a set. The procedure below uses the **return** statement discussed in section 1.2.

```
> MEMBER := proc( a::anything, L::{list, set} )
>    local i;
>    for i from 1 to nops(L) do
>        if a=L[i] then return true end if;
>    end do;
>    false;
> end proc:
```

Here 3 is a member of the list.

```
> MEMBER( 3, [1,2,3,4,5,6] );
```

$$true$$

The type of loop that MEMBER uses occurs so frequently that Maple has a special version of the for loop for it.

```
> MEMBER := proc( a::anything, L::{list, set} )
>     local i;
>     for i in L do
>         if a=i then return true end if;
>     end do;
>     false;
> end proc:
```

The symbol x is not a member of this set.

```
> MEMBER( x, {1,2,3,4} );
```

$$false$$

Instead of using your own MEMBER procedure, you can use the built-in member command.

Exercise

1. Write a Maple procedure called POSITION which returns the position i of an element x in a list L. That is, POSITION(x,L) should return an integer $i > 0$ such that L[i]=x. Return 0 if x is not in the list L.

Binary Search

One of the most basic and well-studied computing problems is that of searching. A typical problem involves searching a list of words (a dictionary, for example) for a specific word w.

Many possible solutions are available. One approach is to search the list by comparing each word in turn with w until Maple either finds w or it reaches the end of the list.

```
> Search := proc(Dictionary::list(string), w::string)
>     local x;
>     for x in Dictionary do
>         if x=w then return true end if
>     end do;
>     false
> end proc:
```

However, if the Dictionary is large, say 50 000 entries, this approach can take a long time.

You can reduce the execution time required by sorting the Dictionary before you search it. If you sort the dictionary into ascending order then you can stop searching as soon as you encounter a word *greater than* w. On average, you only have to look halfway through the dictionary.

Binary searching provides an even better approach. Check the word in the middle of the dictionary. Since you already sorted the dictionary you can tell whether w is in the first or the second half. Repeat the process with the appropriate half of the dictionary. The procedure below searches the dictionary, D, for the word, w, from position, s, to position, f, in D. The `lexorder` command determines the lexicographical ordering of two strings.

```
> BinarySearch :=
> proc(D::list(string), w::string, s::integer, f::integer)
>     local m;
>     if s>f then return false end if; # entry was not found.
>     m := iquo(s+f+1, 2);  # midpoint of D.
>     if w=D[m] then
>         true;
>     elif lexorder(w, D[m]) then
>         BinarySearch(D, w, s, m-1);
>     else
>         BinarySearch(D, w, m+1, f);
>     end if;
> end proc:
```

Here is a short dictionary.

```
> Dictionary := [ "induna", "ion", "logarithm", "meld" ];
```

$$Dictionary := [\text{``induna''}, \text{``ion''}, \text{``logarithm''}, \text{``meld''}]$$

Now search the dictionary for a few words.

```
> BinarySearch( Dictionary, "hedgehogs", 1, nops(Dictionary) );
```

false

```
> BinarySearch( Dictionary, "logarithm", 1, nops(Dictionary) );
```

true

```
> BinarySearch( Dictionary, "melodious", 1, nops(Dictionary) );
```

false

Exercises

1. Can you demonstrate that the `BinarySearch` procedure always terminates? Suppose the dictionary has n entries. How many words in the dictionary D does `BinarySearch` look at in the worst case?

2. Recode `BinarySearch` to use a `while` loop instead of calling itself recursively.

Plotting the Roots of a Polynomial

You can construct lists of any type of object, even lists. A list of two numbers often represents a point in the plane. The `plot` command uses this structure to generate plots of points and lines.

```
> plot( [ [ 0, 0], [ 1, 2], [-1, 2] ],
>     style=point, color=black );
```

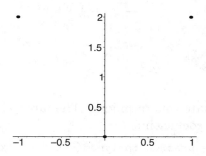

You can use this approach to write a procedure which plots the complex roots of a polynomial. Consider the polynomial $x^3 - 1$.

```
> y := x^3-1;
```

$$y := x^3 - 1$$

Numeric solutions are sufficient for plotting.

```
> R := [ fsolve(y=0, x, complex) ];
```

$$R := [-.5000000000 - .8660254038\,I,$$
$$-.5000000000 + .8660254038\,I, 1.]$$

You need to turn this list of complex numbers into a list of points in the plane. The `Re` and `Im` commands pick the real and imaginary parts, respectively.

```
> points := map( z -> [Re(z), Im(z)], R );
```

$$points := [[-.5000000000, -.8660254038],$$
$$[-.5000000000, .8660254038], [1., 0.]]$$

You can now plot the points.

```
> plot( points, style=point);
```

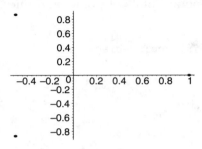

You can automate this technique. The input should be a polynomial in x with constant coefficients.

```
> rootplot := proc( p::polynom(constant, x) )
>    local R, points;
>    R := [ fsolve(p, x, complex) ];
>    points := map( z -> [Re(z), Im(z)], R );
>    plot( points, style=point, symbol=circle );
> end proc:
```

Here is a plot of the roots of the polynomial $x^6 + 3x^5 + 5x + 10$.

```
> rootplot( x^6+3*x^5+5*x+10 );
```

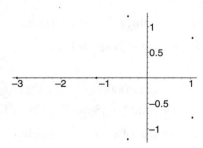

The **randpoly** command generates a random polynomial.

```
> y := randpoly(x, degree=100);
```

$$y := 79\,x^{71} + 56\,x^{63} + 49\,x^{44} + 63\,x^{30} + 57\,x^{24} - 59\,x^{18}$$

```
> rootplot( y );
```

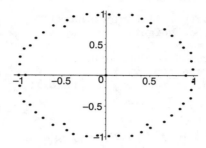

When you write procedures, you often have several choices of how to represent the data with which your procedures work. The choice of data structure can have great impact on how easy it is to write your procedure and its resulting efficiency. Section 2.4 describes an example of choosing a data structure.

1.4 Computing with Formulæ

Maple's real strength stems from its ability to perform symbolic manipulations. This section demonstrates some of these capabilities through sample programs for computation with polynomials. While the examples are specific to polynomials, the techniques and methods apply to more general formulæ.

In mathematics, a *polynomial* in the single variable, x, is most easily recognizable in the expanded form,

$$\sum_{i=0}^{n} a_i x^i, \qquad \text{where if } n > 0, \text{ then } a_n \neq 0.$$

The a_is are the *coefficients*. They can be numbers or even expressions involving variables. The crucial point is that each coefficient is independent of (does not contain) x.

The Height of a Polynomial

The *height* of a polynomial is the largest magnitude (absolute value) of the largest coefficient. The procedure below finds the height of a polynomial, p, in the variable x. The `degree` command finds the degree of a polynomial and the `coeff` command extracts specific coefficients from a polynomial.

```
> HGHT := proc(p::polynom, x::name)
>    local i, c, height;
>    height := 0;
>    for i from 0 to degree(p, x) do
>        c := coeff(p, x, i);
>        height := max(height, abs(c));
>    end do;
>    height;
> end proc:
```

The height of $32x^6 - 48x^4 + 18x^2 - 1$ is 48.

```
> p := 32*x^6-48*x^4+18*x^2-1;
```

$$p := 32\,x^6 - 48\,x^4 + 18\,x^2 - 1$$

```
> HGHT(p,x);
```

$$48$$

A significant weakness of the `HGHT` procedure is its inefficiency with sparse polynomials; that is, polynomials with few terms relative to their degree. For example, to find the height of $x^{4321} - 1$ the `HGHT` procedure has to examine 4322 coefficients.

The `coeffs` command returns the sequence of coefficients of a polynomial.

```
> coeffs( p, x );
```

$$-1, 32, -48, 18$$

You cannot map the `abs` command, or any other command, onto a sequence. One solution is to turn the sequence into a list or a set.

```
> S := map( abs, {%} );
```

$$S := \{1, 18, 32, 48\}$$

The `max` command, however, works on sequences (but not on lists or sets), so now you must turn the set into a sequence again.

```
> max( S[] );
```

$$48$$

The following version of `HGHT` uses this technique.

```
> HGHT := proc(p::polynom, x::name)
>    local S;
>    S := { coeffs(p, x) };
>    S := map( abs, S );
>    max( S[] );
> end proc:
```

Try the procedure out on a random polynomial.

```
> p := randpoly(x, degree=100 );
```

$$p := 79\,x^{71} + 56\,x^{63} + 49\,x^{44} + 63\,x^{30} + 57\,x^{24} - 59\,x^{18}$$

```
> HGHT(p, x);
```

$$79$$

If the polynomial is in expanded form, you can also find its height in the following manner. You can map a command directly onto a polynomial. The `map` command applies the command to each term in the polynomial.

```
> map( f, p );
```

$$\mathrm{f}(79\,x^{71}) + \mathrm{f}(56\,x^{63}) + \mathrm{f}(49\,x^{44}) + \mathrm{f}(63\,x^{30}) + \mathrm{f}(57\,x^{24})$$
$$+ \mathrm{f}(-59\,x^{18})$$

Thus, you can map `abs` directly onto the polynomial.

```
> map( abs, p );
```

$$79\,|x|^{71} + 56\,|x|^{63} + 49\,|x|^{44} + 63\,|x|^{30} + 57\,|x|^{24} + 59\,|x|^{18}$$

Then use `coeffs` to find the sequence of coefficients of that polynomial.

```
> coeffs( % );
```

$$79,\ 56,\ 49,\ 63,\ 57,\ 59$$

Finally, find the maximum.

```
> max( % );
```

$$79$$

Hence, you can calculate the height of a polynomial with this one-liner.

```
> p := randpoly(x, degree=50) * randpoly(x, degree=99);
```

$$p := (77\,x^{48} + 66\,x^{44} + 54\,x^{37} - 5\,x^{20} + 99\,x^5 - 61\,x^3)$$
$$(-47\,x^{57} - 91\,x^{33} - 47\,x^{26} - 61\,x^{25} + 41\,x^{18} - 58\,x^8)$$

```
> max( coeffs( map(abs, expand(p)) ) );
```

$$9214$$

Exercise
1. Write a procedure that computes the Euclidean norm of a polynomial; that is, $\sqrt{\sum_{i=0}^{n} |a_i|^2}$.

The Chebyshev Polynomials, $T_n(x)$

The Chebyshev polynomials, $T_n(x)$, satisfy the following linear recurrence.

$$T_n(x) = 2xT_{n-1}(x) - T_{n-2}(x), \qquad \text{for } n \geq 2.$$

The first two Chebyshev polynomials are $T_0(x) = 1$ and $T_1(x) = x$. This example is similar to the Fibonacci example in section 1.2. Here is a simple procedure, T, that computes $T_n(x)$.

```
> T := proc(n::nonnegint, x::name)
>     option remember, system;
>     if n=0 then
>         return 1;
>     elif n=1 then
>         return x;
>     end if;
>     2*x*T(n-1,x) - T(n-2,x);
> end proc:
```

Maple does not automatically expand the polynomial.

```
> T(4,x);
```

$$2\,x\,(2\,x\,(2\,x^2 - 1) - x) - 2\,x^2 + 1$$

You can expand the polynomial yourself.

```
> expand(%);
```

$$8\,x^4 - 8\,x^2 + 1$$

You may be tempted to rewrite the procedure so that it expands the result before returning it. However, this may be a waste of effort since you do not know whether or not the user of your procedure wants the Chebyshev polynomial in expanded form. Moreover, since the T procedure is recursive, it would expand all the intermediate results as well.

Exercise

1. The Fibonacci polynomials, $F_n(x)$, satisfy the linear recurrence

$$F_n(x) = xF_{n-1}(x) + F_{n-2}(x),$$

where $F_0(x) = 0$ and $F_1(x) = 1$. Write a Maple procedure to compute and factor $F_n(x)$. Can you see any pattern?

Integration by Parts

Maple's indefinite integral evaluator is very powerful. This section describes how you could write your own procedure for integrating formulæ of the form

$$p(x)f(x),$$

where $p(x)$ is a polynomial in x and $f(x)$ is a special function. Here $p(x) = x^2$ and $f(x) = e^x$.

```
> int( x^2*exp(x), x );
```

$$x^2\,e^x - 2\,x\,e^x + 2\,e^x$$

As another example, here $p(x) = x^3$ and $f(x) = \sin^{-1}(x)$.

```
> int( x^3*arcsin(x), x );
```

$$\frac{1}{4}\,x^4 \arcsin(x) + \frac{1}{16}\,x^3\,\sqrt{1 - x^2} + \frac{3}{32}\,x\,\sqrt{1 - x^2} - \frac{3}{32}\,\arcsin(x)$$

Usually you would use *integration by parts* to compute integrals of this form.

```
> int( u(x)*v(x), x ) = u(x)*int(v(x),x) -
> int( diff(u(x),x) * int(v(x),x), x );
```

$$\int u(x)\,v(x)\,dx = u(x)\int v(x)\,dx - \int (\frac{\partial}{\partial x}\,u(x))\int v(x)\,dx\,dx$$

You can verify this formula by differentiating both sides of the equation.

```
> diff(%,x);
```

$$u(x)\,v(x) = u(x)\,v(x)$$

```
> evalb(%);
```

$$true$$

Applying integration by parts to the first example yields

$$\int x^n e^x\,dx = x^n \int e^x\,dx - \int (nx^{n-1}\int e^x\,dx)\,dx = x^n e^x - n\int x^{n-1}e^x\,dx.$$

It introduces a new integral, but the degree of x in that new integral is one smaller than in the old integral. By applying the formula repeatedly, the problem eventually reduces to evaluating $\int e^x$, which is simply e^x.

The following procedure uses integration by parts to calculate the integral

$$\int x^n e^x\,dx\,,$$

by calling itself recursively until $n = 0$.

```
> IntExpMonomial := proc(n::nonnegint, x::name)
>     if n=0 then return exp(x) end if;
>       x^n*exp(x) - n*IntExpMonomial(n-1, x);
> end proc:
```
IntExpMonomial can calculate $\int x^5 e^x\,dx$.

```
> IntExpMonomial(5, x);
```

$$x^5\,e^x - 5\,x^4\,e^x + 20\,x^3\,e^x - 60\,x^2\,e^x + 120\,x\,e^x - 120\,e^x$$

You can simplify this answer by using the `collect` command to group the terms involving $\exp(x)$ together.

```
> collect(%, exp(x));
```

$$(x^5 - 5\,x^4 + 20\,x^3 - 60\,x^2 + 120\,x - 120)\,e^x$$

You can now write a procedure which calculates $\int p(x)e^x\,dx$ for any polynomial p. The idea is that integration is linear:

$$\int af(x) + g(x)\,dx = a\int f(x)\,dx + \int g(x)\,dx.$$

The `IntExpPolynomial` procedure below uses `coeff` to extract the coefficients of p one at a time.

```
> IntExpPolynomial := proc(p::polynom, x::name)
>    local i, result;
>    result := add( coeff(p, x, i)*IntExpMonomial(i, x),
>                   i=0..degree(p, x) );
>    collect(result, exp(x));
> end proc:
```
Here `IntExpPolynomial` calculates $\int (x^2 + 1)(1 - 3x)e^x\,dx$.

```
> IntExpPolynomial( (x^2+1)*(1-3*x), x );
```

$$(24 - 23\,x + 10\,x^2 - 3\,x^3)\,e^x$$

Exercises

1. Modify the procedure `IntExpPolynomial` to be more efficient by processing only the non-zero coefficients of $p(x)$.

2. The procedure `IntExpPolynomial` is quadratic in degree. Modify this procedure again to make it linear in degree.

Computing with Symbolic Parameters

The polynomial $2x^5 + 1$ is an example of an *explicit polynomial* in x. All the elements of the polynomial, except x, are explicit numbers. On the other hand, polynomials like $3x^n + 2$, where n is an unspecified positive integer, or $a + x^5$, where a is an unknown which is independent of x, are examples of *symbolic polynomials*; they contain additional unspecified symbolic parameters.

The procedure `IntExpPolynomial` in section 1.4 calculates the integral $\int p(x)e^x\,dx$ where p is an explicit polynomial. In its present version `IntExpPolynomial` cannot handle symbolic polynomials.

```
> IntExpPolynomial( a*x^n, x );
```

```
Error, invalid input: IntExpPolynomial expects its 1st
argument, p, to be of type polynom, but received a*x^n
```

You may want to extend **IntExpPolynomial** so that it can integrate $p(x)e^x$ for symbolic polynomials p as well. The first problem is that of finding a formula for $\int x^n e^x \, dx$ for any natural number n. Often you can find such a formula by carefully examining the pattern for specific results. Here are the first few results for explicit values of n.

```
> IntExpPolynomial(x, x);
```

$$(x - 1) \, e^x$$

```
> IntExpPolynomial(x^2, x);
```

$$(x^2 - 2x + 2) \, e^x$$

```
> IntExpPolynomial(x^3, x);
```

$$(x^3 - 3x^2 + 6x - 6) \, e^x$$

With sufficient time and ingenuity you would find the formula

$$\int x^n e^x \, dx = n! \, e^x \sum_{i=0}^{n} \frac{(-1)^{n-i} x^i}{i!}.$$

This formula holds only for non-negative integers n. Use the *assume* facility to tell Maple that the unknown n has certain properties.

```
> assume(n, integer);
> additionally(n >= 0);
```

Note that a simple type check is not sufficient to determine that n is an integer.

```
> type(n, integer);
```

$$false$$

You need to use the **is** command, which is part of the assume facility.

```
> is(n, integer), is(n >= 0);
```

$$true, \; true$$

Thus, you can rewrite the `IntExpMonomial` procedure from section 1.4 in the following manner.

```
> IntExpMonomial := proc(n::anything, x::name)
>     local i;
>     if is(n, integer) and is(n >= 0) then
>         n! * exp(x) * sum( ( (-1)^(n-i)*x^i )/i!, i=0..n );
>     else
>         error("Expected a non-negative integer but received", n);
>     end if;
> end proc:
```

This version of `IntExpMonomial` accepts both explicit and symbolic input.

```
> IntExpMonomial(4, x);
```

$$24 \, e^x \left(1 - x + \frac{1}{2} \, x^2 - \frac{1}{6} \, x^3 + \frac{1}{24} \, x^4 \right)$$

In the next example, Maple evaluates the sum in terms of the gamma function. The tilde ($\tilde{\;}$) on n indicates that n carries an assumption.

```
> IntExpMonomial(n, x);
```

$$n\tilde{\;}! \, e^x ((-1)^{n\tilde{\;}} \, e^{(-x)} + x^{(n\tilde{\;}+1)} ((-x)^{(-1-n\tilde{\;})} \, e^{(-x)} \, \Gamma(2 + n\tilde{\;})$$
$$- (n\tilde{\;} + 1) \, (-x)^{(-1-n\tilde{\;})} \, e^{(-x)} \, \Gamma(n\tilde{\;} + 1, \, -x)) / (n\tilde{\;} + 1)!)$$

You can check the answer by differentiating it with respect to x. The `simplify` command reveals $x^n e^x$ as expected.

```
> diff(%, x);
```

$$n\tilde{}!\,e^x\Big($$

$$(-1)^{n\tilde{}}\,e^{(-x)} + \frac{x^{(n\tilde{}+1)}\left((-x)^{(-1-n\tilde{})}\,e^{(-x)}\,\Gamma(2+n\tilde{}) - \%1\right)}{(n\tilde{}+1)!}$$

$$\Big) + n\tilde{}!\,e^x\big(-(-1)^{n\tilde{}}\,e^{(-x)} + x^{(n\tilde{}+1)}\,(n\tilde{}+1)$$

$$\big((-x)^{(-1-n\tilde{})}\,e^{(-x)}\,\Gamma(2+n\tilde{}) - \%1\big)/(x\,(n\tilde{}+1)!)\big)+$$

$$x^{(n\tilde{}+1)}\Big(\frac{(-x)^{(-1-n\tilde{})}\,(-1-n\tilde{})\,e^{(-x)}\,\Gamma(2+n\tilde{})}{x}$$

$$- (-x)^{(-1-n\tilde{})}\,e^{(-x)}\,\Gamma(2+n\tilde{})$$

$$- \frac{(n\tilde{}+1)\,(-x)^{(-1-n\tilde{})}\,(-1-n\tilde{})\,e^{(-x)}\,\Gamma(n\tilde{}+1,\,-x)}{x}$$

$$+ \%1 - (n\tilde{}+1)\,(-x)^{(-1-n\tilde{})}\,e^{(-x)}\,(-x)^{n\tilde{}}\,e^x)/(n\tilde{}+1)!\big)$$

$$\%1 := (n\tilde{}+1)\,(-x)^{(-1-n\tilde{})}\,e^{(-x)}\,\Gamma(n\tilde{}+1,\,-x)$$

```
> simplify(%);
```

$$e^x\,x^{n\tilde{}}$$

Clearly, the use of symbolic constants in this way greatly extends the power of the system.

Exercise

1. Extend the facility above to compute $\int x^n e^{ax+b}\,dx$, where n is an integer and a and b are constants. You must handle the case $n = -1$ separately since

$$\int \frac{e^x}{x}\,dx = -\mathrm{Ei}(1, -x)\,.$$

Use the `ispoly` command from the Maple library to test for the expression $ax + b$ which is linear in x.

1.5   Conclusion

This chapter introduced the basics of Maple programming. It first showed you how to take a few lines of code and turn them into a useful procedure simply by inserting them between `proc()` and `end proc` statements. Then it introduced local and global variables and how to use them. As well, you were introduced to generating error messages, automatic type checking, recursive procedures, and efficiency.

These concepts should equip you for writing many useful procedures. In fact, you may put down this book and start writing some procedures of your own.

The remainder of the book describes procedures in more detail. It presents a formal introduction to the Maple language (chapter 4) and the details of procedure definitions (chapter 5). It contains chapters on special areas of application, including numerical (chapter 8) and graphical programming (chapter 9). Explore these chapters when you are ready to continue.

2   Fundamentals

By now, you have no doubt written a number of procedures and found that Maple's programming language greatly extends the range of tasks you can tackle. Chapter 1 introduced a number of simple examples that are useful as models for creating your own.

When programming in Maple, you may encounter unexpected situations. For instance, you may develop a sequence of commands which work reliably and correctly when you execute them interactively, but then no longer work when you incorporate them into a procedure by encapsulating them between the **proc()** and **end proc** statements.

You are likely to encounter this situation if you write many programs. Fortunately, the solution is almost always simple. A few fundamental rules dictate how Maple reads what you type. An understanding of these basic principles is particularly important within procedures, where you encounter types of objects with which you may be unfamiliar.

Learning the basics is not difficult, especially if you understand five particularly important areas:

1. Maple's evaluation rules;

2. nested procedures;

3. useful details of types: types which modify Maple's evaluation rules, structured types, and type matching;

4. data structures: understanding how to make effective use of them in order to best solve a problem; and

5. remember tables.

This chapter equips you with the fundamentals of Maple programming, thereby allowing you to understand and write nontrivial Maple code.

2.1 Evaluation Rules

Maple does not evaluate lines of code within procedures in quite the same way as it does if you enter those same lines in an interactive session. The rules for evaluation are demonstrated in this section.

Of course, the evaluation rules within a procedure are different for good reasons, some which have to do with efficiency. In an interactive session, Maple evaluates most names and expressions completely. For instance, suppose that you assign a the value b and then assign b the value c. When you subsequently type a, Maple automatically follows your list of assignments to determine that the ultimate value of a is c.

```
> a := b;
```

$$a := b$$

```
> b := c;
```

$$b := c$$

```
> a + 1;
```

$$c + 1$$

In an interactive session, Maple tirelessly follows your chain of assignments, no matter how long the list. Within a procedure, however, Maple is not so diligent.

The substitution of assigned values for a name is called *evaluation*, and each step in this process is known as an *evaluation level*. By using the eval command, you can explicitly ask Maple to perform evaluation of names to specific levels.

```
> eval(a, 1);
```

$$b$$

```
> eval(a, 2);
```

$$c$$

If you do not specify a number of levels, Maple evaluates the name to as many levels as exist.

```
> eval(a);
```

$$c$$

When you enter commands at the prompt, Maple usually evaluates the names as if you had enclosed each one in an **eval()**. The main exception is that evaluation stops whenever evaluating to one more level would turn the name into one of a table, an array, a procedure, or a module. The command **a + 1** above is almost identical to **eval(a) + 1**.

In procedures, some rules are different. If you use the previous assignments within a procedure, you may get unexpected results.

```
> f := proc()
>       local a,b;
>       a := b;
>       b := c;
>       a + 1;
> end proc;
```

$$f := \mathbf{proc}()\,\mathbf{local}\,a,\,b;\;a := b;\;b := c;\;a + 1\,\mathbf{end\ proc}$$

```
> f();
```

$$b + 1$$

The answer is **b + 1** instead of **c + 1**, because **a** is a local variable and Maple evaluates local variables to only one level. The procedure behaves as if the final line were **eval(a,1) + 1**. Evaluating local variables fully is inefficient both in terms of time and memory. To evaluate a variable fully, Maple may have to follow a long list of assignments, resulting in a large expression.

The following sections introduce Maple's evaluation rules systematically. They discuss what types of variables can exist within a procedure and the evaluation rules applied to each.

Parameters

Chapter 1 introduced you to local and global variables, but procedures have a more fundamental type of variable: parameters. Parameters are variables whose name appears between the parentheses of a **proc()** expression. They have a special role within procedures, as Maple replaces them with arguments when you execute the procedure.

Examine the following procedure which squares its first argument and assigns the answer to the second argument, which must be a name.

```
> sqr1 := proc(x::anything, y::name)
>             y := x^2;
> end proc;
```

$$sqr1 := \textbf{proc}(x::anything,\ y::name)\ y := x^2\ \textbf{end proc}$$

```
> sqr1(d, ans);
```

$$d^2$$

```
> ans;
```

$$d^2$$

The procedure squares the value of **d** and assigns the result to the name **ans**. Try the procedure again, but this time use the name **a** which Maple earlier assigned the value **b**. Remember to reset **ans** to a name first.

```
> ans := 'ans';
```

$$ans := ans$$

```
> sqr1(a, ans);
```

$$c^2$$

```
> ans;
```

$$c^2$$

From the answer, Maple clearly remembers that you assigned **b** to the name **a**, and **c** to the name **b**. When did this evaluation occur?

To determine when, you must examine the value of **x** as soon as Maple enters the procedure. Use the debugger to get Maple to stop just after entering **sqr1**.

```
> stopat(sqr1);
```

[*sqr1*]

```
> ans := 'ans':
> sqr1(a, ans);

sqr1:
  1*  y := x^2
```

The value of the formal parameter x is c.

```
DBG > x
```

```
c
sqr1:
  1*  y := x^2
```

```
DBG > cont
```

$$c^2$$

```
> unstopat(sqr1):
```

In fact, Maple evaluates the arguments *before* invoking the procedure.

The steps Maple takes are best thought of in the following manner. When you call a procedure, Maple evaluates the arguments appropriately, given the context in which the call occurs. For example, if you call **sqr1** from inside a procedure, then Maple evaluates **a** to one level. Thus, in the procedure **g** below, Maple evaluates **a** to **b** rather than to **c**.

```
> g := proc()
>       local a,b,ans;
>       a := b;
>       b := c;
>       sqr1(a,ans);
> end proc;
```

$g :=$
proc() **local** a, b, ans; $a := b$; $b := c$; $sqr1(a, ans)$ **end proc**

```
> g();
```

$$b^2$$

Whether you call a procedure from the interactive level or from inside a procedure, Maple evaluates the arguments before invoking the procedure. Once Maple evaluates the arguments, it replaces all occurrences of the procedure's formal parameters with the actual arguments. Then Maple invokes the procedure.

Because Maple only evaluates parameters once, you cannot use them like local variables. The author of procedure **cube**, below, forgot that Maple does not re-evaluate parameters.

```
> cube := proc(x::anything, y::name)
>          y := x^3;
>          y;
> end proc:
```

When you call **cube** as below, Maple does assign **ans** the value 2^3, but the procedure returns the name **ans** rather than its value.

```
> ans := 'ans';
```

$$ans := ans$$

```
> cube(2, ans);
```

$$ans$$

```
> ans;
```

$$8$$

Maple replaces each **y** with **ans**, but Maple does not evaluate these occurrences of **ans** again. Thus, the final line of **cube** returns the name **ans**, not the value that Maple assigned to **ans**.

Use parameters to pass information into the procedure. You may think of parameters as objects evaluated to *zero* levels.

Local Variables

Local variables are temporary storage places within a procedure. You can create local variables by using the **local** declaration statement at the beginning of a procedure. If you do not declare whether a variable is local or global, Maple decides for you. If you make an assignment to a variable within a procedure then Maple assumes that it should be `local`. A local variable is different from any other variable, whether global or local to another procedure, even if they have the same name. The rules for determining local variables become a little more involved when *nested procedures* are written, but the basic concepts are similar. See Section 2.2 for more details.

Maple only evaluates local variables to one level.

```
> f := proc()
>         local a,b;
>         a := b;
>         b := c;
>         a + 1;
> end proc;
```

$$f := \mathbf{proc}()\, \mathbf{local}\, a,\, b;\ a := b;\ b := c;\ a + 1\, \mathbf{end\ proc}$$

When you invoke `f`, Maple evaluates the `a` in `a+1` one level to `b`.

```
> f();
```

$$b + 1$$

Maple always uses last name evaluation for tables, arrays, modules, and procedures. Therefore, if you assign a table, an array, a module, or a procedure to a local variable, Maple does not evaluate that variable unless you use `eval`. Maple creates the local variables of a procedure each time you call the procedure. Thus, local variables are local to a specific invocation of a procedure.

If you have not written many programs you might think that one level evaluation of local variables is a serious limitation, but in fact code which requires further evaluation of local variables is difficult to understand, and is unnecessary. Moreover, because Maple does not attempt further evaluations, it saves many steps, causing procedures to run faster.

Global Variables

Global variables are available from inside any procedure in Maple as well as at the interactive level. Indeed, any name you use at the interactive level is a global variable, allowing you to write a procedure which assigns a value to a variable that is accessible again later from within another procedure, from within the same procedure, or at the interactive level.

```
> h := proc()
>        global x;
>        x := 5;
> end proc:
> h();
```

$$5$$

```
> x;
```

$$5$$

Within procedures, use global variables with caution. The procedure h assigns a value to the global variable x but it does not leave any warning in your worksheet. If you then use x thinking that it is an unknown, you can get unexpected error messages.

```
> diff( x^2, x);
```

```
Error, wrong number (or type) of parameters in function
diff
```

Moreover, if you write yet another procedure which uses the global variable x, then the two procedures may use the same x in incompatible ways.

Whether within a procedure or at the interactive level, Maple always applies the same evaluation rules to global variables. It evaluates all global names fully, except when the value of such a variable is a table, an array, or a procedure, in which case, Maple halts its evaluation at the last name in the chain of assignments. This evaluation rule is called *last name evaluation*.

Hence, *Maple evaluates parameters to zero levels, local variables to one level, and global variables fully*, except for last name evaluation.

As with local variables, the rules for determining which variables are global are fully described in Section 2.2.

Exceptions

This section describes two exceptions of particular note to the rules for evaluation.

The Ditto Operator The *ditto operator*, %, which recalls the last result, is local to procedures but Maple evaluates it *fully*. When you invoke a procedure, Maple initializes the local version of % to NULL.

```
> f := proc()
>    local a,b;
>    print( "Initially [%] has the value", [%] );
>    a := b;
>    b := c;
>    a + 1;
>    print( "Now [%] has the value", [%] );
> end proc:
> f();
```

$$\text{``Initially } [\%] \text{ has the value''}, []$$

$$\text{``Now } [\%] \text{ has the value''}, [c+1]$$

The same special rules apply to the **%%** and **%%%** operators. Using local variables instead of ditto operators makes your procedures easier to read and debug.

Environment Variables The variable `Digits`, which determines the number of digits that Maple uses when calculating with floating-point numbers, is an example of an *environment variable*. Maple evaluates environment variables in the same manner it evaluates global variables; that is, Maple evaluates environment variables fully except for last name evaluation. When a procedure returns, Maple resets all environment variables to the values they had when you invoked the procedure.

```
> f := proc()
>    print( "Entering f.  Digits is", Digits );
>    Digits := Digits + 13;
>    print( "Adding 13 to Digits yields", Digits );
> end proc:
> g := proc()
>    print( "Entering g.  Digits is", Digits );
>    Digits := 77;
>    print( "Calling f from g.  Digits is", Digits );
>    f();
>    print( "Back in g from f.  Digits is", Digits );
> end proc:
```

The default value of `Digits` is 10.

```
> Digits;
```

$$10$$

```
> g();
```

"Entering g. Digits is", 10

"Calling f from g. Digits is", 77

"Entering f. Digits is", 77

"Adding 13 to Digits yields", 90

"Back in g from f. Digits is", 77

When returning from **g**, Maple resets `Digits` to 10.
```
> Digits;
```

$$10$$

See `?environment` for a list of environment variables. You can also make your own environment variables: Maple considers any variable whose name begins with the four characters _Env to be an environment variable.

2.2   Nested Procedures

You can define a Maple procedure inside another Maple procedure. Indeed, you may commonly write such procedures without realizing you are writing nested procedures. In interactive sessions, you are no doubt familiar with using the **map** command to apply some operation to the elements of some type of structure. For example, you may want to divide each element of a list by a number, such as 8.

```
> lst := [8, 4, 2, 16]:
> map( x->x/8, lst);
```

$$[1, \frac{1}{2}, \frac{1}{4}, 2]$$

The **map** command is also very useful inside a procedure. Consider another variation on this command which appears in the following procedure. The intent of this new procedure is to divide each element of a list by the first element of that list.

```
> nest := proc(x::list)
>     local v;
>     v := x[1];
>     map( y -> y/v, x );
> end proc:
> nest(lst);
```

$$[1, \frac{1}{2}, \frac{1}{4}, 2]$$

Maple considers this use of **map** as an example of nested procedures and applies its lexical scoping rules, which declare the **v** within the call to **map** as the same **v** as in the outer procedure, **nest**.

The following section explains Maple's scoping rules. You will learn how Maple decides which variables are local to a procedure and which are global. Understanding Maple's evaluation rules for parameters, and for local and global variables, allows you to make full use of the Maple language.

Local Versus Global Variables

Usually when you write a procedure, you should explicitly declare which variables are global and which are local. Declaring the scope of the variables makes your procedure easier to read and debug. However, sometimes declaring the variables is not the way to go. In the **nest** procedure above, the variable in the **map** command gets its meaning from the surrounding procedure. What happens if you define this variable, **v**, as local to the invocation of the procedure within **map**?

```
> nest2 := proc(x::list)
>     local v;
>     v := x[1];
>     map( proc(y) local v; y/v; end, x );
> end proc:
> nest2(lst);
```

$$[\frac{8}{v}, \frac{4}{v}, \frac{2}{v}, \frac{16}{v}]$$

If you examine **nest2** closely, you should be able to determine why it didn't work the same as **nest**. It is obvious that you don't want to have the variables declared at all within the inner procedure, so that it can get it's proper meaning from the enclosing procedure.

Only two possibilities exist: either a variable is local to a procedure and certain procedures that are completely within it, or it is global to the entire Maple session.

The method Maple uses for determining whether a variable is local or global can be summarized as: The name of the variable is searched for among the parameters, `local` declarations, and `global` declarations of the procedure, and then among the parameters, `local` and `global` declarations, and implicitly declared local variables of any surrounding procedure(s), from the inside out. If found, that specifies the binding of the variable.

If, using the above rule, Maple cannot determine whether a variable should be global or local, the following default decisions are made for you. *If a variable appears on the* left-hand *side of an* explicit *assignment or as the controlling variable of a for loop, then Maple assumes that you intend the variable to be local.* Otherwise, Maple assumes that the variable is global to the whole session. In particular, Maple assumes by default that the variables you only pass as arguments to other procedures, which may set their values, are global.

The Quick-Sort Algorithm

Sorting algorithms are of particular interest to computer scientists. Even if you have never formally studied them you can appreciate that many things need sorting. Sorting a few numbers is quick and easy no matter what approach you use, but sorting large amounts of data can be very time consuming; thus, finding efficient methods is important.

The following quick-sort algorithm is a classic algorithm. The key to understanding this algorithm is to understand the operation of partitioning. This involves choosing any one number from the array that you are about to sort. Then, you reposition the numbers in the array that are less than the number that you chose to one end of the array and reposition numbers that are greater to the other end. Lastly, you insert the chosen number between these two groups.

At the end of the partitioning, you have not yet entirely sorted the array, because the numbers less or greater than the one you chose may still be in their original order. This procedure divides the array into two smaller arrays which are easier to sort than the original larger one. The partitioning operation has thus made the work of sorting much easier. Better yet, you can bring the array one step closer in the sorting process by partitioning each of the two smaller arrays. This operation produces four smaller arrays. You sort the entire array by repeatedly partitioning the smaller arrays.

The **partition** procedure uses an array to store the list because you can change the elements of an array directly. Thus, you can sort the array in place and not waste any space generating extra copies.

The **quicksort** procedure is easier to understand if you look at the procedure **partition** in isolation first. This procedure accepts an array of numbers and two integers. The two integers are element numbers of the array, indicating the portion of the array to partition. While you could possibly choose any of the numbers in the array to partition around, this procedure chooses the last element of the section of the array for that purpose, namely **A[n]**. The intentional omission of **global** and **local** statements is to show which variables Maple thinks are local and which global by default. It is recommended, however, that you not make this omission in your procedures.

```
> partition := proc(A::array(1, numeric),
>                     m::posint, n::posint)
>      i := m;
>      j := n;
>      x := A[j];
>      while i<j do
>          if A[i]>x then
>              A[j] := A[i];
>              j := j-1;
>              A[i] := A[j];
>          else
>              i := i+1;
>          end if;
>      end do;
>      A[j] := x;
>      eval(A);
> end proc:

Warning, 'i' is implicitly declared local to procedure
'partition'
Warning, 'j' is implicitly declared local to procedure
'partition'
Warning, 'x' is implicitly declared local to procedure
'partition'
```

Maple declares i, j, and x local because the **partition** procedure contains explicit assignments to those variables. **partition** also assigns explicitly to **A**, but **A** is a parameter, not a local variable. Because you do not assign to the name **eval**, Maple makes it the global name which refers to the **eval** command.

After partitioning the array a below, all the elements less than 3 precede 3 but they are in no particular order; similarly, the elements larger than 3 come after 3.

```
> a := array( [2,4,1,5,3] );
```

$$a := [2, 4, 1, 5, 3]$$

```
> partition( a, 1, 5);
```

$$[2, 1, 3, 5, 4]$$

The **partition** procedure modifies its first argument, thus changing a.

```
> eval(a);
```

$$[2, 1, 3, 5, 4]$$

The final step in assembling the quick-sort procedure is to insert the **partition** procedure within an outer procedure. The outer procedure first defines the **partition** subprocedure, then partitions the array. Ordinarily, you might want to avoid inserting one procedure within another. However, you will encounter situations in chapter 3 where you will find it necessary to nest the procedures. Since the next step is to partition each of the two subarrays by calling **quicksort** recursively, **partition** must return the location of the element which divides the partition.

```
> quicksort := proc(A::array(1, numeric),
>                   m::integer, n::integer)
>     local partition, p;
>
>     partition := proc(m,n)
>         i := m;
>         j := n;
>         x := A[j];
>         while i<j do
>             if A[i]>x then
>                 A[j] := A[i];
>                 j := j-1;
>                 A[i] := A[j];
>             else
>                 i := i+1;
>             end if;
>         end do;
>         A[j] := x;
```

```
>        p := j;
>     end proc:
>
>     if m<n then    # if m>=n there is nothing to do
>        p:=partition(m, n);
>        quicksort(A, m, p-1);
>        quicksort(A, p+1, n);
>     end if;
>
>     eval(A);
> end proc:
```

Warning, `i` is implicitly declared local to procedure
`partition`
Warning, `j` is implicitly declared local to procedure
`partition`
Warning, `x` is implicitly declared local to procedure
`partition`

```
> a := array( [2,4,1,5,3] );
```

$$a := [2, 4, 1, 5, 3]$$

```
> quicksort( a, 1, 5);
```

$$[1, 2, 3, 4, 5]$$

```
> eval(a);
```

$$[1, 2, 3, 4, 5]$$

Maple determines that the A and p variables in the **partition** sub-procedure are defined by the parameter and local variable (respectively) from the outer **quicksort** procedure and everything works as planned. We could also have passed A as a parameter to the **partition** subprocedure (as we did when **partition** was a stand-alone procedure), but because of the scoping rules, it wasn't necessary.

Creating a Uniform Random Number Generator

If you want to use Maple to simulate physical experiments, you likely need a random number generator. The uniform distribution is particularly simple: any real number in a given range is equally likely. Thus, a *uniform random number generator* is a procedure that returns a random floating-point number within a certain range. This section develops the procedure, `uniform`, which creates uniform random number generators.

The `rand` command generates a procedure which returns random *integers*. For example, `rand(4..7)` generates a procedure that returns random integers between 4 and 7, inclusive.

```
> f := rand(4..7):
> seq( f(), i=1..20 );
```

$$5, 6, 5, 7, 4, 6, 5, 4, 5, 5, 7, 7, 5, 4, 6, 5, 4, 5, 7, 5$$

The `uniform` procedure should be similar to `rand` but should return floating-point numbers rather than integers. You can use `rand` to generate random floating-point numbers between 4 and 7 by multiplying and dividing by `10^Digits`.

```
> f := rand( 4*10^Digits..7*10^Digits ) / 10^Digits:
> f();
```

$$\frac{12210706011}{2000000000}$$

The procedure `f` returns fractions rather than floating-point numbers so you must compose it with `evalf`; that is, use `evalf(f())`. Alternatively, you can perform this operation by using Maple's composition operator, `@`.

```
> (evalf @ f)();
```

$$6.648630719$$

The `uniform` procedure below uses `evalf` to evaluate the constants in the range specification, `r`, to floating-point numbers, the `map` command to multiply both endpoints of the range by `10^Digits`, and `round` to round the results to integers.

```
> uniform := proc( r::constant..constant )
>    local intrange, f;
>    intrange := map( x -> round(x*10^Digits), evalf(r) );
>    f := rand( intrange );
>    (evalf @ eval(f)) / 10^Digits;
> end proc:
```

You can now generate random floating-point numbers between 4 and 7.

```
> U := uniform(4..7):
> seq( U(), i=1..20 );
```

4.559076346, 4.939267370, 5.542851096, 4.260060897,
4.976009937, 5.598293374, 4.547350944,
5.647078832, 5.133877918, 5.249590037,
4.120953928, 6.836344299, 5.374608653,
4.586266491, 5.481365622, 5.384244382,
5.190575456, 5.207535837, 5.553710879,
4.163815544

The `uniform` procedure suffers from a serious flaw: `uniform` uses the current value of `Digits` to construct `intrange`; thus, U depends on the value of `Digits` when `uniform` creates it. On the other hand, the `evalf` command within U uses the value of `Digits` that is current when you invoke U. These two values are not always identical.

```
> U := uniform( cos(2)..sin(1) ):
> Digits := 15:
> seq( U(), i=1..8 );
```

.828316845400000, −.328875163100000,
.790988967100000, .624953401700000,
.362773633800000, .679519822000000,
−.0465278542000000, −.291055180800000

The proper design choice here is that U should depend only on the value of `Digits` when you invoke U. The version of `uniform` below accomplishes this by placing all the computation inside the procedure that `uniform` returns.

```
> uniform := proc( r::constant..constant )
>
>    proc()
>        local intrange, f;
>        intrange := map( x -> round(x*10^Digits),
>                         evalf(r) );
>        f := rand( intrange );
>        evalf( f()/10^Digits );
>    end proc;
> end proc:
```

The **r** within the inner **proc** is not declared as local or global, so it becomes the same **r** as the parameter to the outer **proc**.

The procedure that **uniform** generates is now independent of the value of **Digits** at the time you invoke **uniform**.

```
> U := uniform( cos(2)..sin(1) ):
> Digits := 15:
> seq( U(), i=1..8 );
```

.476383408581006, .554836962987261,
.147655743361511, .273247304736175,
.148172828708797, −.258115633420094,
.558246581434993, .518084711267009

This section introduced you to the rules Maple uses to decide which variables are global or local. You have also seen the principal implications of these rules. In particular, it introduced you to the tools available for writing nested procedures.

2.3   Types

Types that Modify Evaluation Rules

Section 2.1 introduces the details of how Maple evaluates different kinds of variables within a procedure: Maple evaluates global variables fully (except for last-name evaluation) and local variables to one level. Maple evaluates the arguments to a procedure, depending upon the circumstances, *before* invoking the procedure, and then simply substitutes the actual parameters for the formal parameters within the procedure without any further evaluation. All these rules seem to imply that nothing within the procedure in any way affects the evaluation of arguments which occurs *before* Maple invokes the procedure. In reality, the exceptions provide convenient methods for controlling the evaluation of arguments which make your procedures behave more intuitively. They also prevent evaluation which would result in the loss of information you wish available within your procedure.

Maple uses different evaluation rules for some of its own commands, for example, the **evaln** command. You have no doubt used this command to clear the value of previously defined variables. If this command were to evaluate its argument normally, it would be of no use for this purpose.

For example, if you assign x the value π, then Maple evaluates x to π whenever you use the variable x.

```
> x := Pi;
```

$$x := \pi$$

```
> cos(x);
```

$$-1$$

If Maple behaved the same way when you type `evaln(x)`, then Maple would pass the value π to `evaln`, losing all references to the name x. Therefore, Maple evaluates the argument to `evaln` in a special way: it evaluates the argument to a name, not to the value that name may have.

```
> x := evaln(x);
```

$$x := x$$

```
> cos(x);
```

$$\cos(x)$$

You will find it useful to write your own procedures which exhibit this behavior. You may want to write a procedure which returns a value by assigning it to one of the arguments. Section 2.1 describes such a procedure, `sqr1`, but each time you call `sqr1` you must take care to pass it an unassigned name.

```
> sqr1:= proc(x::anything, y::name)
>    y := x^2;
> end proc:
```

This procedure works fine the first time you call it. However, you must make sure that the second argument is indeed a name; otherwise, an error results. In the example below, the error occurs because, upon the second attempt, `ans` has the value 9.

```
> ans;
```

$$ans$$

```
> sqr1(3, ans);
```

$$9$$

```
> ans;
```

$$9$$

```
> sqr1(4, ans);
```

```
Error, invalid input: sqr1 expects its 2nd argument, y,
to be of type name, but received 9
```

You have two ways around this problem. The first is to use either single quotes or the **evaln** command to ensure that Maple passes a name and not a value. The second is to declare the parameter to be of type **evaln**.

Just like the **evaln** command, declaring a parameter to be of type **evaln** causes Maple to evaluate that argument to a name, so you do not have to worry about evaluation when you use the procedure.

```
> cube := proc(x::anything, y::evaln)
>     y := x^3;
> end proc:
> ans;
```

$$9$$

```
> cube(5, ans);
```

$$125$$

```
> ans;
```

$$125$$

In the above case, Maple passes the name **ans** to the **cube** procedure instead of the value 9.

Using the **evaln** declaration is generally a good idea. It ensures that your procedures do what you expect instead of returning cryptic error messages. However, some Maple programmers like to use the single quotes. When the call to the procedure is within a procedure itself, the presence of the single quotes is a reminder that you are assigning a value to a parameter. However, if you plan to use your procedure interactively, you will find using **evaln** far more convenient.

A second type which modifies Maple's evaluation rules is **uneval**. Where **evaln** makes Maple evaluate the argument to a name, **uneval** leaves the argument unevaluated. This type is useful for two reasons. First, sometimes you wish to write a procedure which treats a structure as an object and does not require knowledge of the details. Second, sometimes expanding the argument within the procedure is useful. You may want to write a version of the **map** command which is capable of mapping over sequences. The standard **map** command built into Maple is not capable of this because it evaluates its second argument. If the second argument is the name of a sequence, Maple evaluates the name to the sequence before invoking **map**. Since Maple flattens sequences of sequences, it passes only the first element of the sequence as the second argument to **map** and the other elements become additional arguments.

The **smap** procedure below uses an **uneval** declaration to tell Maple not to evaluate its second argument. Once inside the procedure, the **eval** command fully evaluates S. The **whattype** command returns **exprseq** if you pass it a sequence.

```
> whattype( a, b, c );
```

$$exprseq$$

If S is not a sequence, **smap** simply calls **map**. **args[3..-1]** is the sequence of arguments to **smap** after S. If S is a sequence, enclosing it in square brackets forms a list. You can then map f onto the list and use the selection operator, **[]**, to turn the resulting list back into a sequence.

```
> smap := proc( f::anything, S::uneval )
>    local s;
>    s := eval(S);
>    if whattype(s) = 'exprseq' then
>        map( f, [s], args[3..-1] )[];
>    else
>        map( f, s, args[3..-1] );
>    end if;
> end proc:
```

Now you can map over sequences as well as lists, sets, and other expressions.

```
> S := 1,2,3,4;
```

$$S := 1, 2, 3, 4$$

```
> smap(f, S, x, y);
```

$$f(1, x, y), f(2, x, y), f(3, x, y), f(4, x, y)$$

```
> smap(f, [a,b,c], x, y);
```

$$[f(a, x, y), f(b, x, y), f(c, x, y)]$$

Both `evaln` and `uneval` greatly extend the flexibility of Maple's programming language and the types of procedures you can write.

Structured Types

Sometimes a simple type check, either through declared formal parameters or explicitly with the `type` command, does not provide enough information. A simple check tells you that 2^x is an exponentiation but it does not distinguish between 2^x and x^2.

```
> type( 2^x, '^' );
```

$$true$$

```
> type( x^2, '^' );
```

$$true$$

To make such distinctions you need *structured types*. For example, 2 is a `constant` and x is a `name`, so 2^x has type `constant^name` but x^2 does not.

```
> type( 2^x, constant^name );
```

$$true$$

```
> type( x^2, constant^name );
```

$$false$$

Suppose you want to solve a set of equations. Before proceeding you want to remove any equations that are trivially true, like $4 = 4$. Thus, you need to write a procedure that accepts a set of equations as input. The procedure **nontrivial** below uses automatic type checking to ensure that the argument is indeed a set of equations.

```
> nontrivial := proc( S::set( '=' ) )
>    remove( evalb, S );
> end proc:
> nontrivial( { x^2+2*x+1=0, y=y, z=2/x } );
```

$$\{x^2 + 2\,x + 1 = 0, \ z = \frac{2}{x}\}$$

You can easily extend **nontrivial** so that it accepts general relations rather than just equations, and so that it allows both sets and lists of relations. An expression matches a set of types if it matches one of the types in the set.

```
> nontrivial := proc( S::{ set(relation), list(relation) } )
>    remove( evalb, S );
> end proc:
> nontrivial( [ 2<=78, 1/x=9 ] );
```

$$[\frac{1}{x} = 9]$$

You can extend **nontrivial** even further: if an element in S is not a relation but an algebraic expression, f, then **nontrivial** should treat it as the equation $f = 0$.

```
> nontrivial := proc( S::{  set( {relation, algebraic} ),
>                           list( {relation, algebraic} ) } )
>    local istrivial;
>    istrivial := proc(x)
>        if type(x, relation) then evalb(x);
>        else evalb( x=0 );
>        end if;
>    end proc;
>    remove( istrivial, S );
> end proc:
> nontrivial( [ x^2+2*x+1, 23>2, x=-1, y-y ] );
```

$$[x^2 + 2\,x + 1, \ x = -1]$$

Automatic type checking is a very powerful tool. It allows you to do a large amount of checking for invalid arguments automatically. You should make using it a habit. Structured types allow checking even when you design a procedure to accept a variety of inputs, or to rely on a particular structure in its arguments.

Automatic type checking has two weaknesses. First, if the structure of the type is complicated, permitting several structures, then the code for the type checking can become cumbersome. The second is that Maple does not save any of the information about the structure of the arguments. It parses and checks them, but then the structure is lost. If you wish to extract a particular component of the structure you must write more code to do so.

The complexity of the types is rarely of concern in practice. A procedure which relies on arguments with a complicated structure is usually hard to use. The **typematch** command addresses the duplication of effort in parsing the arguments. This command provides a more flexible alternative method of type checking.

Type Matching

Section 1.4 describes the following pair of procedures that implement indefinite integration of any polynomial multiplied by e^x.

```
> IntExpMonomial := proc(n::nonnegint, x::name)
>     if n=0 then return exp(x)   end if;
>     x^n*exp(x) - n*IntExpMonomial(n-1, x);
> end proc:
> IntExpPolynomial := proc(p::polynom, x::name)
>     local i, result;
>     result := add( coeff(p, x, i)*IntExpMonomial(i, x),
>                     i=0..degree(p, x) );
>     collect(result, exp(x));
> end proc:
```

You may want to modify **IntExpPolynomial** so that it can also perform definite integration. The new version of **IntExpPolynomial** should allow its second argument to be a name, in which case **IntExpPolynomial** should perform indefinite integration, or the form *name=range*. You could use the **type** command and **if** statements to do this, but then the procedure becomes difficult to read.

```
> IntExpPolynomial := proc(p::polynom, xx::{name, name=range})
>     local i, result, x, a, b;
>     if type(xx, name) then
>         x:=xx;
>     else
>         x := lhs(xx);
>         a := lhs(rhs(xx));
>         b := rhs(rhs(xx));
>     end if;
>     result := add( coeff(p, x, i)*IntExpMonomial(i, x),
```

```
>                        i=0..degree(p, x) );
>      if type(xx, name) then
>          collect(result, exp(x));
>      else
>          eval(result, x=b) - eval(result, x=a);
>      end if;
> end proc:
```

Using the `typematch` command makes your procedure much easier to read. The `typematch` command not only tests if an expression matches a certain type, it can also assign variables to pieces of the expression. Below, `typematch` checks that `expr` is of the form `name=integer..integer` *and* it assigns the name to y, the left-hand limit to a, and the right-hand limit to b.

```
> expr := myvar=1..6;
```

$$expr := myvar = 1..6$$

```
> typematch( expr, y::name=a::integer..b::integer );
```

$$true$$

```
> y, a, b;
```

$$myvar, 1, 6$$

The version of `IntExpPolynomial` below uses the `typematch` command.

```
> IntExpPolynomial := proc(p::polynom, expr::anything )
>     local i, result, x, a, b;
>     if not typematch( expr, {x::name,
>           x::name=a::anything..b::anything} ) then
>         error( "expects a name or name=range but received",
>                 expr );
>     end if;
>     result := add( coeff(p, x, i)*IntExpMonomial(i, x),
>                     i=0..degree(p, x) );
>     if type(expr, name) then
>         collect(result, exp(x));
>     else
>         eval(result, x=b) - eval(result, x=a);
>     end if;
> end proc:
```

Now `IntExpPolynomial` can perform definite, as well as indefinite, integrals.

```
> IntExpPolynomial( x^2+x^5*(1-x), x=1..2 );
```

$$-118\,e^2 + 308\,e$$

```
> IntExpPolynomial( x^2*(x-1), x);
```

$$(-4\,x^2 + 8\,x - 8 + x^3)\,e^x$$

2.4   Choosing a Data Structure: Connected Graphs

When writing programs you have to decide how to represent the data. Sometimes the choice is straightforward but often it requires considerable thought and planning. Some choices of data structure may make your procedures more efficient or easier to write and debug. No doubt you are familiar with Maple's many available data structures, such as sequences, lists, tables, and sets.

This section uses a variety of structures and discusses their advantages. This section also illustrates, by means of an example, the problem of choosing a data structure.

Suppose you have a number of cities with roads between them. Write a procedure that determines whether you can travel between any two cities.

You can express this problem in terms of graph theory. Maple has a **networks** package that helps you work with graphs and more general structures. You do not need to understand graph theory or the **networks** package to benefit from the examples in this section; these examples primarily use the **networks** package as a shortcut to the drawing of G, below.

```
> with(networks):
```

Make a new graph G and add a few cities (or *vertices*, in the terminology of graph theory).

```
> new(G):
> cities := {Zurich, Rome, Paris, Berlin, Vienna};
```

$$cities := \{Zurich,\ Rome,\ Paris,\ Berlin,\ Vienna\}$$

```
> addvertex(cities, G);
```

$$Zurich,\ Rome,\ Paris,\ Berlin,\ Vienna$$

Add roads between Zurich and each of Paris, Berlin, and Vienna. The **connect** command names the roads $e1$, $e2$, and $e3$.

```
> connect( {Zurich}, {Paris, Berlin, Vienna}, G );
```

$$e1,\ e2,\ e3$$

Add roads between Rome and Zurich and between Berlin and both Paris and Vienna.

```
> connect( {Rome}, {Zurich}, G);
```

$$e4$$

```
> connect( {Berlin}, {Vienna, Paris}, G);
```

$$e5,\ e6$$

Now draw the graph G.

```
> draw(G);
```

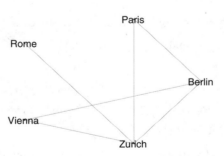

If you look at the drawing above, you can convince yourself that, in this particular case, you could travel between any two cities. Instead of visual inspection, you can also use the **connectivity** command.

```
> evalb( connectivity(G) > 0 );
```

$$true$$

The data structures that the **networks** package uses are quite involved, because that package supports more general structures than you
need in this example. The question then is: how would *you* represent the
cities and roads? Since cities have distinct names and the order of the
cities is irrelevant, you could represent the cities as a set of names.

```
> vertices(G);
```

$$\{Zurich,\ Rome,\ Paris,\ Berlin,\ Vienna\}$$

The **networks** package assigns distinct names to the roads, so it can
also represent them as set of names.

```
> edges(G);
```

$$\{e1,\ e2,\ e3,\ e4,\ e5,\ e6\}$$

You can also represent a road as the set consisting of the two cities
the road connects.

```
> ends(e2, G);
```

$$\{Zurich,\ Berlin\}$$

Thus, you can represent the roads as a set of sets.

```
> roads := map( ends, edges(G), G);
```

$$roads := \{\{Zurich,\ Rome\},\ \{Zurich,\ Paris\},$$
$$\{Zurich,\ Berlin\},\ \{Zurich,\ Vienna\},\ \{Paris,\ Berlin\},$$
$$\{Berlin,\ Vienna\}\}$$

Unfortunately, if you want to know which cities are directly connected
to Rome, for example, you have to search through the whole set of roads.
Therefore, representing the data as a set of cities and a set of roads is computationally inefficient for determining whether you can travel between
any two cities.

You can also represent the data as an *adjacency matrix*: a square matrix with a row for each city. The (i, j)th entry in the matrix is 1 if the ith and the jth city have a road between them, and 0 otherwise. The following is the adjacency matrix for the graph G.

```
> adjacency(G);
```

$$\begin{bmatrix} 0 & 1 & 0 & 1 & 1 \\ 1 & 0 & 0 & 0 & 1 \\ 0 & 0 & 0 & 0 & 1 \\ 1 & 0 & 0 & 0 & 1 \\ 1 & 1 & 1 & 1 & 0 \end{bmatrix}$$

The adjacency matrix is an inefficient representation if few roads exist relative to the number of cities. In that case, the matrix contains many zeros, representing an overall lack of roads. Also, though each row in the matrix corresponds to a city, you cannot tell which row corresponds to which city.

Here is yet another way of representing the cities and roads: Paris has two roads between it and both Zurich and Berlin; thus, Berlin and Zurich are the neighbors of Paris.

```
> neighbors(Paris, G);
```

$$\{Zurich,\ Berlin\}$$

You can represent the data as a table of neighbors; one entry should be in the table for each city.

```
> T := table( map( v -> (v)=neighbors(v,G), cities ) );
```

$T :=$ table([$Zurich = \{Rome,\ Paris,\ Berlin,\ Vienna\}$,
$Rome = \{Zurich\},\ Paris = \{Zurich,\ Berlin\}$,
$Berlin = \{Zurich,\ Paris,\ Vienna\}$,
$Vienna = \{Zurich,\ Berlin\}$
])

The representation of a system of cities and roads as a table of neighbors is ideally suited to answering the question of whether it is possible to travel between any two cities. You can begin at one city. The table allows you to efficiently find the neighboring cities to which you can travel.

Similarly, you can find the neighbors of the neighbors, and thus you can quickly determine how far you can travel.

The **connected** procedure below determines whether you can travel between any two cities. It uses the **indices** command to extract the set of cities from the table.

```
> indices(T);
```

$$[Zurich], [Rome], [Paris], [Berlin], [Vienna]$$

Since the **indices** command returns a sequence of lists, you must use the **op** and **map** command to generate the set.

```
> map( op, {%} );
```

$$\{Zurich, \ Rome, \ Paris, \ Berlin, \ Vienna\}$$

The **connected** procedure initially visits the first city, v. Then **connected** adds v to the set of cities that it has already visited and v's neighbors to the set of cities to which it can travel. As long as **connected** can travel to more cities, it will. When **connected** has no more new cities to which it can travel, it determines whether it has seen all the cities.

```
> connected := proc( T::table )
>    local canvisit, seen, v, V;
>    V := map( op, { indices(T) } );
>    seen := {};
>    canvisit := { V[1] };
>    while canvisit <> {} do
>        v := canvisit[1];
>        seen := seen union {v};
>        canvisit := ( canvisit union T[v] ) minus seen;
>    end do;
>    evalb( seen = V );
> end proc:
> connected(T);
```

$$true$$

You can add the cities Montreal, Toronto, and Waterloo, and the highway between them.

```
> T[Waterloo] := {Toronto};
```

$$T_{Waterloo} := \{\,Toronto\,\}$$

```
> T[Toronto] := {Waterloo, Montreal};
```

$$T_{Toronto} := \{\,Waterloo,\ Montreal\,\}$$

```
> T[Montreal] := {Toronto};
```

$$T_{Montreal} := \{\,Toronto\,\}$$

Now you can no longer travel between any two cities; for example, you cannot travel from Paris to Waterloo.

```
> connected(T);
```

$$false$$

Exercises

1. The system of cities and roads above splits naturally into two components: the Canadian cities and the roads between them, and the European cities and the roads between them. In each component you can travel between any two cities but you cannot travel between the two components. Write a procedure that, given a table of neighbors, splits the system into such components. You may want to think about the form in which the procedure should return its result.

2. The **connected** procedure above cannot handle the empty table of neighbors.

```
> connected( table() );
```

```
Error, (in connected) invalid subscript selector
```

Correct this shortcoming.

The importance of this example is not to teach you about networks, but to emphasize how the choice of data structures suited to the problem allows you to create an efficient and concise version of the procedure **connected**. Sets and tables were the best choices here. The best choice for a problem that you wish to tackle may be very different. Before writing code to perform your task, pause to consider which structures best suit your needs. A good program design begins with choosing structures and methods which mirror the data and task at hand.

2.5   Remember Tables

Sometimes procedures are designed such that they are called repeatedly with the same arguments. Each time, Maple has to recompute the same answer, unless you take advantage of Maple's concept of *remember tables*.

Any Maple procedure can have a remember table. The purpose of a remember table is to improve the efficiency of a procedure by storing previous results so that Maple can retrieve them from the table instead of recomputing them.

A remember table uses the sequence of actual parameters to the procedure call as the table index, and the results of the procedure calls as the table values. Whenever you invoke a procedure which has a remember table, Maple searches the table for an index which is the sequence of actual parameters. If such an index is found, it returns the corresponding value in the table as the result of the procedure call. Otherwise, Maple executes the body of the procedure.

Maple tables are hash tables, so looking up previously computed results is very fast. The purpose of remember tables is to make use of fast table lookup in order to avoid recomputing results. Since remember tables can become large, they are most useful when procedures need the same results repeatedly and the results are expensive to compute.

The remember Option

Use the **remember** option to indicate to Maple that it should store the result of a call to a procedure in a remember table. The **Fibonacci** procedure in section 1.2 is an example of a recursive procedure with the **remember** option.

```
> Fibonacci := proc(n::nonnegint)
>     option remember;
>     if n<2 then return n end if;
>     Fibonacci(n-1) + Fibonacci(n-2);
> end proc:
```

Section 1.2 demonstrates that the **Fibonacci** procedure is very slow without the **remember** option, since it must compute the lower Fibonacci numbers many times.

When you ask **Fibonacci** to calculate the third Fibonacci number, it adds four entries to its remember table. The remember table is the fourth operand of a procedure.

```
> Fibonacci(3);
```

2

```
> op(4, eval(Fibonacci));
```

$$\text{table}([0 = 0,\ 1 = 1,\ 2 = 1,\ 3 = 2])$$

Adding Entries Explicitly

You can also define entries in procedure remember tables yourself. To do so, use the following syntax.

```
f(x) := result:
```

Below is another procedure which generates the Fibonacci numbers. The **fib** procedure uses two entries in its remember table, where **Fibonacci** uses an **if** statement.

```
> fib := proc(n::nonnegint)
>    option remember;
>    fib(n-1) + fib(n-2);
> end proc:
> fib(0) := 0:
> fib(1) := 1:
```

You must add entries in the remember table *after* making the procedure. The **option remember** statement does *not* create the remember table, but rather asks Maple to automatically *add* entries to it. The procedure works without this option, but less efficiently.

You could even write a procedure which chooses which values to add to its remember table. The following version of **fib** only adds entries to its remember table when you call it with an odd-valued argument.

```
> fib := proc(n::nonnegint)
>    if type(n,odd) then
>        fib(n) := fib(n-1) + fib(n-2);
>    else
>        fib(n-1) + fib(n-2);
>    end if;
> end proc:
> fib(0) := 0:
> fib(1) := 1:
> fib(9);
```

34

```
> op(4, eval(fib));
```

$$\text{table}([0 = 0, 1 = 1, 3 = 2, 5 = 5, 7 = 13, 9 = 34])$$

As in this case, sometimes you can dramatically improve the efficiency of a procedure by remembering only some of the values instead of none.

Removing Entries from a Remember Table

You can remove entries from a remember table in the same manner you remove entries from any other table: assign a table entry to its own name. The **evaln** command evaluates an object to its name.

```
> T := op(4, eval(fib) );
```

$$T := \text{table}([0 = 0, 1 = 1, 3 = 2, 5 = 5, 7 = 13, 9 = 34])$$

```
> T[7] := evaln( T[7] );
```

$$T_7 := T_7$$

Now the **fib** procedure's remember table has only five entries.

```
> op(4, eval(fib) );
```

$$\text{table}([0 = 0, 1 = 1, 3 = 2, 5 = 5, 9 = 34])$$

Maple can also remove remember table entries automatically. If you give your procedure the **system** option, then Maple may remove entries in the procedure's remember table when Maple performs a garbage collection. Thus, you should *never* give the **system** option to procedures like **fib** that rely on entries in its remember table to terminate.

You can remove a procedure's remember table altogether by substituting NULL for the procedure's fourth operand.

```
> subsop( 4=NULL, eval(Fibonacci) ):
> op(4, eval(Fibonacci));
```

You should use remember tables only with procedures whose results depend exclusively on parameters. The procedure below depends on the value of the environment variable **Digits**.

```
> f := proc(x::constant)
>    option remember;
>    evalf(x);
> end proc:
> f(Pi);
```

$$3.141592654$$

Even if you change the value of `Digits`, `f(Pi)` remains unchanged because Maple retrieves the value from the remember table.

```
> Digits := Digits + 34;
```

$$Digits := 44$$

```
> f(Pi);
```

$$3.141592654$$

2.6 Conclusion

A thorough understanding of the concepts in this chapter will provide you with an excellent foundation for understanding Maple's language. The time you spend studying this chapter will save you hours puzzling over trivial problems in subroutines and procedures which appear to behave erratically. With the knowledge contained here, you should now see the source of such problems with clarity. Just as you may have done after finishing chapter 1, you may wish to put this book down for a while and practice creating more of your own procedures.

Chapter 3 introduces you to more advanced techniques in Maple programming. For example, it discusses procedures which return procedures, procedures which query the user for input, and packages which you can design yourself.

The remaining chapters of this manual are independent from one another. You can focus on the topics of interest to you, for example, the Maple debugger or Maple graphics programming. If you wish a more formal presentation of the Maple language, take a look at chapters 4 and 5.

3   Advanced Programming

As you progress in learning the Maple programming language and tackling more challenging projects, you may discover that you would like more detailed information. The topics in this chapter are more advanced than those in previous chapters, and some are difficult to follow without a sound understanding of Maple's evaluation rules, scoping rules, and other principal concepts.

The first two sections in this chapter begin where section 2.2 left off, using and returning procedures within the same procedure. Armed with a basic knowledge of Maple's evaluation rules, you will discover that such procedures are not difficult to write.

Surprisingly, local variables can exist long after the procedure which created them has finished. This feature can be particularly useful when you wish a procedure to return a procedure, but the new procedure needs a unique place to store information. Maple's `assume` facility, for example, uses such variables. The second section clearly explains and demonstrates how to use them effectively.

Two special topics make up the remainder of this chapter: interactive input and extending Maple. Interactive input allows you to write interactive procedures, making them more intuitive by querying the user for missing information. Perhaps you wish to write an interactive tutorial or a test. You are already aware of the customization power which you gain through the ability to write procedures; Maple also supplies some particularly useful mechanisms for modifying or extending Maple's functionality other than by writing a completely separate group of commands. In conjunction with the topics you find in the specialized chapters in the remainder of this book, the topics here will equip you to use Maple to its fullest.

3.1 Procedures Which Return Procedures

Of all the types of procedures you may want to write, procedures which return procedures are likely to cause the most trouble. Creating these procedures builds upon the material presented in chapter 2, which covered procedures within procedures, how Maple evaluates parameters, and how Maple assigns and evaluates both local and global variables. You also learned, for example, that an inner procedure recognizes the variable declarations of an outer procedure.

Some of the standard Maple commands return procedures. For example, **rand** returns a procedure which in turn produces randomly chosen integers from a specified range. If you use the **type=numeric** option with **dsolve**, it returns a procedure which supplies a numeric estimate of the solution to a differential equation.

You may wish to incorporate such features into your own programs. The areas which require your particular attention are those of conveying values from the outer procedure to the inner procedure, and the use of local variables to store information unique to a returned procedure. This section discusses the former. The latter is the topic of the next section, section 3.2.

Creating a Newton Iteration

Newton's method is one way of locating the roots of a function. First, you pick a point on the x-axis that you think might be close to a root. Next, you find the slope of the curve at the point you picked. Draw the tangent to the curve at that point and observe where the tangent intersects the x-axis. For most functions, this second point is closer to the real root than your initial guess. Thus, to find the root, all you need to do is use the new point as a new guess and keep drawing tangents and finding new points.

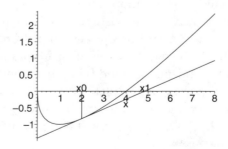

To find a numerical solution to the equation $f(x) = 0$, you may use Newton's method: guess an approximate solution, x_0; then use the following formula, which is the mathematical description of the above process, to generate better approximations.

$$x_{k+1} = x_k - \frac{f(x_k)}{f'(x_k)}$$

You can implement this algorithm in Maple in a number of ways. The program below takes a function and creates a new procedure, which takes an initial guess and, for that particular function, generates the next guess. Of course, the new procedure will not work for other functions. To find the roots of a new function, use **MakeIteration** to generate a new guess-generating procedure. The **unapply** command turns an expression into a procedure.

```
> MakeIteration := proc( expr::algebraic, x::name )
>     local iteration;
>     iteration := x - expr/diff(expr, x);
>     unapply(iteration, x);
> end proc:
```

Test the procedure on the expression $x - 2\sqrt{x}$.

```
> expr := x - 2*sqrt(x);
```

$$expr := x - 2\sqrt{x}$$

```
> Newton := MakeIteration( expr, x);
```

$$Newton := x \rightarrow x - \frac{x - 2\sqrt{x}}{1 - \frac{1}{\sqrt{x}}}$$

It only takes **Newton** a few iterations to find the solution, $x = 4$.

```
> x0 := 2.0;
```

$$x0 := 2.0$$

```
> to 4 do x0 := Newton(x0);  end do;
```

$$x0 := 4.828427124$$

$$x0 := 4.032533198$$

$$x0 := 4.000065353$$

$$x0 := 4.000000000$$

The `MakeIteration` procedure above expects its first argument to be an algebraic expression. You can also write a version of `MakeIteration` that works on functions. Since `MakeIteration` below knows that the parameter f is a procedure, you must use the `eval` command to evaluate it fully.

```
> MakeIteration := proc( f::procedure )
>    (x->x) - eval(f) / D(eval(f));
> end proc:
> g := x -> x - cos(x);
```

$$g := x \rightarrow x - \cos(x)$$

```
> SirIsaac := MakeIteration( g );
```

$$SirIsaac := (x \rightarrow x) - \frac{x \rightarrow x - \cos(x)}{x \rightarrow 1 + \sin(x)}$$

Note that `SirIsaac` does not contain references to the name g; thus, you can change g without breaking `SirIsaac`. You can find a good approximate solution to $x - \cos(x) = 0$ in a few iterations.

```
> x0 := 1.0;
```

$$x0 := 1.0$$

```
> to 4 do x0 := SirIsaac(x0) end do;
```

$$x0 := .7503638679$$

$$x0 := .7391128909$$

$$x0 := .7390851334$$

$$x0 := .7390851332$$

A Shift Operator

Consider the problem of writing a procedure that takes a function, f, as input and returns a function, g, such that $g(x) = f(x+1)$. You can write such a procedure in the following manner.

```
> shift := (f::procedure) -> ( x->f(x+1) ):
```

Try performing a shift on $\sin(x)$.

```
> shift(sin);
```

$$x \to \sin(x+1)$$

Maple's lexical scoping rules declare the f within the inner procedure to be the same f as the parameter within the outer procedure. Therefore, the command **shift** works as written.

The version of **shift** above works with univariate functions but it does not work with functions of two or more variables.

```
> h := (x,y) -> x*y;
```

$$h := (x, y) \to x\,y$$

```
> hh := shift(h);
```

$$hh := x \to h(x+1)$$

```
> hh(x,y);
```

```
Error, (in h) h uses a 2nd argument, y, which is
missing
```

If you want **shift** to work with multivariate functions, you must rewrite it to deal with the additional parameters. In a procedure, **args** is the sequence of actual parameters, and **args[2..-1]** is the sequence of actual parameters except the first one; see section 4.4. It follows that the procedure x->f(x+1,args[2..-1]) passes all its arguments except the first directly to f.

```
> shift := (f::procedure) -> ( x->f(x+1, args[2..-1]) ):
```

```
> hh := shift(h);
```

$$hh := x \rightarrow h(x+1, \text{args}_{2..-1})$$

```
> hh(x,y);
```

$$(x+1)\,y$$

The function **hh** depends on **h**; if you change **h**, you implicitly change **hh**;

```
> h := (x,y,z) -> y*z^2/x;
```

$$h := (x,\,y,\,z) \rightarrow \frac{y\,z^2}{x}$$

```
> hh(x,y,z);
```

$$\frac{y\,z^2}{x+1}$$

3.2   When Local Variables Leave Home

Section 2.2 states that local variables are not only local to a procedure but also to an invocation of that procedure. Very simply, calling a procedure creates and uses new local variables each time. If you invoke the same procedure twice, the local variables it uses the second time are distinct from those it used the first time.

What may surprise you is that the local variables do not necessarily disappear when the procedure exits. You can write procedures which return a local variable, either explicitly or implicitly, to the interactive session, where it may survive indefinitely. You may find these renegade local variables confusing, particularly since they may have the same name as some global variables, or even other local variables which another procedure or a different call to the same procedure created. In fact, you can create as many distinct variables as you want, all with the same name.

The procedure below creates a new local variable, **a**, and then returns this new variable.

```
> make_a := proc()
>        local a;
>        a;
> end proc;
```

$$make\_a := \textbf{proc}()\,\textbf{local}\,a;\ a\,\textbf{end proc}$$

Since a set in Maple contains *unique* elements, you can easily verify that each a that make_a returns is unique.

```
> test := { a, a, a };
```

$$test := \{a\}$$

```
> test := test union { make_a() };
```

$$test := \{a,\ a\}$$

```
> test := test union { 'make_a'()$5 };
```

$$test := \{a,\ a,\ a,\ a,\ a,\ a,\ a\}$$

Obviously, Maple identifies variables by more than their names.

Remember that no matter how many variables you create with the same name, when you type a name in an interactive session, Maple interprets that name to be of a *global* variable. Indeed, you can easily find the global a in the above set test .

```
> seq( evalb(i=a), i=test);
```

$$true,\ false,\ false,\ false,\ false,\ false,\ false$$

You can use local variables to make Maple print things it would not ordinarily be able to display. The above set **test** is an example. Another example is expressions which Maple would ordinarily simplify automatically. For example, Maple automatically simplifies the expression $a + a$ to $2a$, so displaying the equation $a+a = 2a$ is not easy. You can create the illusion that Maple is showing you these steps using procedure make_a, above.

```
> a + make_a() = 2*a;
```

$$a + a = 2\,a$$

To Maple, these two variables are distinct, even though they share the same name.

You cannot easily assign a value to such escapees. Whenever you type a name in an interactive session, Maple thinks you mean the global variable of that name. While this prevents you from using the assignment *statement*, it does not prevent you from using the assignment *command*. The trick is to write a Maple expression which extracts the variable you want. For example, in the equation above, you may extract the local **a** by removing the global **a** from the left-hand side of the equation.

```
> eqn := %;
```

$$eqn := a + a = 2\,a$$

```
> another_a := remove( x->evalb(x=a), lhs(eqn) );
```

$$another\_a := a$$

You may then assign the global name **a** to this extracted variable and so verify the equation.

```
> assign(another_a = a);
> eqn;
```

$$2\,a = 2\,a$$

```
> evalb(%);
```

$$true$$

Should your expression be complicated, you may need a fancier command to extract the desired variable.

You may have encountered this situation before without realizing it, when you were using the **assume** facility and wished to remove an assumption. The **assume** facility attaches various definitions to the variable you specify, with one result being that the name subsequently appears as a *local* name with an appended tilde. Maple does not understand if you type the tilde name because no relationship exists with the *global* variable name containing a tilde.

```
> assume(b>0);
> x := b + 1;
```

$$x := b^{\sim} + 1$$

```
> subs( 'b~'=c, x);
```

$$b^{\sim} + 1$$

When you clear the definition of the named variable the association between the name and the local name with the tilde is lost, but expressions created with the local name still contain it.

```
> b := evaln(b);
```

$$b := b$$

```
> x;
```

$$b^{\sim} + 1$$

If you later wish to reuse your expression, you must either perform a substitution before removing the assumption or perform some manipulations of your expressions similar to the equation eqn.

Creating the Cartesian Product of a Sequence of Sets

An important use for returning local objects arises when the returned object is a procedure. When you write a procedure which returns a procedure, you will often find it useful to have the procedure create a variable which holds information pertinent only to the returned procedure. This allows different procedures (or different invocations of the same procedure) to pass information between themselves.

The program introduced in this section uses this idea. When you pass a sequence of sets to the procedure it constructs a new procedure. The new procedure returns the next term in the Cartesian product each time you invoke it. Local variables from the outer procedure are used to keep track of which term to return next.

The *Cartesian product* of a sequence of sets is the set of all lists whose *i*th entry is an element of the *i*th set. Thus, the Cartesian product of $\{\alpha, \beta, \gamma\}$ and $\{x, y\}$ is

$$\{\alpha, \beta, \gamma\} \times \{x, y\} = \{[\alpha, x], [\beta, x], [\gamma, x], [\alpha, y], [\beta, y], [\gamma, y]\}.$$

The number of elements in the Cartesian product of a sequence of sets grows very rapidly as the sequence gets longer or the sets get larger. It therefore requires a large amount of memory to store all the elements of the Cartesian product. One way around this is to write a procedure that returns a new element of the Cartesian product each time you call it. By calling such a procedure repeatedly you can process every element in the Cartesian product without ever storing all its elements at once.

The procedure below returns the next element of the Cartesian product of the list s of sets. It uses an array, c, of counters to keep track of which element comes next. For example, c[1]=3 and c[2]=1 correspond to the third element of the first set and the first element of the second set.

```
> s := [ {alpha, beta, gamma}, {x, y} ];
```

$$s := [\{\alpha, \beta, \gamma\}, \{x, y\}]$$

```
> c := array( 1..2, [3, 1] );
```

$$c := [3, 1]$$

```
> [ seq( s[j][c[j]], j=1..2 ) ];
```

$$[\gamma, x]$$

Before you call the **element** procedure you must initialize all the counters to 1, except the first one, which should be 0.

```
> c := array( [0, 1] );
```

$$c := [0, 1]$$

In **element** below, nops(s) is the number of sets and nops(s[i]) is the number of elements in the ith set. When you have seen all the elements, the procedure re-initializes the array of counters and returns **FAIL**. Therefore, you can trace through the Cartesian product again by calling **element** again.

```
> element := proc(s::list(set), c::array(1, nonnegint))
>    local i, j;
>    for i to nops(s) do
>        c[i] := c[i] + 1;
>        if c[i] <= nops( s[i] ) then
>            return [ seq(s[j][c[j]], j=1..nops(s)) ] ;
>        end if;
>        c[i] := 1;
>    end do;
>    c[1] := 0;
>    FAIL;
> end proc:


> element(s, c); element(s, c); element(s, c);
```

$$[\alpha, x]$$

$$[\beta, x]$$

$$[\gamma, x]$$

```
> element(s, c); element(s, c); element(s, c);
```

$$[\alpha, y]$$

$$[\beta, y]$$

$$[\gamma, y]$$

```
> element(s, c);
```

$$FAIL$$

Instead of writing a new procedure for each Cartesian product you want to study, you can write a procedure, CartesianProduct, that returns such a procedure. CartesianProduct below first creates a list, s, of its arguments, which should all be sets. Then it initializes the array, c, of counters and defines the subprocedure element. Finally, the element subprocedure is invoked inside a proc structure.

```
> CartesianProduct := proc()
>    local s, c, element;
>    global S, C;
>    s := [args];
>    if not type(s, list(set)) then
>        error "expected a sequence of sets, but received",
>                args ;
```

```
>     end if;
>     c := array( [0, 1$(nops(s)-1)] );
>
>     element := proc(s::list(set), c::array(1, nonnegint))
>        local i, j;
>        for i to nops(s) do
>           c[i] := c[i] + 1;
>           if c[i] <= nops( s[i] ) then
>              return [ seq(s[j][c[j]], j=1..nops(s)) ] ;
>           end if;
>           c[i] := 1;
>        end do;
>        c[1] := 0;
>        FAIL;
>     end proc;
>
>     proc()
>        element(s, c);
>     end proc;
> end proc:
```

Again, you can find all six elements of $\{\alpha, \beta, \gamma\} \times \{x, y\}$.

```
> f := CartesianProduct( {alpha, beta, gamma}, {x,y} );
```

$$f := \mathbf{proc}() \; element(s, c) \, \mathbf{end \; proc}$$

```
> to 7 do f() end do;
```

$$[\alpha, x]$$

$$[\beta, x]$$

$$[\gamma, x]$$

$$[\alpha, y]$$

$$[\beta, y]$$

$$[\gamma, y]$$

$$FAIL$$

You can use **CartesianProduct** to study several products simultaneously.

```
> g := CartesianProduct( {x, y}, {N, Z, R},
>                         {56, 23, 68, 92} );
```

$$g := \mathbf{proc}()\ element(s,\ c)\ \mathbf{end\ proc}$$

The following are the first few elements of $\{x, y\} \times \{N, Z, R\} \times \{56, 23, 68, 92\}$.

```
> to 5 do g() end do;
```

$$[x,\ N,\ 23]$$

$$[y,\ N,\ 23]$$

$$[x,\ Z,\ 23]$$

$$[y,\ Z,\ 23]$$

$$[x,\ R,\ 23]$$

Because the variables s in f and g are local variables to `CartesianProduct`, they are not shared by different *invocations* of `CartesianProduct`. Similarly, the variable c in f and g is also not shared. You can see that the two arrays of counters are different by invoking f and g a few more times.

```
> to 5 do f(), g() end do;
```

$$[\alpha,\ x],\ [y,\ R,\ 23]$$

$$[\beta,\ x],\ [x,\ N,\ 56]$$

$$[\gamma,\ x],\ [y,\ N,\ 56]$$

$$[\alpha,\ y],\ [x,\ Z,\ 56]$$

$$[\beta,\ y],\ [y,\ Z,\ 56]$$

The `element` procedure in g is also local to `CartesianProduct`. Therefore, you can change the value of the global variable `element` without breaking g.

```
> element := 45;
```

$$element := 45$$

```
> g();
```

$$[x,\ R,\ 56]$$

These examples demonstrate not only that local variables can escape the bounds of the procedures which create them, but that this mechanism allows you to write procedures which create specialized procedures.

Exercises

1. The procedure that `CartesianProduct` generates does not work if one of the sets is empty.

    ```
    > f := CartesianProduct( {}, {x,y} );
    ```

    $$f := \mathbf{proc}()\ element(s,\ c)\ \mathbf{end\ proc}$$

    ```
    > f();
    ```

    ```
    Error, (in element) invalid subscript selector
    ```

    Improve the type-checking in `CartesianProduct` so that it generates an informative error message in each such case.

2. A *partition* of a positive integer, n, is a list of positive integers whose sum is n. The same integer can appear several times in the partition but the order of the integers in the partition is irrelevant. Thus, the following are all the partitions of 5:

    $$[1,1,1,1,1], [1,1,1,2], [1,1,3], [1,2,2], [1,4], [2,3], [5].$$

    Write a procedure that generates a procedure that returns a new partition of n each time you call it.

3.3   Interactive Input

Normally you pass input to Maple procedures as parameters. Sometimes, however, you may want to write a procedure that asks the user directly for input. For example, you could write a procedure that drills students on some topic; the procedure could generate random problems and verify the students' answers. The input may be the value of a certain parameter, or the answer to a question such as whether a parameter is positive or not. The two commands in Maple for reading input from the terminal are the `readline` command and the `readstat` command.

Reading Strings from the Terminal

The `readline` command reads one line of text from a file or the keyboard. You may use the `readline` command as follows.

```
readline( filename )
```

If *filename* is the special name `terminal`, then `readline` reads a line of text from the keyboard. `readline` returns the text as a string.

Here is a simple application, prompting the user for an answer to a question.

```
> DetermineSign := proc(a::algebraic) local s;
>     printf("Is the sign of %a positive? "
>            "Answer yes or no:\n",a);
>     s := readline(terminal);
>     evalb( s="yes" or s = "y" );
> end proc:


> DetermineSign(u-1);
```

```
Is the sign of u-1 positive?  Answer yes or no:
```

```
> y
```

$$true$$

Section 10.5 gives more details on the `readline` command.

Reading Expressions from the Terminal

You may want to write procedures that require the user to input an expression rather than a string. The `readstat` command reads one expression from the keyboard.

```
readstat( prompt )
```

The *prompt* is an optional string.

```
> readstat("Enter degree: ");
```

Enter degree: n-1;

$$n - 1$$

Notice that the **readstat** command insists on a terminating semicolon (or colon). Unlike the **readline** command, which only reads one line, the **readstat** command works like the rest of Maple: it allows you to break a large expression across multiple lines. Another advantage of using the **readstat** command is that if the user makes a mistake in the input, the **readstat** command will automatically re-prompt the user for input, giving the user an opportunity to correct the error.

```
> readstat("Enter a number: ");
```

Enter a number: 5^^8;
syntax error, '^' unexpected:
5^^8;
  ^

Enter a number: 5^8;

$$390625$$

Here is an application of the **readstat** command for implementing an interface to the **limit** command. The procedure does the following: given the function $f(x)$, assume x is the variable if only one variable is present; otherwise, ask the user what the variable is, and also ask the user for the limit point.

```
> GetLimitInput := proc(f::algebraic)
>     local x, a, K;
>     # choose all variables in f
>     K := select(type, indets(f), name);
>
>     if nops(K) = 1 then
>         x := K[1];
>     else
>         x := readstat("Input limit variable: ");
>         while not type(x, name) do
>             printf("A variable is required: received %a\n", x);
>             x := readstat("Please re-input limit variable: ");
>         end do;
>     end if;
```

```
>     a := readstat("Input limit point: ");
>     x = a;
> end proc:
```

The expression $\sin(x)/x$ depends only on one variable, so `GetLimitInput` does not ask for any limit variable.

```
> GetLimitInput( sin(x)/x );
```

Input limit point: 0;

$$x = 0$$

Below, the user first tries to use the number 1 as the limit variable. Since 1 is not a name, `GetLimitInput` asks for another limit variable.

```
> GetLimitInput( exp(u*x) );
```

Input limit variable: 1;
A variable is required: received 1

Please re-input limit variable: x;

Input limit point: infinity;

$$x = \infty$$

You can specify a number of options to `readstat`; see section 10.5.

Converting Strings to Expressions

Occasionally, you may need more control over how and when Maple evaluates user input to your procedure than the `readstat` command allows. In such cases, you can use the `readline` command to read the input as a string, and the `parse` command to convert the string to an expression. The string must represent a complete expression.

```
> s := "a*x^2 + 1";
```

$$s := \text{``a*x^2 + 1''}$$

```
> y := parse( s );
```

$$y := a\,x^2 + 1$$

When you parse the string s you get an expression. In this case, you get a sum.

```
> type(s, string), type(y, '+');
```

$$true,\ true$$

The **parse** command does not evaluate the expression it returns. You must use **eval** to evaluate the expression explicitly. Below, Maple does not evaluate the variable **a** to its value, 2, until you explicitly use the **eval** command.

```
> a := 2;
```

$$a := 2$$

```
> z := parse( s );
```

$$z := a\,x^2 + 1$$

```
> eval(z);
```

$$2\,x^2 + 1$$

See section 10.7 for more details about the **parse** command.

The techniques you have seen in this section are all very simple, but you can use them to create powerful applications such as Maple tutorials, procedures that drill students, or interactive lessons.

3.4   Extending Maple

Even though you may find it useful to write your own procedures to perform new tasks, sometimes extending the abilities of Maple's own commands is most beneficial. Many of Maple's existing commands provide this service. This section familiarizes you with the most helpful methods, including making your own types and operators, modifying how Maple displays expressions, and extending the abilities of such useful commands as `simplify` and `expand`.

Defining New Types

If you use a complicated structured type you may find it easier to assign the structured type to a variable of the form `'type/name'`. That way you only have to write the structure once, thus reducing the risk of errors. When you have defined the variable `'type/name'`, you can use *name* as a type.

```
> 'type/Variables' := {name, list(name), set(name)}:
> type( x, Variables );
```

$$true$$

```
> type( { x[1], x[2] }, Variables );
```

$$true$$

When the structured type mechanism is not powerful enough, you can define a new type by assigning a procedure to a variable of the form `'type/name'`. When you test whether an expression is of type *name*, Maple invokes the procedure `'type/name'` on the expression if such a procedure exists. Your procedure should return **true** or **false**. The `'type/permutation'` procedure below determines if p is a permutation of the first n positive integers. That is, p should contain exactly one copy of each integer from 1 through n.

```
> 'type/permutation' := proc(p)
>    local i;
>    type(p,list) and { op(p) } = { seq(i, i=1..nops(p)) };
> end proc:
> type( [1,5,2,3], permutation );
```

$$false$$

```
> type( [1,4,2,3], permutation );
```

$$true$$

Your type-testing procedure may have more than one parameter. When you test if an expression, *expr*, has type *name*(*parameters*), then Maple invokes

```
'type/name'( expr, parameters )
```

if such a procedure exists. The `'type/LINEAR'` procedure below determines if f is a polynomial in V of degree 1.

```
> 'type/LINEAR' := proc(f, V::name)
>    type( f, polynom(anything, V) ) and degree(f, V) = 1;
> end proc:
```

```
> type( a*x+b, LINEAR(x) );
```

$$true$$

```
> type( x^2, LINEAR(x) );
```

$$false$$

```
> type( a, LINEAR(x) );
```

$$false$$

Exercises

1. Modify the `'type/LINEAR'` procedure so that you can use it to test if an expression is linear in a set of variables. For example, $x + ay + 1$ is linear in both x and y, but $xy + a + 1$ is not.

2. Define the type `POLYNOM(X)` which tests if an algebraic expression is a polynomial in X where X may be a name, a list of names, or a set of names.

Neutral Operators

Maple understands a number of operators, for example +, *, ^, and, not, and union. All of these operators have special meaning to Maple: some represent algebraic operations, such as addition or multiplication; some represent logical operations; and some represent operations performed on sets. Maple also has a special class of operators, the *neutral operators*, on which it does not impose any meaning. Instead, Maple allows *you* to define the meaning of any neutral operator. The name of a neutral operator begins with the ampersand character, &. Section 4.4 describes the naming conventions for neutral operators.

```
> 7 &^ 8 &^ 9;
```

$$(7 \&^\smallfrown 8) \&^\smallfrown 9$$

```
> evalb( 7 &^ 8 = 8 &^ 7 );
```

false

```
> evalb( (7&^8)&^9 = 7&^(8&^9) );
```

false

Internally, Maple represents neutral operators as procedure calls. Thus, 7&^8 is just a convenient way of writing &^(7,8).

```
> &^(7, 8);
```

$$7 \&^\smallfrown 8$$

Maple uses the infix notation only if your neutral operator has exactly two arguments.

```
> &^(4),  &^(5, 6), &^(7, 8, 9);
```

$$\&^\smallfrown(4), 5 \&^\smallfrown 6, \&^\smallfrown(7, 8, 9)$$

You can define the actions of a neutral operator by assigning a procedure to its name. The example below implements the Hamiltonians by assigning a neutral operator to a procedure that multiplies two Hamiltonians. The next paragraph explains all you need to know about the Hamiltonians to understand the example.

The *Hamiltonians* or *Quaternions* extend the complex numbers in the same way the complex numbers extend the real numbers. Each Hamiltonian has the form $a + bi + cj + dk$ where a, b, c, and d are real numbers. The special symbols i, j, and k satisfy the following multiplication rules: $i^2 = -1$, $j^2 = -1$, $k^2 = -1$, $ij = k$, $ji = -k$, $ik = -j$, $ki = j$, $jk = i$, and $kj = -i$.

The '&^' procedure below uses I, J, and K as the three special symbols. However, I is implemented as the *complex* imaginary unit in Maple. Therefore, you should assign another letter to represent the imaginary unit by using the `interface` function. See `?interface` for more information.

```
> interface(imaginaryunit=j);
```

You can multiply many types of expressions by using '`&^`', making it convenient to define a new type, `Hamiltonian`, by assigning a structured type to the name '`type/Hamiltonian`'.

```
> 'type/Hamiltonian' := { '+', '*', name, realcons,
>    specfunc(anything, '&^') };
```

$$type/Hamiltonian :=$$
$$\{name, *, +, realcons, \text{specfunc}(anything, \&\char`^)\}$$

The '`&^`' procedure multiplies the two Hamiltonians, x and y. If either x or y is a real number or variable, then their product is the usual product denoted by $*$ in Maple. If x or y is a sum, '`&^`' maps the product onto the sum; that is, '`&^`' applies the distributive laws: $x(u + v) = xu + xv$ and $(u + v)x = ux + vx$. If x or y is a product, '`&^`' extracts any real factors. You must take special care to avoid infinite recursion when x or y is a product that does not contain any real factors. If none of the multiplication rules apply, '`&^`' returns the product unevaluated.

```
> '&^' := proc( x::Hamiltonian, y::Hamiltonian )
>    local Real, unReal, isReal;
>    isReal := z -> evalb( is(z, real) = true );
>
>    if isReal(x) or isReal(y) then
>        x * y;
>
>    elif type(x, '+') then
>        # x is a sum, u+v, so x&^y = u&^y + v&^y.
>        map('&^', x, y);
>
>    elif type(y, '+') then
>        # y is a sum, u+v, so x&^y = x&^u + x&^v.
>        map2('&^', x, y);
>
>    elif type(x, '*') then
>        # Pick out the real factors of x.
>        Real, unReal := selectremove(isReal, x);
>        # Now x&^y = Real * (unReal&^y)
>        if Real=1 then
>            if type(y, '*') then
>                Real, unReal := selectremove(isReal, x);
>                Real * ''&^''(x, unReal);
>            else
>                ''&^''(x, y);
```

```
>           end if;
>        else
>           Real * '&^'(unReal, y);
>        end if;
>
>   elif type(y, '*') then
>        # Similar to the x-case but easier since
>        # x cannot be a product here.
>        Real, unReal := selectremove(isReal, y);
>        if Real=1 then
>           ''&^''(x, y);
>        else
>           Real * '&^'(x, unReal);
>        end if;
>
>   else
>        ''&^''(x,y);
>   end if;
> end proc:
```

You can place all the special multiplication rules for the symbols I, J, and K in the remember table of '&^'. See section 2.5.

```
> '&^'(I,I) := -1: '&^'(J,J) := -1: '&^'(K,K) := -1:
> '&^'(I,J) := K: '&^'(J,I) := -K:
> '&^'(I,K) := -J: '&^'(K,I) := J:
> '&^'(J,K) := I: '&^'(K,J) := -I:
```

Since '&^' is a neutral operator, you can write products of Hamiltonians using &^ as the multiplication symbol.

```
> (1 + 2*I + 3*J + 4*K) &^ (5 + 3*I - 7*J);
```

$$20 + 41\,I + 20\,J - 3\,K$$

```
> (5 + 3*I - 7*J) &^ (1 + 2*I + 3*J + 4*K);
```

$$20 - 15\,I - 4\,J + 43\,K$$

```
> 56 &^ I;
```

$$56\,I$$

Below, a is an unknown Hamiltonian until you tell Maple that a is an unknown real number.

```
> a &^ J;
```

$$a \,\&\,\hat{}\; J$$

```
> assume(a, real);
> a &^ J;
```

$$a\tilde{}\; J$$

Exercise

1. The inverse of a general Hamiltonian, $a + bi + cj + dk$, is $(a - bi - cj - dk)/(a^2 + b^2 + c^2 + d^2)$. You can demonstrate this fact by assuming that a, b, c, and d are real and define a general Hamiltonian, h.

   ```
   > assume(a, real); assume(b, real);
   ```

   ```
   > assume(c, real); assume(d, real);
   ```

   ```
   > h := a + b*I + c*J + d*K;
   ```

   $$h := a\tilde{} + b\tilde{}\; I + c\tilde{}\; J + d\tilde{}\; K$$

   By the formula above, the following should be the inverse of h.

   ```
   > hinv := (a-b*I-c*J-d*K) / (a^2+b^2+c^2+d^2);
   ```

   $$hinv := \frac{a\tilde{} - b\tilde{}\; I - c\tilde{}\; J - d\tilde{}\; K}{a^{\tilde{}2} + b^{\tilde{}2} + c^{\tilde{}2} + d^{\tilde{}2}}$$

   Now all you have to check is that **h &^ hinv** and **hinv &^ h** both simplify to 1.

   ```
   > h &^ hinv;
   ```

$$\frac{a\tilde{}\,(a\tilde{} - b\tilde{}\,I - c\tilde{}\,J - d\tilde{}\,K)}{\%1}$$
$$+ \frac{b\tilde{}\,(I\,a\tilde{} + b\tilde{} - c\tilde{}\,K + d\tilde{}\,J)}{\%1}$$
$$+ \frac{c\tilde{}\,(J\,a\tilde{} + b\tilde{}\,K + c\tilde{} - d\tilde{}\,I)}{\%1}$$
$$+ \frac{d\tilde{}\,(K\,a\tilde{} - b\tilde{}\,J + c\tilde{}\,I + d\tilde{})}{\%1}$$
$$\%1 := a\tilde{}^2 + b\tilde{}^2 + c\tilde{}^2 + d\tilde{}^2$$

```
> simplify(%);
```

$$1$$

```
> hinv &^ h;
```

$$\frac{a\tilde{}\,(a\tilde{} - b\tilde{}\,I - c\tilde{}\,J - d\tilde{}\,K)}{\%1}$$
$$+ \frac{a\tilde{}\,b\tilde{}\,I + b\tilde{}^2 + b\tilde{}\,c\tilde{}\,K - b\tilde{}\,d\tilde{}\,J}{\%1}$$
$$+ \frac{a\tilde{}\,c\tilde{}\,J - b\tilde{}\,c\tilde{}\,K + c\tilde{}^2 + c\tilde{}\,d\tilde{}\,I}{\%1}$$
$$+ \frac{a\tilde{}\,d\tilde{}\,K + b\tilde{}\,d\tilde{}\,J - c\tilde{}\,d\tilde{}\,I + d\tilde{}^2}{\%1}$$
$$\%1 := a\tilde{}^2 + b\tilde{}^2 + c\tilde{}^2 + d\tilde{}^2$$

```
> simplify(%);
```

$$1$$

Write a procedure, '&/', that computes the inverse of a Hamiltonian. You may want to implement the following rules.

```
&/( &/x ) = x,   &/(x&^y) = (&/y) &^ (&/x),
         x &^ (&/x) = 1 = (&/x) &^ x.
```

Extending Certain Commands

If you introduce your own data structures, Maple cannot know how to manipulate them. In most cases, you design new data structures because you want to write special-purpose procedures that manipulate them. However, sometimes extending the capabilities of one or more of Maple's built-in commands is more intuitive. You can extend several Maple commands, among them **expand**, **simplify**, **diff**, **series**, and **evalf**.

Suppose you choose to represent a polynomial $a_n u^n + a_{n-1} u^{n-1} + \cdots + a_1 u + a_0$ by using the data structure

```
POLYNOM( u, a_0, a_1, ..., a_n )
```

You can then extend the **diff** command so that you can differentiate polynomials represented in that way. If you write a procedure with a name of the form `'diff/F'` then **diff** invokes it on any unevaluated calls to F. Specifically, if you use **diff** to differentiate $F(\texttt{arguments})$ with respect to x, then **diff** invokes `'diff/F'` as follows.

```
'diff/F'( arguments, x )
```

The procedure below differentiates a polynomial in u with constant coefficients with respect to x.

```
> 'diff/POLYNOM' := proc(u)
>     local i, s, x;
>     x := args[-1];
>     s := seq( i*args[i+2], i=1..nargs-3 );
>     'POLYNOM'(u, s) * diff(u, x);
> end proc:
```

```
> diff( POLYNOM(x, 1, 1, 1, 1, 1, 1, 1, 1, 1, 1), x );
```

$$\text{POLYNOM}(x, 1, 2, 3, 4, 5, 6, 7, 8, 9)$$

```
> diff( POLYNOM(x*y, 34, 12, 876, 11, 76), x );
```

$$\text{POLYNOM}(x\,y, 12, 1752, 33, 304)\,y$$

The implementation of the Hamiltonians that section 3.4 describes does not know that multiplication of Hamiltonians is associative, that is $(xy)z = x(yz)$. Sometimes, using associativity simplifies a result. Recall that I here is *not* the complex imaginary unit, but rather, one of the special symbols I, J, and K that are part of the definition of the Hamiltonians.

```
> x &^ I &^ J;
```

$$(x \,\&^{\wedge}\, I) \,\&^{\wedge}\, J$$

```
> x &^ ( I &^ J );
```

$$x \,\&^{\wedge}\, K$$

You can extend the `simplify` command so that it applies the associative law to unevaluated products of Hamiltonians. If you write a procedure with a name of the form `'simplify/F'`, then `simplify` invokes it on any unevaluated function calls to F. Thus, you must write a procedure `'simplify/&^'` that applies the associative law to Hamiltonians.

The procedure below uses the `typematch` command to determine if its argument is of the form `(a&^b)&^c` and, if so, it picks out the a, b, and c.

```
> s := x &^ y &^ z;
```

$$s := (x \,\&^{\wedge}\, y) \,\&^{\wedge}\, z$$

```
> typematch( s, ''&^''( ''&^''( a::anything, b::anything ),
>                       c::anything ) );
```

$$true$$

```
> a, b, c;
```

$$x, y, z$$

You can give the user details about the simplifications your procedure makes through the `userinfo` command. The `'simplify/&^'` procedure prints out an informative message if you set `infolevel[simplify]` or `infolevel[all]` to at least 2.

```
> 'simplify/&^' := proc( x )
>    local a, b, c;
>    if typematch( x,
>            '&^'( '&^'( a::anything, b::anything ),
>                  c::anything ) ) then
>       userinfo(2, simplify, "applying the associative law");
>       a &^ ( b &^ c );
>    else
>       x;
>    end if;
> end proc:
```

Applying the associative law does make some products of Hamiltonians simpler.

```
> x &^ I &^ J &^ K;
```

$$((x \,\&^{\wedge}\, I) \,\&^{\wedge}\, J) \,\&^{\wedge}\, K$$

```
> simplify(%);
```

$$-x$$

If you set `infolevel[simplify]` large enough, Maple prints out information on what `simplify` tries in order to make your expression simpler.

```
> infolevel[simplify] := 5;
```

$$infolevel_{simplify} := 5$$

```
> w &^ x &^ y &^ z;
```

$$((w \,\&^{\wedge}\, x) \,\&^{\wedge}\, y) \,\&^{\wedge}\, z$$

```
> simplify(%);
```

```
simplify/&^:    "applying the associative law"
simplify/&^:    "applying the associative law"
```

$$w \,\&^{\wedge}\, ((x \,\&^{\wedge}\, y) \,\&^{\wedge}\, z)$$

The help pages for `expand`, `series`, and `evalf` provide details on how you may extend those commands. See also section 8.4.

You may employ any or all of the above methods, as you see fit. Maple's design affords you the opportunity to customize it to suit your needs, allowing you great flexibility.

3.5   Conclusion

The topics in this chapter and chapters 1 and 2 form the building blocks of the programming features in Maple. Although the topics in this chapter are more specialized than those of earlier chapters, they are still very important and are among the most useful. In particular, the first two sections which delve into the workings of procedures which return procedures and local variables are fundamental as you move on to more advanced programming. The later topics, including interactive input and extending Maple, while not as fundamental, are also extremely beneficial.

The remaining chapters in this book fall into two categories. Chapters 4 and 5 present in a formal manner the structure of the Maple language and the details of procedures. The other chapters address specific topics, such as plotting, numerical programming, and the Maple debugger.

4 The Maple Language

This chapter describes the Maple language in detail. The language definition breaks down into four parts: characters, tokens, syntax (how you enter commands), and semantics (the meaning Maple gives to the language). The syntax and semantics are what define a language. Syntax consists of rules to combine words into sentences; syntax is grammar, and is purely mechanical. Semantics is the extra information or meaning that syntax cannot capture, and determines what Maple does when it receives a command.

Syntax The *syntax* defines what input constitutes a valid Maple expression, statement, or procedure. It answers such questions as:

- Do I need the parentheses in x^(y^z)?

- How do I input a string which is longer than a line?

- How can I input the floating-point number 2.3×10^{-3}?

These are all questions about language *syntax*. They are concerned solely with the input of expressions and programs to Maple, not what Maple does with them.

If the input is not syntactically correct, Maple reports a *syntax* error. Consider some interactive examples.

Two adjacent minus signs are not valid.

```
> --1;
```

```
syntax error, '-' unexpected:
--1;
 ^
```

Maple accepts many kinds of floating-point formats,

```
> 2.3e-3, 2.3E-03, +0.0023;
```

$$.0023, .0023, .0023$$

but you must place at least one digit between the decimal point and the exponent suffix.

```
> 2.e-3;
```

```
syntax error, missing operator or
2.e-3
      ^
```

The correct way to write this is `2.0e-3`.

Semantics The *semantics* of the language specifies how expressions, statements, and programs execute, that is, what Maple does with them. This answers questions such as:

- Does `x/2*z` equal `x/(2*z)` or `(x/2)*z`? What about `x/2/z`?

- If x has the value 0, what will happen if I compute $\sin(x)/x$?

- Why does computing $\sin(0)/\sin(0)$ result in 1 and not in an error?

- What is the value of `i` after executing the following loop?

  ```
  > for i from 1 to 5 do print(i^2) end do;
  ```

The following is a common mistake. Many users think that `x/2*z` is equal to `x/(2*z)`.

```
> x/2*z, x/(2*z);
```

$$\frac{1}{2}\,x\,z,\ \frac{1}{2}\frac{x}{z}$$

Syntax Errors in Files Maple reports syntax errors which occur when reading in files and indicates the line number. Write the following program in a file called `integrand`.

```
f:= proc(x)
    t:= 1 - x^2
    t*sqrt(t)
end proc:
```

Then read it in to your Maple session by using the **read** command.

```
> read integrand;

syntax error, missing operator or
t*sqrt(t)
^
```

Maple reports an error at the beginning of line 3. There should be a ";" separating the two calculations, `t := 1 - x^2` and `t*sqrt(t)`.

4.1   Language Elements

To simplify the presentation of Maple syntax, consider it in two parts: first, the language *elements* and second, the language *grammar* which explains how to combine the language elements.

The Character Set

The Maple character set consists of letters, digits, and special characters. The letters are the 26 lower-case letters

a, b, c, d, e, f, g, h, i, j, k, l, m, n, o, p, q, r, s, t, u, v, w, x, y, z,

and the 26 upper-case letters

A, B, C, D, E, F, G, H, I, J, K, L, M, N, O, P, Q, R, S, T, U, V, W, X, Y, Z.

The 10 digits are

0, 1, 2, 3, 4, 5, 6, 7, 8, 9.

There are also 32 *special characters*, as shown in Table 4.1. Sections later in this chapter state the uses of each.

Table 4.1 Special Characters

	blank	(	left parenthesis
;	semicolon	)	right parenthesis
:	colon	[	left bracket
+	plus	]	right bracket
−	minus	{	left brace
*	asterisk	}	right brace
/	slash	`	back quote
^	caret	'	single quote (apostrophe)
!	exclamation	"	double quote
=	equal	|	vertical bar
<	less than	&	ampersand
>	greater than	_	underscore
@	at sign	%	percent
$	dollar	\	backslash
.	period	#	sharp
,	comma	?	question mark

Tokens

Maple's language definition combines characters into tokens. Tokens consist of keywords (reserved words), programming-language operators, names, strings, natural integers, and punctuation marks.

Reserved Words Table 4.2 lists the *reserved words* in Maple. They have special meanings, and thus you cannot use them as variables in programs.

Many other symbols in Maple have predefined meanings. For example, mathematical functions such as `sin` and `cos`, Maple commands such as `expand` and `simplify`, and type names such as `integer` and `list`. However, you can safely use these commands in Maple programs in certain contexts. But the reserved words in table 4.2 have a special meanings, and thus you cannot change them.

Programming-Language Operators Three types of *Maple language operators* exist, namely *binary*, *unary*, and *nullary* operators. Tables 4.3 and 4.4 list these operators and their uses. The three nullary operators, %, %%, and %%% are special Maple *names* which refer to the three previously computed expressions.

The `?precedence` help page gives the order of precedence of all programming-language operators.

Table 4.2 Reserved Words

Keywords	Purpose
break, next	loop control
if, then, elif, else	if statement
for, from, in, by, to, while, do	for and while loops
proc, local, global, option, error, return options, description	procedures
export, module, use	modules
end	ends structure
assuming	assume facility
try, catch, finally	exception handling
read, save	read and save statements
quit, done, stop	ending Maple
union, minus, intersect, subset	set operators
and, or, not, xor, implies	Boolean operators
mod	modulus operator

Table 4.3 Programming Binary Operators

Operator	Meaning	Operator	Meaning
+	addition	<	less than
–	subtraction	<=	less or equal
*	multiplication	>	greater than
/	division	>=	greater or equal
^	exponentiation	<>	not equal
$	sequence operator	->	arrow operator
@	composition	union	set union
@@	repeated composition	minus	set difference
&string	neutral operator	intersect	set intersection
,	expression separator	::	type declaration, pattern binding
||	concatenation		
.	decimal point	and	logical and
..	ellipsis	or	logical or
mod	modulo	.	non-commutative multiplication
:=	assignment		

Table 4.4 Programming Unary Operators

Operator	Meaning
+	unary plus (prefix)
–	unary minus (prefix)
!	factorial (postfix)
$	sequence operator (prefix)
not	logical not (prefix)
&*string*	neutral operator (prefix)
.	decimal point (prefix or postfix)
%*integer*	label (prefix)

Names Maple's language definition predefines many other tokens, including names. For example, mathematical functions like `sin` and `cos`, or commands like `expand` or `simplify`, or type names like `integer` or `list` are all examples of names.

The simplest instance of a *name* consists of letters, digits, and underscores, and does not begin with a number. Maple reserves names beginning with an underscore for internal use only.

Names of the form ˜`name` are allowed for spreadsheet references.

Strings Maple's language definition also predefines strings. Some simple strings are `"h"`, `"hi"`, `"result"` and `"Input value1"`. Generally, enclosing any sequence of characters in double quotes forms a string.

> `"The modulus should be prime";`

"The modulus should be prime"

> `"There were %d values";`

"There were %d values"

You should not confuse the double quote character, `"`, which delimits a string, with the back quote character, `` ` ``, which forms a *symbol* or the single quote, `'`, which delays evaluation. A string's length has no practical limit in Maple. On most Maple implementations, this means that a string can contain more than half a million characters.

To make the double quote character appear in a string, type a backslash character and a double quote (`"`) where you want the double quote character to appear.

```
> "a\"b";
```

$$\text{``a\textbackslash ``b''}$$

Similarly, to allow a backslash (escape character) to appear as one of the characters in a string, type two consecutive backslashes \\.

```
> "a\\b";
```

$$\text{``a\textbackslash\textbackslash b''}$$

The special backslash characters mentioned above only count as one character, as is demonstrated by using the **length** command.

```
> length(%);
```

$$3$$

A reserved word enclosed in double quotes also becomes a valid Maple string, distinct from its usage as a token.

```
> "while";
```

$$\text{``while''}$$

The enclosing double quotes themselves do not form part of the string.

```
> length("abcde");
```

$$5$$

To access individual characters or substrings, strings can be subscripted in much the same way as lists. An integer range provides access.

```
> S := "This is a string";
```

$$S := \text{``This is a string''}$$

```
> S[6..9];
```

$$\text{``is a''}$$

```
> S[-6..-1];
```

$$\text{"string"}$$

As well, iterations can be performed over the characters in a string.

```
> seq(i,i="over a string");
```

$$\text{"o", "v", "e", "r", " ", "a", " ", "s", "t", "r", "i", "n", "g"}$$

Integers A *natural integer* is any sequence of one or more digits. Maple ignores any leading zeroes.

```
> 03141592653589793238462643;
```

$$3141592653589793238462643$$

The length limit for integers is system-dependent, but is generally much larger than users require.

An *integer* is either a natural integer or a signed integer. Either **+natural** or **-natural** indicates a signed integer.

```
> -12345678901234567890;
```

$$-12345678901234567890$$

```
> +12345678901234567890;
```

$$12345678901234567890$$

Token Separators

You can separate tokens by using either *white space* or punctuation marks. This tells Maple where one token ends and the next begins.

Blanks, Lines, Comments, and Continuation The *white space* characters are space, tab, return, and line-feed. This book uses the terminology *newline* to refer to either return or line-feed since the Maple system does not distinguish between these characters. The terminology *blank* refers to either space or tab. The white space characters separate tokens, but are not themselves tokens.

White space characters cannot normally occur within a token.

```
> a: = b;
```

```
syntax error, '=' unexpected:
a: = b;
     ^
```

You can use white space characters freely between tokens.

```
> a * x + x*y;
```

$$a\,x + x\,y$$

The only instances in which white space can become part of a token are names and strings, formed by enclosing a sequence of characters in back quotes and double quotes, respectively. In these cases, the white space characters are as significant as any other character.

On a line, unless you are in the middle of a string, Maple considers all characters which follow a sharp character "#" to be part of a *comment*.

Since white space and newline characters are functionally the same, you can continue statements from line to line.

```
> a:= 1 + x +
>      x^2;
```

$$a := 1 + x + x^2$$

The problem of continuation from one line to the next is less trivial when long numbers or long strings are involved since these two classes of tokens are not restricted to a few characters in length. The general mechanism in Maple to specify continuation of one line onto the next is as follows: if the special character backslash, \, immediately precedes a newline character, then the parser ignores both the backslash and the newline. If a backslash occurs in the middle of a line, Maple usually ignores it; see `?backslash` for exceptions. You can use this to break up a long sequence of digits into groups of smaller sequences, to enhance readability.

```
> "The input should be either a list of\
>  variables or a set of variables";
```

"The input should be either a list of variables or \
a set of variables"

Table 4.5 Maple Punctuation Marks

;	semicolon	(	left parenthesis
:	colon	)	right parenthesis
'	single quote	[	left bracket
`	back quote	]	right bracket
|	vertical bar	{	left brace
<	left angle bracket	}	right brace
>	right angle bracket	,	comma

```
> G:= 0.5772156649\0153286060\
> 6512090082\4024310421\5933593992;
```

$$G := .5772156649015328606065120900824024\backslash$$
$$3104215933593992$$

Punctuation Marks   Table 4.5 lists the *punctuation marks*.

; and : Use the semicolon and the colon to separate statements. The distinction between these marks is that a colon during an interactive session prevents the result of the statement from printing.

```
> f:=x->x^2;
```

$$f := x \to x^2$$

```
> p:=plot(f(x), x=0..10):
```

' Enclosing an expression, or part of an expression, in a pair of single quotes delays evaluation of the expression (subexpression) by one level. See section 4.4.

```
> ''sin''(Pi);
```

$$\text{'sin'}(\pi)$$

```
> %;
```

$$\sin(\pi)$$

```
> %;
```

$$0$$

' To form symbols, use the back quote character.

```
> limit(f(x), x=0, 'right'):
```

() The left and right parentheses group terms in an expression and group parameters in a function call.

```
> (a+b)*c; cos(Pi):
```

[] Use the left and right square brackets to form indexed (subscripted) names and to select components from aggregate objects such as arrays, rtables, tables, and lists. See section 4.4.

```
> a[1]: L:=[2,3,5,7]: L[3]:
```

[] **and** {} Use the left and right square brackets also to form lists, and the left and right braces to form sets. See section 4.4.

```
> L:=[2,3,5,2]: S:={2,3,5,2}:
```

<> **and** | The left and right angle brackets in conjunction with the vertical bar are used to construct rtable-based Matrices and Vectors.

```
> <<1,2,3> | <4,5,6>>:
```

, Use the comma to form a sequence, to separate the arguments of a function call, and to separate the elements of a list or set. See section 4.4.

```
> sin(Pi), 0, limit(cos(xi)/xi, xi=infinity):
```

4.2 Escape Characters

The *escape characters* are ?, !, #, and \. Their special meanings are outlined below.

? The question mark character, if it appears as the first non-blank character on a line, invokes Maple's *help* facility. The words following ? on the same line determine the arguments to the help procedure. Use either "," or "/" to separate the words.

! The exclamation mark character, if it appears as the first non-blank character on a line, passes the remainder of the line as a command to the host operating system. This facility is not available on all platforms.

The hash mark character indicates that Maple is to treat the characters following it on the line as a *comment*. In other words, Maple ignores them. They have no effect on any calculation that Maple does.

**** Use the backslash character for *continuation* of lines and for grouping of characters within a token. See section 4.1.

4.3 Statements

There are eight types of statements in Maple. They are the

1. assignment statement

2. selection statement

3. repetition statement

4. **read** statement

5. **save** statement

6. empty statement

7. **quit** statement

8. expressions

Section 4.4 discusses expressions at length.

Throughout the remainder of this section, *expr* stands for any expression, *statseq* stands for a sequence of statements separated by semicolons.

The Assignment Statement

The syntax of the assignment statement is

```
name := expr;
name_1, ..., name_n := expr_1, ..., expr_n;
```

This assigns, or sets, the value of the variable *name* to be the result of executing the expression *expr*. Multiple assignments can also be performed.

Names A *name* in Maple may be a *symbol* or an *indexed name* (subscript). Names stand for unknowns in formulæ. They also serve as programming variables. A name only becomes a programming variable when Maple assigns it a value. Otherwise, if Maple does not assign the name a value, then it remains an unknown.

> 2*y - 1;

$$2\,y - 1$$

> x := 3; x^2 + 1;

$$x := 3$$

$$10$$

> a[1]^2;   a[1] := 3;   a[1]^2;

$$a_1{}^2$$

$$a_1 := 3$$

$$9$$

> f[Cu] := 1.512;

$$f_{Cu} := 1.512$$

To define a function, use the *arrow notation*, ->.

> phi := t -> t^2;

$$\phi := t \to t^2$$

Note that the following does *not* define a function; instead an entry is created in the remember table for `phi`. See section 2.5.

> phi(t) := t^2;

$$\phi(t) := t^2$$

Section 5.1 contains more on how to define functions.

Indexed Names Another form of a name in Maple is the *indexed name* or subscripted name, which has the form

name [sequence]

Note that since an indexed name is itself a valid name, you can add a succession of subscripts.

> A[1,2];

$$A_{1,2}$$

> A[i,3*j-1];

$$A_{i,3j-1}$$

> b[1][1], data[Cu,gold][1];

$$b_{11},\ data_{Cu,gold_1}$$

The use of the indexed name `A[1,2]` does not imply that `A` is an array, as in some languages. The statement

> a := A[1,2] + A[2,1] - A[1,1]*A[2,2];

$$a := A_{1,2} + A_{2,1} - A_{1,1}\,A_{2,2}$$

forms a formula in the four indexed names. (However, if `A` does evaluate to an array or table, then `A[1,1]` refers to the $(1,1)$ element of the array or table.)

Table 4.6 Maple Concatenation Operator

v || 5	p || "n"	a || (2*i)	V || (1..n)	r || i || j

The Concatenation Operator Generally, you can form a *name* by using the *concatenation* operator in one of the following three forms.

```
name || natural
name || string
name || ( expression )
```

Since a *name* can appear on the left-hand side, Maple allows a succession of concatenations. Some examples of the use of the concatenation operator for name formation are given in Table 4.6.

The concatenation operator is a binary operator which requires a name or a string as its left operand. Although Maple usually evaluates expressions from left to right, it evaluates concatenations from right to left. Maple evaluates the right-most operand, then concatenates to the left operand. If it evaluates the right operand to an integer, string or name, then the result of the concatenation is a string or name (depending on the type of the left-most operand). If it evaluates the right operand to some other type of object, say a formula, then the result of the operation is an unevaluated concatenated object.

> p || n;

$$pn$$

> "p" || n;

$$\text{“pn”}$$

> n := 4: p || n;

$$p4$$

> p || (2*n+1);

$$p9$$

```
> p || (2*m+1);
```

$$p||(2\,m+1)$$

If the right hand *expression* is a sequence or a range and the operands of the range are integers or character strings, then Maple creates a sequence of names.

```
> x || (a, b, 4, 67);
```

$$xa,\ xb,\ x4,\ x67$$

```
> x || (1..5);
```

$$x1,\ x2,\ x3,\ x4,\ x5$$

```
> X || ("a".."g");
```

$$Xa,\ Xb,\ Xc,\ Xd,\ Xe,\ Xf,\ Xg$$

If more than one range appears, it composes the extended sequence of names.

```
> x || (1..2) || (1..3);
```

$$x11,\ x12,\ x13,\ x21,\ x22,\ x23$$

Maple never fully evaluates the left-most object, but rather evaluates it to a name. Concatenations can also be formed with the `cat` command.

```
cat( sequence )
```

Note that all the arguments of the `cat` command are evaluated normally (as for any other function call); therefore

```
> cat( "a", "b", "c" );
```

$$\text{``abc''}$$

is equivalent to

```
> "" || a || b || c;
```

$$\text{``abc''}$$

Protected Names Many names in Maple have a predefined meaning, and you cannot directly assign a value to them. For example, the names of built-in functions such as **sin**, the sine function, utility operations such as **degree**, which computes the degree of a polynomial, commands such as **diff** for differentiation, and type names like **integer** and **list**, are all protected names. When the user attempts to assign to any of these names, an error occurs.

```
> list := [1,2];
```

```
Error, attempting to assign to 'list' which is
protected
```

The system protects these names from accidental assignment. It *is* possible to assign to these names by first unprotecting them as follows.

```
> unprotect(sin);
> sin := "a sin indeed";
```

$$\text{sin} := \text{``a sin indeed''}$$

However, now the areas of Maple that rely on the sine function will not work properly.

```
> plot( 1, 0..2*Pi, coords=polar );
```

```
Plotting error, empty plot
```

On the other hand, to write programs in which you want to prevent a user from assigning to certain names, use the **protect** command.

```
> mysqr := x -> x^2;
```

$$mysqr := x \to x^2$$

```
> protect( mysqr );
> mysqr := 9;
```

```
Error, attempting to assign to 'mysqr' which is
protected
```

Unassignment: Clearing a Name

When names do not carry assigned values they act as unknowns. When assigned values, they act as variables. It is often desirable to *unassign* (or clear) a name which previously carried an assigned value, so that you can use the name as an unknown again. The way to do this in Maple is to *assign the name to be itself*. Maple understands this to mean clear the name. The command

```
evaln(name)
```

evaluates *name* to a name (as opposed to evaluating *name* to its value as in other function calls). You can thus unassign a name as follows.

```
> a := evaln(a);
```

$$a := a$$

```
> i := 4;
```

$$i := 4$$

```
> a[i] := evaln(a[i]);
```

$$a_4 := a_4$$

```
> a || i := evaln(a || i);
```

$$a4 := a4$$

In the special case where *name* is a string you may also unassign a variable by delaying evaluation of the right-hand side with single quotes ('). See section 4.4.

```
> a := 'a';
```

$$a := a$$

Related Functions You can use the `assigned` command to test if a name has an assigned value.

```
> assigned(a);
```

$$false$$

The `assign` command assigns a variable.

```
> assign( a=b );
> assigned(a);
```

$$true$$

```
> a;
```

$$b$$

Maple normally evaluates all the arguments of **assign**. Therefore, because there was the previous assignment, **assign(a=b)**, Maple assigns **b** the value 2 here.

```
> assign( a=2 );
> b;
```

$$2$$

One level evaluation of **a** reveals that **a** still has the value **b**.

```
> eval( a, 1 );
```

$$b$$

Changing the value of **a** does not affect the value of **b**.

```
> a := 3;
```

$$a := 3$$

```
> b;
```

$$2$$

Often, applications of the **assign** command are to a set or list of equations.

```
> eqn1   :=  x + y = 2:
> eqn2   :=  x - y = 3:
> sol := solve( {eqn1, eqn2}, {x, y} );
```

$$sol := \{y = \frac{-1}{2}, \, x = \frac{5}{2}\}$$

Maple assigns the variables x and y according to the set **sol** of equations.

```
> assign(sol);
> x;
```

$$\frac{5}{2}$$

```
> assigned(x);
```

$$true$$

It is recommended that you not assign values to expressions like **f(x)**. See section 2.5 for details.

The Selection Statement

The selection or conditional statement has four forms. The syntax of the first two forms is

```
if expr then statseq
end if;

if expr then statseq1
    else statseq2
end if;
```

Maple executes the selection statement as follows. It evaluates the expression in the **if** clause (*expr*). If the result is the Boolean value **true**, then Maple executes the statement sequence in the **then** clause. If the result is the Boolean value **false** or **FAIL**, then Maple executes the statements in the **else** clause.

```
> x := -2:
> if x<0 then 0 else 1 end if;
```

$$0$$

The *expr* must evaluate to one of the Boolean values **true**, **false**, or **FAIL**; see section 4.4.

```
> if x then 0 else 1 end if;
```

```
Error, invalid boolean expression
```

Omit the **else** clause if you do not want to include an alternative course of action when the condition is false.

```
> if x>0 then x := x-1 end if;
> x;
```

$$-2$$

The selection statement may be nested, that is, the statement sequence in the **then** clause or **else** clause may be any statement, including an **if** statement.

Compute the sign of a number.

```
> if x > 1 then 1
> else if x=0 then 0 else -1 end if
> end if;
```

The following example demonstrates a use of **FAIL**.

```
> r := FAIL:
> if r then
>     print(1)
> else
>     if not r then
>         print(0)
>     else
>         print(-1)
>     end if
> end if;
```

$$-1$$

If Maple has many cases to consider, the use of nested **if** statements becomes messy and unreadable. Maple provides the following two alternatives.

```
if expr then statseq
     elif expr then statseq
end if;

if expr then statseq
     elif expr then statseq
     else statseq
end if;
```

The **elif** *expr* **then** *statseq* construct may appear more than once.

Here you can implement the sign function by using an **elif** clause.

```
> x := -2;
```

$$x := -2$$

```
> if x<0 then -1
> elif x=0 then 0
> else 1
> end if;
```

$$-1$$

In this form, you can view the selection statement as a case statement with the optional **else** clause as the default case. For example, if you are writing a program that accepts a parameter n with four possible values, $0, 1, 2, 3$, then you might write

```
> n := 5;
```

$$n := 5$$

```
> if    n=0 then 0
> elif n=1 then 1/2
> elif n=2 then sqrt(2)/2
> elif n=3 then sqrt(3)/2
> else error "bad argument: %1", n;
> end if;
```

```
Error, bad argument: 5
```

The Repetition Statement

The most general repetition statement in Maple is the `for` loop. However, you can replace many loops with more efficient and concise special forms. See section 4.5.

The `for` loop has two forms: the `for-from` loop and the `for-in` loop.

The `for-from` Loop   A typical `for-from` loop has the following form.

```
> for i from 2 to 5 do i^2 end do;
```

$$4$$

$$9$$

$$16$$

$$25$$

This sequence of results arose as follows. First, Maple assigns `i` the value 2. Since 2 is less than 5, Maple executes the statement between the `do` and the `end do`. Then it increments `i` by 1 to 3, tests again, the loop executes, and so on until `i` is (strictly) larger than 5. In this case the final value of `i` is

```
> i;
```

$$6$$

The syntax of the `for-from` loop is

```
for name from expr by expr to expr
while expr do statseq
end do;
```

You may omit any of the clauses `for` *name*, `from` *expr*, `by` *expr*, `to` *expr*, or `while` *expr*. You may omit the sequence of statements *statseq*. Except for the `for` clause, which must always appear first, the other clauses may appear in any order. If you omit a clause, it has a default value, which is shown in Table 4.7.

You could also write the previous example as the following.

Table 4.7 Clauses and Their Default Values

Clause	Default Value
for	dummy variable
from	1
by	1
to	infinity
while	true

```
> for i from 2 by 1 to 5 while true do i^2 end do:
```

If the **by** clause is negative, the **for** loop counts downward.

```
> for i from 5 to 2 by -1 do i^2 end do;
```

$$25$$

$$16$$

$$9$$

$$4$$

To find the first prime number greater than 10^7 you could write

```
> for i from 10^7 while not isprime(i) do end do;
```

Now i is the first prime larger than 10^7.

```
> i;
```

$$10000019$$

Notice that the body of the loop is empty. Maple allows for the empty statement. Try improving the program by considering only the odd numbers.

```
> for i from 10^7+1 by 2 while not isprime(i) do end do;
> i;
```

$$10000019$$

Here is an example of repeating an action n times. Throw a die five times.

```
> die := rand(1..6):
> to 5 do die(); end do;
```

$$4$$

$$3$$

$$4$$

$$6$$

$$5$$

Omitting all clauses produces an infinite loop.

```
do statseq end do;
```

This is equivalent to

```
for name from 1 by 1 to infinity
while true do statseq
end do;
```

Such a loop statement will loop forever unless the **break** construct (see section 4.3) or a **return** statement (see section 5.5) terminates it, or if Maple encounters the **quit** statement, or if an error occurs.

The while Loop The while loop is a for loop with all its clauses omitted except the while clause, that is

```
while expr do statseq end do;
```

The expression *expr* is called the *while condition*. It must be a Boolean valued expression, that is, it must evaluate to **true**, **false**, or **FAIL**. For example,

```
> x := 256;
```

$$x := 256$$

```
> while x>1 do x := x/4 end do;
```

$$x := 64$$

$$x := 16$$

$$x := 4$$

$$x := 1$$

The **while** loop works as follows. First, Maple evaluates the **while** condition. If it evaluates to **true**, Maple executes the body of the loop. This loop repeats until the **while** condition evaluates to **false** or **FAIL**. Note that Maple evaluates the **while** condition *before* it executes the body of the loop. An error occurs if the **while** condition does not evaluate to one of **true**, **false**, or **FAIL**.

```
> x := 1/2:
> while x>1 do x := x/2 end do;
> x;
```

$$\frac{1}{2}$$

```
> while x do x := x/2 end do;
```

```
Error, invalid boolean expression
```

The for-in Loop   Suppose you have a list of integers L and want to find the integers in the list that are at most 7. You could write

```
> L := [7,2,5,8,7,9];
```

$$L := [7, 2, 5, 8, 7, 9]$$

```
> for i in L do
>     if i <= 7 then print(i) end if;
> end do;
```

$$7$$

$$2$$

$$5$$

$$7$$

This example cycles through the components of an object. The object, this time, is a list. But in other examples, the object might be a set, a sum of terms, a product of factors, or the characters of a string. The syntax for the `for-in` loop is

```
for name in expr
while expr do statseq
end do;
```

The loop index (the *name* specified in the `for` clause of the statement) takes on the operands of the first *expr*. See section 4.4 for a description of the operands associated with each data type. You can test the value of the index in the optional **while** clause, and, of course, the value of the index is available when you execute the *statseq*. Note that the value of the index variable name remains assigned at the end of the loop if the object contains at least one operand.

The `break` and `next` Commands   Within the Maple language reside two additional loop control constructs: `break` and `next`. When Maple evaluates the special name **break**, the result is to exit from the innermost repetition statement within which it occurs. Execution then proceeds with the first statement following this repetition statement.

```
> L := [2, 5, 7, 8, 9];
```

$$L := [2, 5, 7, 8, 9]$$

```
> for i in L do
>     print(i);
>     if i=7 then break end if;
> end do;
```

$$2$$

$$5$$

$$7$$

When Maple evaluates the special name **next**, it then proceeds immediately to the next iteration. For example, suppose you want to skip over the elements in a list that are equal to 7.

```
> L := [7,2,5,8,7,9];
```

$$L := [7, 2, 5, 8, 7, 9]$$

```
> for i in L do
>       if i=7 then next end if;
>       print(i);
> end do;
```

$$2$$

$$5$$

$$8$$

$$9$$

An error occurs if Maple evaluates the names **break** or **next** in a context other than within a repetition statement.

```
> next;
```

```
Error, break or next not in loop
```

The read **and** save **Statements**

The file system is an important part of Maple. The user may interact with the file system either explicitly by using the **read** and **save** statements, or implicitly by executing a command that automatically loads information from a file. For example, the computation of an integral may load many commands from the Maple library. The **read** and **save** statements read and save Maple data and programs to and from files. See also Chapter 10.

Saving a Maple Session   The **save** statement allows you to save the values of a sequence of variables. It takes the general form

```
save nameseq, filename;
```

Here *nameseq* must be a sequence of names of assigned variables. Maple saves each variable name and its value in an assignment statement in the file *filename*. Maple evaluates each argument, except the last one, to a name. It evaluates the last argument normally.

Clear Maple by using the **restart** command and assign three new values.

```
> restart:
> r0 := x^3:
> r1 := diff(r0,x):
> r2 := diff(r1,x):
```

The next statement saves `r0`, `r1` and `r2` in the ASCII file `my_file`:

```
> save r0, r1, r2, "my_file":
```

This is now the contents of the file `my_file`.

```
r0 := x^3;
r1 := 3*x^2;
r2 := 6*x;
```

The expression *filename* must evaluate to a name which specifies the name of a file. You can read it back into Maple later using the **read** command.

The read Statement   The **read** statement

```
read filename;
```

reads a file into the Maple session. The *filename* must evaluate to the name of the file. The file must be either a Maple internal format file (a `.m` file), or a text file.

If the file is a plain text file, then it must contain a sequence of valid Maple statements, separated by semicolons or colons. The effect of reading the file is identical to entering the same sequence of statements interactively. The system displays the result of executing each statement that it reads in from the file.

4.4   Expressions

Expressions are the fundamental entities in the Maple language. The various types of expressions include constants, names of variables and unknowns, formulæ, Boolean expressions, series, and other data structures. Technically speaking, procedures are also valid expressions since you may use them wherever an expression is legal. Chapter 5 describes them separately.

Table 4.8 Primitive Functions

`type(f, t)`	tests if f is of type t
`nops(f)`	returns the number of operands of f
`op(i, f)`	selects the ith operand of f
`subsop(i=g, f)`	replaces the ith operand of f with g

Expression Trees: Internal Representation

Consider the following formula.

```
> f := sin(x) + 2*cos(x)^2*sin(x) + 3;
```

$$f := \sin(x) + 2\cos(x)^2 \sin(x) + 3$$

To represent this formula, Maple builds an *expression tree.*

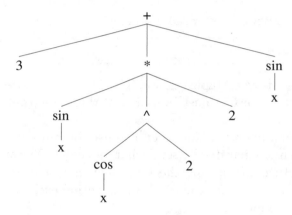

The first node of the expression tree labeled "+" is a sum. This indicates the expression's *type*. This expression has three branches corresponding to the three terms in the sum. The nodes of each branch tell you each term's type in the sum. And so on down the tree until you get to the leaves of the tree, which are names and integers in this example.

When programming with expressions, you need a way to determine what type of expression you have, how many operands or branches an expression has, and a way of selecting those operands. You also need a way of building new expressions, for example, by replacing one operand of an expression with a new value. Table 4.8 lists the primitive functions for doing this.

```
> type(f, '+');
```

$$true$$

```
> type(f, '*');
```

$$false$$

```
> nops(f);
```

$$3$$

```
> op(1, f);
```

$$\sin(x)$$

```
> subsop(2=0, f);
```

$$\sin(x) + 3$$

By determining the type of an expression, the number of operands it has, and selecting each operand of the expression, you can systematically work all the way through an expression.

```
> t := op(2, f);
```

$$t := 2\cos(x)^2 \sin(x)$$

```
> type(t, '*');
```

$$true$$

```
> nops(t);
```

$$3$$

```
> type(op(1,t), integer);
```

$$true$$

```
> type(op(2,t), '^');
```

$$true$$

```
> type(op(3,t), function);
```

$$true$$

The op command has several other useful forms. The first is

```
op(i..j, f)
```

which returns the sequence

```
op(i, f), op(i+1, f), ..., op(j-1, f), op(j, f)
```

of operands of f. Another short-form notation is,

```
op([i, j, k], f)
```

which gives the same result as

```
op(k, op(j, op(i, f)))
```

The last object in the list may also be a range

```
op([i, j, k1..k2], f)
```

which returns the sequence

```
op(k1, op(i, f)), op(k1+1, op(i, f)), ...,
              op(k2, op(i, f))
```

You may want to see the whole sequence of operands of an expression. You can do this with

```
op(f)
```

which is equivalent to op(1..nops(f),f). The special operand op(0,f) generally returns the type of an expression. An exception occurs when f is a function, in which case it returns the name of the function.

```
> op(0, f);
```

$$+$$

```
> op(1..3, f);
```

$$\sin(x), \ 2\cos(x)^2\sin(x), \ 3$$

```
> op(0, op(1,f));
```

$$\sin$$

```
> op(0, op(2,f));
```

$$*$$

```
> op(0, op(3,f));
```

$$Integer$$

Evaluation and Simplification Consider this example in detail.

```
> x := Pi/6:
> sin(x) + 2*cos(x)^2*sin(x) + 3;
```

$$\frac{17}{4}$$

What does Maple do when it executes the second command? Maple first reads and *parses* the input line. As it is parsing the input line it builds an expression tree to represent the value

$$\sin(x) + 2\cos(x)^2\sin(x) + 3.$$

Next it evaluates the expression tree, then simplifies the result. Evaluation means substituting values for variables and invoking any functions. Here x evaluates to $\pi/6$. Hence, with these substitutions the expression is as follows.

$$\sin(\pi/6) + 2\cos(\pi/6)^2\sin(\pi/6) + 3$$

Invoking the sin and cos functions, Maple obtains a new expression tree,

$$1/2 + 2 \times (1/2\sqrt{3})^2 \times 1/2 + 3.$$

Table 4.9 Subtypes of Integers

negint	negative integer
posint	positive integer
nonnegint	non-negative integer
nonposint	non-positive integer
even	even integer
odd	odd integer
prime	prime integer

Finally, Maple does the arithmetic in this expression tree to obtain the fraction 17/4. In the following example, evaluation occurs, but no simplification is possible.

```
> x := 1;
```

$$x := 1$$

```
> sin(x) + 2*cos(x)^2*sin(x) + 3;
```

$$\sin(1) + 2\cos(1)^2 \sin(1) + 3$$

We now present in detail every kind of expression, beginning with the constants. The presentation states how to input the expression, gives examples of how and where to use the expression, and the action of the type, nops, op, and subsop commands on the expression.

The numeric constants in Maple are integers, fractions, floating-point (decimal) numbers, infinity, and undefined. The complex numeric constants are the complex integers (Gaussian integers), complex rationals, and complex floating-point numbers. The full set of real and complex numeric constants is exactly what is recognized by type(..., complex(extended_numeric)).

The Types and Operands of Integers, Strings, Indexed Names, and Concatenations

The type of an integer is integer. The type command also understands the subtypes of integers listed in Table 4.9. The op and nops commands consider an integer to have only one operand, namely, the integer itself.

```
> x := 23;
```

$$x := 23$$

```
> op(0, x);
```

Integer

```
> op(x);
```

23

```
> type(x, prime);
```

true

The type of a string is **string**. A string also has only one operand; the string itself.

```
> s := "Is this a string?";
```

$s :=$ "Is this a string?"

```
> type(s, string);
```

true

```
> nops(s);
```

1

```
> op(s);
```

"Is this a string?"

The type of an indexed name is **indexed**. The operands of an indexed name are the indices or subscripts and the zeroth operand is the base name. The **type** command also understands the composite type **name** which Maple defines as either a **string** or an **indexed** name.

```
> x := A[1][2,3];
```

$$x := A_{12,3}$$

```
> type(x, indexed);
```

$$true$$

```
> nops(x);
```

$$2$$

```
> op(x);
```

$$2, 3$$

```
> op(0,x);
```

$$A_1$$

```
> y:=%;
```

$$y := A_1$$

```
> type(y, indexed);
```

$$true$$

```
> nops(y), op(0,y), op(y);
```

$$1, A, 1$$

The type of an unevaluated concatenation is "||". This type has two operands, the left-hand side expression and the right-hand side expression.

```
> c := p || (2*m + 1);
```

$$c := p||(2\,m + 1)$$

```
> type(c, '||');
```

$$true$$

> op(0, c);

$$\|$$

> nops(c);

$$2$$

> op(c);

$$p,\, 2\,m + 1$$

Fractions and Rational Numbers

A *fraction* is input as

```
integer/natural
```

Maple does arithmetic with fractions and integers *exactly*. Maple always immediately simplifies a fraction so that the denominator is positive, and reduces the fraction to lowest terms by canceling out the greatest common divisor of the numerator and denominator.

> -30/12;

$$\frac{-5}{2}$$

If the denominator is 1 after simplification of a fraction, Maple automatically converts it to an integer. The type of a fraction is **fraction**. The **type** command also understands the composite type name **rational**, which is an **integer** or a **fraction**, that is, a rational number.

> x := 4/6;

$$x := \frac{2}{3}$$

> type(x,rational);

$$true$$

A fraction has two operands, the numerator and denominator. In addition to the **op** command, you may use the commands **numer** and **denom** to extract the numerator and denominator of a fraction, respectively.

```
> op(1,x), op(2,x);
```

$$2, 3$$

```
> numer(x), denom(x);
```

$$2, 3$$

Floating-Point (Decimal) Numbers

An *unsigned float* has one of the following six forms:

```
natural.natural
natural.
.natural
natural exponent
natural.natural exponent
.natural exponent
```

where the *exponent* suffix is the letter "e" or "E" followed by a signed integer with no spaces in the middle. A *floating-point number* is an *unsigned float* or a signed float (**+unsigned_float** or **-unsigned_float** indicates a signed float).

```
> 1.2, -2., +.2;
```

$$1.2, -2., .2$$

```
> 2e2, 1.2E+2, -.2e-2;
```

$$200., 120., -.002$$

Note that

```
> 1.e2;
```

```
syntax error, missing operator or ';':
1.e2;
  ^
```

is not valid, and that spaces are significant.

```
> .2e -1 <> .2e-1;
```

$$-.8 \neq .02$$

The type of a floating-point number is `float`. The `type` command also understands the composite types `numeric`, which recognizes `integer`, `fraction` and `float`, and `extended_numeric`, which recognizes `integer`, `fraction`, `float`, `infinity`, and `undefined`. For information about the full suite of numeric types and subtypes, see `?numeric_type`.

A floating-point number has two parts, the mantissa (or significand) m and the exponent e, representing the number $m \times 10^e$. The decimal point is taken to be after the rightmost digit of m. To get access to the parts of a floating-point number, use the Maple commmands `SFloatMantissa` and `SFloatExponent`.

```
> x := 231.3;
```

$$x := 231.3$$

```
> SFloatMantissa(x);
```

$$2313$$

```
> SFloatExponent(x);
```

$$-1$$

The `Float` command can also be used to construct floating-point numbers in Maple:

```
Float(m, e)
```

This constructs the floating-point number $m \times 10^e$. Again, the mantissa (or significand) is m, the exponent is e, and the decimal point is to the right of m.

The mantissa, m, is a Maple integer, and hence it is subject to the same restrictions in terms of number of digits as any Maple integer, which is machine dependent, but is always at least $268\,435\,448$. The exponent, e, is subject to a smaller restriction, which is again machine dependent but is always at least $2\,147\,483\,646$. The exact values of these limits can be obtained from the `Maple_floats` command.

You can also input a floating-point number $m \times 10^e$ by simply forming the literal expression `m * 10^e`. However this is less efficient, particularly for large exponents.

Arithmetic with Floating-Point Numbers For arithmetic operations and the standard mathematical functions, if one of the operands (or arguments) is a floating-point number or evaluates to a floating-point number, then floating-point arithmetic takes place automatically. The global name `Digits`, which has 10 as its default, determines the number of digits which Maple uses when calculating with floating-point numbers (the number of digits in the significand).

```
> x := 2.3:   y := 3.7:
> 1 - x/y;
```

$$.3783783784$$

In general, you may use the `evalf` command to force the evaluation of a non-floating-point expression to a floating-point expression where possible.

```
> x := ln(2);
```

$$x := \ln(2)$$

```
> evalf(x);
```

$$.6931471806$$

An optional second argument to the `evalf` command specifies the precision at which Maple is to do this evaluation.

Table 4.10 Types of Complex Numbers

complex(integer)	both a and b are integers, possibly 0
complex(rational)	both a and b are rationals
complex(float)	both a and b are floating-point constants
complex(numeric)	any of the above

```
> evalf[15](x);
```

$$.693147180559945$$

Complex Numerical Constants

By default, I denotes the complex unit $\sqrt{-1}$ in Maple. In fact, all of the following are equivalent.

```
> sqrt(-1), I, (-1)^(1/2);
```

$$I, I, I$$

A complex number $a + bi$ is input as the sum `a + b*I` or as `Complex(a, b)` in Maple. Maple uses a special representation for complex numeric constants, such as `1.3 + 4.2*I`. Note that in an expression such as `x + y*I`, where x and y are symbols, Maple does *not* assume that x is the real part and y is the imaginary part. Use the commands `Re` and `Im` to select the real and imaginary parts, respectively.

```
> x := 2+3*I;
```

$$x := 2 + 3\,I$$

```
> Re(x), Im(x);
```

$$2, 3$$

The type of a complex number is `complex(numeric)`. This means that the real and imaginary parts are of type `numeric`, that is, integers, fractions, or floating-point numbers. Other useful type names are listed in Table 4.10.

Arithmetic with complex numbers is done automatically.

```
> x := (1 + I);   y := 2.0 - I;
```

$$x := 1 + I$$

$$y := 2.0 - 1. I$$

```
> x+y;
```

$$3.0 + 0. I$$

Maple also knows how to evaluate elementary functions and many special functions over the complex numbers. It does this automatically if a and b are numeric constants and one of a or b is a decimal number.

```
> exp(2+3*I), exp(2+3.0*I);
```

$$e^{(2+3\,I)}, \; -7.315110095 + 1.042743656\,I$$

If the arguments are not complex floating-point constants, you can expand the expression in some cases into the form $a + bi$, where a and b are real, using the **evalc** command.

Here the result is not in the form $a+bi$ since a is not of type **numeric**.

```
> 1/(a - I);
```

$$\frac{1}{a - I}$$

```
> evalc(%);
```

$$\frac{a}{a^2 + 1} + \frac{I}{a^2 + 1}$$

If you prefer to use another letter, say j, for the imaginary unit, use the **interface** command as follows.

```
> interface(imaginaryunit = j);
> solve( {z^2=-1}, {z} );
```

$$\{z = j\}, \{z = -j\}$$

The following command reinstates **I** as the imaginary unit.

```
> interface(imaginaryunit = I);
> solve( {z^2=-1}, {z} );
```

$$\{z = I\}, \{z = -I\}$$

Labels

A *label* in Maple has the form

```
%natural
```

that is, the unary operator % followed by a natural integer. The percentage sign takes on double duty, as a label and as the ditto operator, which represents the result of the last one, two, or three commands.

A label is only valid after Maple's pretty-printer introduces it. The purpose is to allow the naming (labeling) of common subexpressions, which serves to decrease the size of the printed output, making it more comprehensible. After the pretty-printer introduces it, you may use a label just like an assigned name in Maple.

```
> solve( {x^3-y^3=2, x^2+y^2=1}, {x, y} );
```

$$\{y = \%1, \, x = -\frac{1}{3}\,\%1\,(-4\,\%1^3 - 3 - \%1^2 + 6\,\%1 + 2\,\%1^4)\}$$
$$\%1 := \mathrm{RootOf}(3\,\_Z^2 + 3 - 3\,\_Z^4 + 2\,\_Z^6 + 4\,\_Z^3)$$

After you obtain the above printout, the label %1 is an assigned name and its value is the `RootOf` expression shown.

```
> %1;
```

$$\mathrm{RootOf}(3\,\_Z^2 + 3 - 3\,\_Z^4 + 2\,\_Z^6 + 4\,\_Z^3)$$

Two options are available for adjusting this facility. The option

```
interface(labelwidth=n)
```

specifies that Maple should not display expressions less than n characters wide (approximately) as labels. The default is 20 characters. You may turn off this facility entirely using

```
> interface(labelling=false);
```

Sequences

A *sequence* is an expression of the form

---

expression_1, *expression_2*, ..., *expression_n*

The comma operator joins expressions into a sequence. It has the lowest precedence of all operators except assignment. A key property of sequences is that if any of *expression_i* themselves are sequences, this flattens out the result into a single unnested sequence.

```
> a := A, B, C;
```

$$a := A, B, C$$

```
> a,b,a;
```

$$A, B, C, b, A, B, C$$

A zero-length sequence is syntactically valid. It arises, for example, in the context of forming an empty list, an empty set, a function call with no parameters, or an indexed name with no subscripts. Maple initially assigns the special name NULL to the zero-length sequence, and you may use it whenever necessary.

You cannot use the **type** command to test the type of a sequence, nor can you use the **nops** or **op** commands to count the number of operands in a sequence or select them. Their use is not possible because a sequence becomes the arguments to these commands.

```
> s := x,y,z;
```

$$s := x, y, z$$

The command

```
> nops(s);
```

```
Error, wrong number (or type) of parameters in function
nops
```

is the same as the command

```
> nops(x,y,z);
```

```
Error, wrong number (or type) of parameters in function
nops
```

Here the arguments to the **nops** command are x, y, z, which constitute too many arguments. If you desire to count the number of operands in a sequence or select an operand from a sequence, you should first put the sequence in a list as follows

```
> nops([s]);
```

$$3$$

Alternatively, you can use the *selection operation* discussed in section 4.4 to select the operands of a sequence.

Please note that many Maple commands return sequences. You may wish to put sequences into a list or set data structure. For example, when the arguments to the **solve** command are not sets, it returns a sequence of values if it finds multiple solutions.

```
> s := solve(x^4-2*x^3-x^2+4*x-2, x);
```

$$s := 1, 1, \sqrt{2}, -\sqrt{2}$$

The elements of the above sequence are values, not equations, because you did not use sets in the call to **solve**. Putting the solutions in a set removes duplicates.

```
> s := {s};
```

$$s := \{1, \sqrt{2}, -\sqrt{2}\}$$

The seq Command The **seq** command creates sequences, a key tool for programming. Section 4.5 describes it in detail. The syntax takes either of the following general forms.

```
seq(f, i = a .. b)
seq(f, i = X)
```

Here f, a, b, and X are expressions and i is a name. In the first form, the expressions a and b must evaluate to two numerical constants or two single character strings. The result is the sequence produced by evaluating

f after successively assigning the index i the values a, $a{+}1$, ..., b, (or up to the last value not exceeding b). If the value a is greater than b then the result is the NULL sequence.

```
> seq(i^2,i=1..4);
```

$$1, 4, 9, 16$$

```
> seq(i,i="d".."g");
```

$$\text{``d''}, \text{``e''}, \text{``f''}, \text{``g''}$$

In the second form, seq(f, $i{=}X$), the result is the sequence produced by evaluating f after successively assigning the index i the operands of the expression X (or the individual characters, if X is a string). Section 4.4 states the operands of a general expression.

```
> a := x^3+3*x^2+3*x+1;
```

$$a := x^3 + 3\,x^2 + 3\,x + 1$$

```
> seq(i,i=a);
```

$$x^3, 3\,x^2, 3\,x, 1$$

```
> seq(degree(i,x), i=a);
```

$$3, 2, 1, 0$$

```
> seq(i,i="maple");
```

$$\text{``m''}, \text{``a''}, \text{``p''}, \text{``l''}, \text{``e''}$$

The \$ Operator The sequence operator, \$, also forms sequences. The primary purpose of \$ is to represent a symbolic sequence such as x\$n as in the following examples.

```
> diff(ln(x), x$n);
```

$$\text{diff}(\ln(x), x\,\$\,n)$$

```
> seq( diff(ln(x), x$n), n=1..5);
```

$$\frac{1}{x}, \ -\frac{1}{x^2}, \ \frac{2}{x^3}, \ -\frac{6}{x^4}, \ \frac{24}{x^5}$$

The general syntax of the $ operator is

```
f $ i = a .. b
f $ n
$ a .. b
```

where *f*, *a*, *b*, and *n* are expressions and *i* must evaluate to a name. In general, this operator is less efficient than **seq** and hence the **seq** command is preferred for programming.

In the first form, Maple creates a sequence by *substituting* the values $a, a+1, \ldots, b$ for *i* in *f*.

The second form *f*$n is a shorthand notation for

```
f $ dummy = 1 .. n
```

where *dummy* is a dummy index variable. If the value of *n* is an integer, the result of the second form is the sequence consisting of the value of *f* repeated *n* times.

```
> x$3;
```

$$x, \ x, \ x$$

The third form $a..b is a shorthand notation for

```
dummy $ dummy = a .. b
```

If the values of *a* and *b* are numerical constants, this form is short for creating a numerical sequence $a, a+1, \ldots, b$ (or up to the last value not exceeding *b*).

```
> $0..4;
```

$$0, \ 1, \ 2, \ 3, \ 4$$

The $ command differs from the **seq** command in that *a* and *b* do not need to evaluate to numbers. However, when *a* and *b* do evaluate to specific values, **seq** is more efficient than $. See section 4.5.

Sets and Lists

A *set* is an expression of the form

{ *sequence* }

and a *list* is an expression of the form

[*sequence*]

Note that a *sequence* may be empty, so {} represents the empty set and [] the empty list. A set is an *unordered* sequence of *unique* expressions. Maple removes duplicates and reorders the terms in a manner convenient for internal storage. A list is an *ordered* sequence of expressions with the order of the expressions specified by the user. Maple retains duplicate entries in a list.

```
> {y[1],x,x[1],y[1]};
```

$$\{x, y_1, x_1\}$$

```
> [y[1],x,x[1],y[1]];
```

$$[y_1, x, x_1, y_1]$$

A set is an expression of type **set**. Similarly, a list is an expression of type **list**. The operands in a list or set are the elements in the set or list. Select the elements of a list or set using either the **op** command or a subscript.

```
> t := [1, x, y, x-y];
```

$$t := [1, x, y, x - y]$$

```
> op(2,t);
```

$$x$$

```
> t[2];
```

$$x$$

Maple's ordering for sets is the order in which it stores the expressions in memory. The user should not make assumptions about this ordering. For example, in a different Maple session, the set above might appear in the ordering {y[1], x, x[1]}. You can sort elements of a list by using the sort command.

Selection Operation   The selection operation, [], selects components from an aggregate object. The aggregate objects include tables, arrays, sequences, lists, and sets. The syntax for the selection operation is

---

name [*sequence*]

If *name* evaluates to a table or array, Maple returns the table (array) entry.

> A := array([w,x,y,z]);

$$A := [w,\ x,\ y,\ z]$$

> A[2];

$$x$$

If *name* evaluates to a list, set, or sequence, and *sequence* evaluates to an integer, a range, or NULL, Maple performs a selection operation.

If *sequence* evaluates to an integer i, then Maple returns the ith operand of the set, list, or sequence. If *sequence* evaluates to a range, then Maple returns a set, list, or sequence containing the operands of the aggregate object as the range specifies. If *sequence* evaluates to NULL, then Maple returns a sequence containing all of the operands of the aggregate object.

> s := x,y,z:
> L := [s,s];

$$L := [x,\ y,\ z,\ x,\ y,\ z]$$

> S := {s,s};

$$S := \{z,\ x,\ y\}$$

```
> S[2];
```

$$x$$

```
> L[2..3];
```

$$[y, z]$$

```
> S[];
```

$$z, x, y$$

Negative integers count operands from the right.

```
> L := [t,u,v,w,x,y,z];
```

$$L := [t, u, v, w, x, y, z]$$

```
> L[-3];
```

$$x$$

```
> L[-3..-2];
```

$$[x, y]$$

You can also use **select**, **remove**, and **selectremove** to select elements from a list or set. See section 4.5.

Functions

A *function call* in Maple takes the form

```
f( sequence )
```

Often f will be a *name*, that is, the name of the function.

```
> sin(x);
```

$$\sin(x)$$

```
> min(2,3,1);
```

$$1$$

```
> g();
```

$$g()$$

```
> a[1](x);
```

$$a_1(x)$$

Maple executes a function call as follows. First, it evaluates f (typically yielding a procedure). Next, Maple evaluates the operands of *sequence* (the arguments) from left to right. (If any of the arguments evaluate to a sequence, Maple flattens the sequence of evaluated arguments into one sequence.) If f evaluated to a procedure, Maple invokes it on the argument sequence. Chapter 5 discusses this in detail.

```
> x := 1:
> f(x);
```

$$f(1)$$

```
> s := 2,3;
```

$$s := 2, 3$$

```
> f(s,x);
```

$$f(2, 3, 1)$$

```
> f := g;
```

$$f := g$$

```
> f(s,x);
```

$$g(2, 3, 1)$$

```
> g := (a,b,c) -> a+b+c;
```

$$g := (a,\ b,\ c) \to a + b + c$$

```
> f(s,x);
```

$$6$$

A function object's type is **function**. The operands are the arguments. The zeroth operand is the name of the function.

```
>  m := min(x,y,x,z);
```

$$m := \min(1,\ y,\ z)$$

```
> op(0,m);
```

$$min$$

```
> op(m);
```

$$1,\ y,\ z$$

```
> type(m,function);
```

$$true$$

```
> f := n!;
```

$$f := n!$$

```
> type(f, function);
```

$$true$$

```
> op(0, f);
```

$$factorial$$

```
> op(f);
```

$$n$$

In general, the function name f may be one of the following.

- name

- procedure definition

- integer

- float

- parenthesized algebraic expression

- function

Allowing f to be a procedure definition allows you to write, for example

```
> proc(t) t*(1-t) end proc (t^2);
```

$$t^2 \left(1 - t^2\right)$$

instead of

```
> h := proc(t) t*(1-t) end proc;
```

$$h := \mathbf{proc}(t)\, t * (1 - t)\, \mathbf{end\ proc}$$

```
> h(t^2);
```

$$t^2 \left(1 - t^2\right)$$

If f is an integer or a float, Maple treats f as a constant operator. That is $f(x)$ returns f.

```
> 2(x);
```

$$2$$

The following rules define the meaning of a parenthesized algebraic expression.

```
> (f + g)(x), (f - g)(x), (-f)(x), (f@g)(x);
```

$$f(x) + g(x),\; f(x) - g(x),\; -f(x),\; f(g(x))$$

@ denotes functional composition; that is, **f@g** denotes $f \circ g$. These rules together with the previous rule mean that

```
> (f@g + f^2*g + 1)(x);
```

$$f(g(x)) + f(x)^2\, g(x) + 1$$

Notice that **@@** denotes the corresponding exponentiation. That is, **f@@n** denotes $f^{(n)}$ which means f composed with itself n times.

```
> (f@@3)(x);
```

$$(f^{(3)})(x)$$

```
> expand(%);
```

$$f(f(f(x)))$$

Finally, f may be a function, as in

```
> cos(0);
```

$$1$$

```
> f(g)(0);
```

$$f(g)(0)$$

```
> D(cos)(0);
```

$$0$$

For more information on how to define a function, see chapter 5.

Table 4.11 The Arithmetic Operators

+	addition
−	subtraction
*	multiplication
.	non-commutative multiplication
/	division
^	exponentiation

The Arithmetic Operators

Table 4.11 contains Maple's six arithmetic operators. You may use all these items as binary operators. You may also use the operators + and − as prefix operators representing unary plus and unary minus.

You can find the types and operands of the arithmetic operations listed below.

- The type of a sum or difference is +.

- The type of a product or quotient is * and the type of a power is ^.

- The operands of the sum $x - y$ are the terms x and $-y$.

- The operands of the product xy^2/z are factors x, y^2, and z^{-1}.

- The operands of the power x^a are the base x and the exponent a.

```
> whattype(x-y);
```

$$+$$

```
> whattype(x^y);
```

$$\hat{}$$

Arithmetic   Maple always computes the five arithmetic operations $x + y$, $x - y$, $x \times y$, x/y, and x^n, where n is an integer, if x and y are numbers. If the operands are floating-point numbers, Maple performs the arithmetic computation in the floating-point environment.

```
> 2 + 3,  6/4,  1.2/7,  (2 + I)/(2 - 2*I);
```

$$5, \frac{3}{2}, .1714285714, \frac{1}{4} + \frac{3}{4}I$$

> `3^(1.2), I^(1.0 - I);`

$$3.737192819, \, 0. + 4.810477381\,I$$

The only other simplification done for numerical constants is reduction of fractional powers of integers and fractions. For integers n, m and fraction b,
$$(n/m)^b \to (n^b)/(m^b).$$
For integers n, q, r, d and fraction $b = q + r/d$ with $0 < r < d$,
$$n^b = n^{q+r/d} \to n^q \times n^{r/d}.$$

> `2^(3/2), (-2)^(7/3);`

$$2\sqrt{2}, \, 4\,(-2)^{(1/3)}$$

Automatic Simplifications Maple automatically does these simplifications

> `x - x,   x + x,   x + 0,   x*x,   x/x,   x*1,   x^0,   x^1;`

$$0, \, 2\,x, \, x, \, x^2, \, 1, \, x, \, 1, \, x$$

for a symbol x, or an arbitrary expression. But these simplifications are not valid for all x. Some exceptions which Maple catches are

> `infinity - infinity;`

$$undefined$$

> `infinity/infinity;`

$$undefined$$

> `0/0;`

`Error, numeric exception: division by zero`

In the following, a, b, c denote numerical constants and x, y, z denote general symbolic expressions. Maple understands that addition and multiplication are associative and commutative, and so simplifies the following.

$$ax + bx \rightarrow (a + b)x$$

$$x^a \times x^b \rightarrow x^{a+b}$$

$$a(x + y) \rightarrow ax + ay$$

The first two simplifications mean that Maple adds like terms in polynomials automatically. The third means that Maple distributes numerical constants (integers, fractions, and floats) over sums, but does not do the same for non-numerical constants.

```
> 2*x + 3*x, x*y*x^2, 2*(x + y), z*(x + y);
```

$$5\,x, \; x^3\,y, \; 2\,x + 2\,y, \; z\,(x + y)$$

The most difficult and controversial simplifications have to do with simplying powers x^y for non-integer exponents y.

Simplification of Repeated Exponentiation In general, Maple does not do the simplification $(x^y)^z \rightarrow x^{(yz)}$ automatically because this procedure does not always provide an accurate answer. For example, letting $y = 2$ and $z = 1/2$, the first simplification would imply that $\sqrt{x^2} = x$, which is not necessarily true. Maple only does the first transformation above if it is provably correct for all complex x with the possible exception of a finite number of values, such as, 0 and ∞. Maple does $(x^a)^b \rightarrow x^{ab}$ if b is an integer, $-1 < a \le 1$, or x is a positive real constant.

```
> (x^(3/5))^(1/2), (x^(5/3))^(1/2);
```

$$x^{(3/10)}, \; \sqrt{x^{(5/3)}}$$

```
> (2^(5/3))^(1/2), (x^(-1))^(1/2);
```

$$2^{(5/6)}, \; \sqrt{\dfrac{1}{x}}$$

Maple does not simplify $a^b c^b \rightarrow (ac)^b$ automatically, even if the answer is correct.

```
> 2^(1/2)+3^(1/2)+2^(1/2)*3^(1/2);
```

$$\sqrt{2} + \sqrt{3} + \sqrt{2}\,\sqrt{3}$$

The reason is that combining $\sqrt{2}\sqrt{3}$ to $\sqrt{6}$ would introduce a third unique square root. Calculating with roots is, in general, difficult and expensive, so Maple is careful not to create new roots. You may use the **combine** command to combine roots if you desire.

Non-Commutative Multiplication

The non-commutative multiplication operator **&*** acts as an inert operator (for example, the *neutral operators* described in section 4.4), but the parser understands its binding strength to be equivalent to the binding strength of ***** and **/**.

The **evalm** command in the Maple Library interprets **&*** as the table-based matrix multiplication operator.[1] The **evalm** command also understands the form **&*()** as a generic matrix identity.

```
> with(LinearAlgebra):
> A := matrix(2,2,[a,b,c,d]);
```

$$A := \begin{bmatrix} a & b \\ c & d \end{bmatrix}$$

```
> evalm( A &* &*() );
```

$$\begin{bmatrix} a & b \\ c & d \end{bmatrix}$$

```
> B := matrix(2,2,[e,f,g,h]);
```

$$B := \begin{bmatrix} e & f \\ g & h \end{bmatrix}$$

```
> evalm( A &* B - B &* A );
```

$$\begin{bmatrix} b\,g - c\,f & a\,f + b\,h - e\,b - f\,d \\ c\,e + d\,g - g\,a - h\,c & c\,f - b\,g \end{bmatrix}$$

---

[1]The Maple library interprets . (dot) as the rtable-based Matrix multiplication operator.

The Composition Operators

The composition operators are @ and @@. The @ operator represents function composition, that is, f@g in Maple denotes $f \circ g$.

> (f@g)(x);

$$f(g(x))$$

> (sin@cos)(Pi/2);

$$0$$

The @@ operator is the corresponding exponentiation operator representing repeated functional composition, that is, $f^{(n)}$ is denoted f@@n in Maple.

> (f@@2)(x);

$$(f^{(2)})(x)$$

> expand(%);

$$f(f(x))$$

> (D@@n)(f);

$$(D^{(n)})(f)$$

Usually $f^n(x)$ denotes composition; for example, D^n denotes the differential operator composed n times. Also $\sin^{-1}(x)$ denotes the inverse of the sine function, that is, composition to the power -1. But, sometimes mathematicians use $f^n(x)$ to denote ordinary powering, for example, $\sin^2(x)$ is the square of sine of x. Maple always uses $f^n(x)$ to denote repeated composition, and $f(x)^n$ to denote powering.

> sin(x)^2, (sin@@2)(x), sin(x)^(-1), (sin@@(-1))(x);

$$\sin(x)^2, \ (\sin^{(2)})(x), \ \frac{1}{\sin(x)}, \ \arcsin(x)$$

The Ditto Operators

The value of the nullary operator, %, is the most recent expression. The first and second expressions preceding the most recent are the values of the nullary operators %% and %%%, respectively. The most common use of these operators is in an interactive Maple session where they refer to the previously computed results. The sequence of expressions defining these three nullary operators is the last three non-NULL values generated in the Maple session.

The Factorial Operator

Maple uses the unary operator ! as a postfix operator which denotes the factorial function of its operand n. The input n! is shorthand for the functional form factorial(n).

> 0!, 5!;

$$1, 120$$

For negative integers, the factorial returns an error.

> (-2)!;

Error, numeric exception: division by zero

For floating-point n, generalized factorial function values n! are calculated by using GAMMA(n+1).

> 2.5!;

$$3.323350970$$

The type of an unevaluated factorial is !. Note that in Maple, n!! does not denote the double factorial function. It denotes repeated factorial, $n!! = (n!)!$.

> 3!!;

$$720$$

The mod **Operator**

The **mod** operator evaluates an expression modulo m, for a non-zero integer m. That is, Maple writes $a \bmod m$ as **a mod m**. Maple uses one of two representations for an integer modulo m.

- In the *positive representation*, **integer** mod **m** is an integer between zero and **m-1**, inclusive. The following assignment selects the positive representation explicitly.

  ```
  > `mod` := modp;
  ```

  This is the default representation.

- In the *symmetric representation*, **integer** mod **m** is an integer between **-floor((abs(m)-1)/2)** and **floor(abs(m)/2)**. The following assignment selects the symmetric representation.

  ```
  > `mod` := mods;
  ```

Notice that you need back quotes around **mod** since it is a reserved word.

You may invoke the commands **modp** and **mods** directly if you desire. For example

```
> modp(9,5), mods(9,5);
```

$$4, -1$$

The **mod** operator understands the inert operator **&^** for powering. That is, **i&^j** mod **m** calculates i^j mod m. Instead of first computing the integer i^j, which may be too large to compute, and then reducing modulo m, Maple computes the power using binary powering with remainder.

```
> 2^(2^100) mod 5;
```

```
Error, numeric exception: overflow
```

```
> 2 &^ (2^100) mod 5;
```

$$1$$

The first operand of the **mod** operator may be a general expression. Maple evaluates the expression over the ring of integers modulo m. For polynomials, this means that it reduces rational coefficients modulo m.

The `mod` operator knows many functions for polynomial and matrix arithmetic over finite rings and fields. For example, `Factor` for polynomial factorization, and `Nullspace` for matrix null-space.

> `1/2 mod 5;`

$$3$$

> `9*x^2 + x/2 + 13 mod 5;`

$$4\,x^2 + 3\,x + 3$$

> `Factor(4*x^2 + 3*x + 3) mod 5;`

$$4\,(x + 4)\,(x + 3)$$

Do not confuse, for example, the commands `factor` and `Factor`. The former evaluates immediately; the latter is an inert command which Maple does not evaluate until you make the call to `mod`.

The `mod` command also knows how to compute over a Galois field $GF(p^k)$, that is, the finite field with p^k elements. See the `?mod` online documentation for a list of the commands that `mod` knows, and for further examples.

The Neutral Operators

Maple possesses a *user-defined* or *neutral* operators facility. Form a neutral operator symbol by using the ampersand character "`&`" followed by one or more characters. The two varieties of `&`-names depend on whether the sequence of characters is alphanumeric or non-alphanumeric:

- Any Maple *name* not requiring back quotes, preceded by the `&` character; for example, `&wedge`.

- The `&` character followed by one or more non-alphanumeric characters; for example, `&+` or `&++`.

The following characters cannot appear in an `&`-name after the initial `&`:

& | ( ) [ ] { } ; : ' ` # \ %

as well as *newline* and *blank* characters.

Maple singles out the particular neutral operator symbol `&*` as a special token representing the non-commutative multiplication operator. The special property of &* is that the parser understands its binding strength to be equivalent to Maple's other multiplication operators. All other neutral operators have binding strength greater than the standard algebraic operators. See ?precedence for the order of precedence of all programming-language operators. See section 4.4 which describes where to use &* in Maple.

You can use neutral operators as unary prefix operators, infix binary operators, or function calls. In any of these cases, they generate function calls with the name of the function being that of the neutral operator. (In the usual pretty-printing mode, these particular function calls are printed in binary operator format when exactly two operands exist and in unary operator format when exactly one operand exists, but the internal representation is an unevaluated function.) For example,

```
> a &~ b &~ c;
```

$$(a \, \&^{\sim} b) \, \&^{\sim} c$$

```
> op(%);
```

$$a \, \&^{\sim} b, \, c$$

```
> op(0,%%);
```

$$\&^{\sim}$$

Maple imposes no semantics on the neutral operators. The user may define the operator to have a meaning by assigning the name to a Maple procedure. You can define manipulations on expressions containing such operators via Maple's interface to user-defined procedures for various standard library functions, including simplify, diff, combine, series, evalf, and many others. See section 3.4.

Relations and Logical Operators

You can form new types of expressions from ordinary algebraic expressions by using the *relational operators* <, >, <=, >=, =, and <>. The semantics of these operators is dependent on whether they occur in an *algebraic* context or in a *Boolean* context.

In an algebraic context, the relational operators are simply place holders for forming equations or inequalities. Maple fully supports addition of equations or inequalities and multiplication of an equation or inequality by an algebraic expression. In the case of adding or subtracting two equations, for example, Maple applies the addition or subtraction to each side of the equations, thus yielding a new equation. In the case of multiplying an equation by an expression, Maple distributes the multiplication to each side of the equation. You may perform similar operations with inequalities.

```
> e  :=  x + 3*y = z;
```

$$e := x + 3\,y = z$$

```
> 2*e;
```

$$2\,x + 6\,y = 2\,z$$

The type of an equation is = or **equation**. An equation has two operands, the left-hand side, and the right-hand side. You can use the commands **lhs** and **rhs** to select the operands of an equation instead of **op**.

```
> op(0,e);
```

$$=$$

```
> lhs(e);
```

$$x + 3\,y$$

The **type** command also understands the types <>, <, and <=. Maple automatically converts inequalities involving > or >= to < and <=, respectively. All the relational types have two operands.

```
> e := a > b;
```

$$e := b < a$$

```
> op(e);
```

$$b,\, a$$

In a Boolean context, Maple evaluates a relation to the value **true** or the value **false**. A Boolean context includes the condition in an **if** statement and the condition in the **while** clause of a loop. You may also use the **evalb** command to evaluate a relation in a Boolean context.

In the case of the operators <, <=, >, and >=, the difference of the operands must evaluate to a numeric constant and Maple compares this constant with zero.

```
> if 2<3 then "less" else "not less" end if;
```

$$\text{``less''}$$

In the case of the relations = and <>, the operands may be arbitrary expressions (algebraic or non-algebraic). This equality test for expressions deals only with syntactic equality of the Maple representations of the expressions, which is not the same as mathematical equivalence.

```
> evalb( x + y = y + x );
```

$$true$$

```
> evalb( x^2 - y^2  =  (x - y)*(x + y) );
```

$$false$$

In the latter example, applying the **expand** command results in an equation which evaluates to **true**.

```
> evalb( x^2 - y^2  =  expand( (x - y)*(x + y) ) );
```

$$true$$

You may use the **is** command instead of **evalb** to evaluate relations in a Boolean context. The **is** command tries much harder than **evalb** to determine whether relations are true.

```
> is( x^2 - y^2  =  (x - y)*(x + y) );
```

$$true$$

```
> is( 3<Pi );
```

$$true$$

The Logical Operators   Generally, you can form an expression by using the *logical operators* and, or, and not, where the first two are binary operators and the third is a unary (prefix) operator. An expression containing one or more logical operators is automatically evaluated in a Boolean context.

```
> 2>3 or not 5>1;
```

$$false$$

The precedence of the logical operators or, or, and not is analogous to multiplication, addition, and exponentiation, respectively. Here no parentheses are necessary.

```
> (a and b) or ((not c) and d);
```

$$a \textbf{ and } b \textbf{ or } \textbf{ not } c \textbf{ and } d$$

The type names for the logical operators and, or, and not are and, or, and not, respectively. The first two have two operands, the latter one operand.

```
> b := x and y or z;
```

$$b := x \textbf{ and } y \textbf{ or } z$$

```
> whattype(b);
```

$$or$$

```
> op(b);
```

$$x \textbf{ and } y,\ z$$

Among operators of the same precedence, the evaluation of Boolean expressions involving the logical operators and and or proceeds from left to right and terminates as soon as Maple can determine the truth of the whole expression. Consider the evaluation of the following.

```
a and b and c
```

If the result of evaluating *a* is false, you know that the result of the whole Boolean expression will be false, regardless of what *b* and *c* evaluate to. These evaluation rules are commonly known as *McCarthy evaluation rules*. They are quite crucial for programming. Consider the following statement

```
if x <> 0 and f(x)/x > 1 then ... end if;
```

If Maple always evaluated both operands of the **and** clause, then when *x* is 0, evaluation would result in a division by zero error. The advantage of the above code is that Maple will attempt to check the second condition only when $x \neq 0$.

Boolean Expressions In general, a Boolean context requires a Boolean expression. Use the Boolean constants **true**, **false**, and **FAIL**, the *relational operators* and the *logical operators* for forming Boolean expressions. The **type** command understands the name **boolean** to include all of these.

The evaluation of Boolean expressions in Maple uses the following *three-valued logic*. In addition to the special names **true** and **false**, Maple also understands the special name **FAIL**. Maple sometimes uses the value **FAIL** as the value that a procedure returns when it is unable to completely solve a problem. In other words, you can view it as the value *don't know*.

```
> is(sin(1),positive);
```

$$true$$

```
> is(a-1,positive);
```

$$FAIL$$

In the context of the Boolean clause in an **if** statement or a **while** statement, Maple determines the branching of the program by treating the value **FAIL** the same as the value **false**. Without three valued logic, whenever you use the **is** command you would have to test for **FAIL** separately. You would write

```
if is(a - 1, positive) = true then ...
```

The three valued logic allows you to write

Table 4.12 Truth Tables

and	false	true	FAIL		or	false	true	FAIL
false	false	false	false		false	false	true	FAIL
true	false	true	FAIL		true	true	true	true
FAIL	false	FAIL	FAIL		FAIL	FAIL	true	FAIL

not	false	true	FAIL
	true	false	FAIL

```
if is(a - 1, positive) then ...
```

The evaluation of a Boolean expression yields `true`, `false`, or `FAIL` according to table 4.12.

Note that three-valued logic leads to asymmetry in the use of `if` statements and `while` statements. For example, the following two statements are not equivalent.

```
if condition then statseq_1 else statseq_2 end if;
if not condition then statseq_2 else statseq_1 end if;
```

Depending on the desired action in the case where *condition* has the value `FAIL`, either the first or the second of these two `if` statements may be correct for a particular context.

Tables

The `table` data type in Maple is a special data type for representing data in tables. Create a table either explicitly via the `table` command or implicitly by assignment to an indexed name. For example, the statements

```
> a := table([(Cu,1) = 64]);
```

$$a := \text{table}([(Cu, 1) = 64])$$

```
> a[Cu,1] := 64;
```

$$a_{Cu, 1} := 64$$

have the same effect. They both create a `table` object with one component. The purpose of a table is to allow fast access to data with

```
> a[Cu,1];
```

$$64$$

The type of a table object is **table**. The first operand is the indexing function. The second operand is a list of the components. Note that tables (and arrays, which are a special case of a table) have special evaluation rules; in order to access the table (or array) object, you must first apply the **eval** command.

```
> op(0,eval(a));
```

$$table$$

Table **a** has no indexing function and only one entry.

```
> op(1,eval(a));
> op(2,eval(a));
```

$$[(Cu,\,1) = 64]$$

The **array** data type in Maple is a specialization of the **table** data type. An array is a **table** with specified dimensions, with each dimension an integer range. Create an array via the **array** command call.

```
> A := array(symmetric, 1..2, 1..2, [(1,1) = 3]);
```

$$A := \begin{bmatrix} 3 & A_{1,2} \\ A_{1,2} & A_{2,2} \end{bmatrix}$$

```
> A[1,2] := 4;
```

$$A_{1,2} := 4$$

```
> print(A);
```

$$\begin{bmatrix} 3 & 4 \\ 4 & A_{2,2} \end{bmatrix}$$

The ranges `1..2,1..2` specify two dimensions and bounds for the integers. You may include entries in the array command or insert them explicitly as shown. You may leave entries unassigned. In this example, the (2, 2) entry is unassigned.

```
> op(0,eval(A));
```

$$array$$

As for tables, the first operand is the indexing function (if any).

```
> op(1,eval(A));
```

$$symmetric$$

The second operand is the sequence of ranges.

```
> op(2,eval(A));
```

$$1..2, \ 1..2$$

The third operand is a list of entries.

```
> op(3, eval(A));
```

$$[(1, \ 1) = 3, \ (1, \ 2) = 4]$$

The example above displays only two entries in the array A since Maple knows the $(2, 1)$ entry implicitly through the indexing function.

Series

The **series** data type in Maple represents an expression as a truncated power series with respect to a specified indeterminate, expanded about a particular point. Although you cannot input a series directly into Maple as an expression, you can create a series data type with the **taylor** or **series** commands which have the following syntax

```
taylor( f, x=a, n )
taylor( f, x )
series( f, x=a, n )
series( f, x )
```

If you do not specify the expansion point, it is by default $x = 0$. If you do not specify the order n, it is the value of the global variable `Order`, which by default is 6.

```
> s := series( exp(x), x=0, 4 );
```

$$s := 1 + x + \frac{1}{2}\,x^2 + \frac{1}{6}\,x^3 + \mathrm{O}(x^4)$$

The type name for the series data type is **series**.

```
> type(s, series);
```

$$\textit{true}$$

The zeroth operand is the expression $x - a$ where x denotes the specified indeterminate and a denotes the particular point of expansion.

```
> op(0, s);
```

$$x$$

The odd (first, third, ...) operands are the coefficients of the series and the even operands are the corresponding integer exponents.

```
> op(s);
```

$$1,\ 0,\ 1,\ 1,\ \frac{1}{2},\ 2,\ \frac{1}{6},\ 3,\ \mathrm{O}(1),\ 4$$

The coefficients may be general expressions but Maple restricts the exponents to *word-size* integers on the host computer, with a typical limit of nine or ten digits, ordered from least to greatest. Usually, the final pair of operands in the series data type are the special *order* symbol $O(1)$ and the integer n which indicates the order of truncation.

The **print** routine displays the final pair of operands by using the notation $O(x^n)$ rather than more directly as $O(1)x^n$, where x is `op(0,s)`.

If Maple knows that the series is exact then it will not contain an order term. An example of this occurs when you apply the **series** command to a polynomial whose degree is less than the truncation degree for the series. A very special case is the *zero series*, which Maple immediately simplifies to the integer zero.

The **series** data structure represents generalized power series, which include Laurent series with finite principal parts. More generally, Maple allows the series coefficients to depend on x provided their growth is less than polynomial in x. $O(1)$ represents such a coefficient, rather than an arbitrary constant. An example of a non-standard generalized power series is

```
> series( x^x, x=0, 3 );
```

$$1 + \ln(x)\, x + \frac{1}{2} \ln(x)^2\, x^2 + \mathrm{O}(x^3)$$

Maple can compute more general series expansions than the **series** data type supports. The Puisseux series is such an example. In these cases, the **series** command does not return a series data type, it returns a general algebraic expression.

```
> s := series( sqrt(sin(x)), x );
```

$$s := \sqrt{x} - \frac{1}{12}\, x^{(5/2)} + \frac{1}{1440}\, x^{(9/2)} + \mathrm{O}(x^{(13/2)})$$

```
> type(s, series);
```

$$\textit{false}$$

```
> type(s, '+');
```

$$\textit{true}$$

Ranges

You often need to specify a *range* of numbers. For example, when you want to integrate a function over a range. In Maple, use the ellipsis operation to form ranges.

---

expression_1 .. *expression_2*

Specify the operator "`..`" using two consecutive periods. The ellipsis operator simply acts as a place holder in the same manner as using the relational operators in an algebraic context, primarily as a notational tool. A range has type "`..`" or **range**. A range has two operands, the left-limit and the right-limit, which you can access with the **lhs** and **rhs** commands.

```
> r:=3..7;
```

$$r := 3..7$$

```
> op(0,r);
```

$$..$$

```
> lhs(r);
```

$$3$$

A typical application of ranges occurs in Maple's **int**, **sum**, and **product** commands. Interpret the operands of the ellipsis to mean the lower and upper limits of integration, summation, or products, respectively.

```
>   int( f(x), x=a..b );
```

$$\int_a^b f(x)\, dx$$

You can use the range construct, with Maple's built-in command **op**, to extract a *sequence* of operands from an expression. The notation

```
op(a..b, c)
```

is equivalent to

```
seq(op(i,c),i=a..b)
```

For example,

```
> a := [ u, v, w, x, y, z ];
```

$$a := [u,\, v,\, w,\, x,\, y,\, z]$$

```
> op(2..5,a);
```

$$v, \, w, \, x, \, y$$

You can also use the range construct in combination with the concatenation operator to form a *sequence* as follows.

```
> x || (1..5);
```

$$x1, \, x2, \, x3, \, x4, \, x5$$

See section 4.3.

Unevaluated Expressions

Maple normally evaluates all expressions, but sometimes you need to tell Maple to delay evaluating an expression.

An expression enclosed in a pair of single quotes

```
'expression'
```

is called an *unevaluated expression*. For example, the statements

```
> a := 1;  x := a + b;
```

$$a := 1$$

$$x := 1 + b$$

assign the value $1 + b$ to the name x, while the statements

```
> a := 1;  x := 'a' + b;
```

$$a := 1$$

$$x := a + b$$

assign the value $a + b$ to the name x if b has no value.

The effect of evaluating a quoted expression is to strip off one level of quotes, so in some cases nested levels of quotes are very useful. Note the distinction between *evaluation* and *simplification* in the statement

```
> x := '2 + 3';
```

$$x := 5$$

which assigns the value 5 to the name x even though this expression contains quotes. The evaluator simply strips off the quotes, but the *simplifier* transforms the expression $2 + 3$ into the constant 5.

The result of evaluating an expression with two levels of quotes is an expression of type **uneval**. This expression has only one operand, namely the expression inside the outermost pair of quotes.

```
> op(''x - 2'');
```

$$x - 2$$

```
> whattype(''x - 2'');
```

$$uneval$$

A special case of unevaluation arises when a name, which Maple may have assigned a value, needs unassigning so that in the future the name simply stands for itself. You can accomplish this by assigning the quoted name to itself.

```
> x := 'x';
```

$$x := x$$

Now x stands for itself as if Maple had never assigned it a value.

Another special case of unevaluation arises in the function call

```
'f'(sequence)
```

Suppose the arguments evaluate to the sequence a. Since the result of evaluating $'f'$ is not a procedure, Maple returns the unevaluated function call $f(a)$.

```
> ''sin''(Pi);
```

$$'\mathrm{sin}'(\pi)$$

```
> %;
```

$$\sin(\pi)$$

```
> %;
```

$$0$$

You will find this facility useful when writing procedures which implement simplification rules. See section 3.4.

Constants

Maple has a general concept of *symbolic constants*, and initially assigns the global variable **constants** the following expression sequence of names

```
> constants;
```

$$false, \; \gamma, \; \infty, \; true, \; Catalan, \; FAIL, \; \pi$$

implying that Maple understands these particular names to be of type **constant**. The user may define additional names (specifically, they must be the simplest type of names called *strings*—see section 4.3) to be constants by redefining the value of this global variable.

```
> type(g,constant);
```

$$false$$

```
> constants := constants, g;
```

$$constants := false, \; \gamma, \; \infty, \; true, \; Catalan, \; FAIL, \; \pi, \; g$$

```
> type(g,constant);
```

$$true$$

Generally, a Maple expression is of type **constant** if it is of type **complex(numeric)**, or one of the initially-known constants, or an unevaluated function with all arguments of type **constant**, or a sum, product, or power with all operands of type **constant**. For example, the following expressions are of type **constant**: 2, sin(1), f(2,3), exp(gamma), 4+Pi, 3+I, 2*gamma/Pi^(1/2)

Structured Types

Sometimes a simple type check does not give enough information. For example, the command

```
> type( x^2, '^' );
```

$$true$$

tells you that x^2 is an exponentiation but it does not tell you whether or not the exponent is, say, an integer. In such cases, you need *structured types*.

```
> type( x^2, name^integer );
```

$$true$$

Since x is a **name** and 2 is an **integer**, the command returns **true**. The square root of x does not have this type.

```
> type( x^(1/2), name^integer );
```

$$false$$

The expression (x+1)^2 does not have type **name^integer**, because x+1 is not a name.

```
> type( (x+1)^2, name^integer );
```

$$false$$

The type **anything** matches any expression.

```
> type( (x+1)^2, anything^integer );
```

$$true$$

An expression matches a set of types if the expression matches one of the types in the set.

```
> type( 1, {integer, name} );
```

$$true$$

```
> type( x, {integer, name} );
```

$$true$$

The type **set(type)** matches a set of elements of type *type*.

```
> type( {1,2,3,4}, set(integer) );
```

$$true$$

```
> type( {x,2,3,y}, set( {integer, name} ) );
```

$$true$$

Similarly, the type **list(type)** matches a list of elements of type *type*.

```
> type( [ 2..3, 5..7 ], list(range) );
```

$$true$$

Note that e^2 is not of type **anything^2**.

```
> exp(2);
```

$$e^2$$

```
> type( %, anything^2 );
```

$$false$$

The reason is that e^2 is simply the pretty-printed version of **exp(2)**.

```
> type( exp(2), 'exp'(integer) );
```

$$true$$

You should use single quotes (') around Maple commands in type expressions to delay evaluation.

```
> type( int(f(x), x), int(anything, anything) );
Error, testing against an invalid type
```

Here Maple evaluated `int(anything, anything)` and got

```
> int(anything, anything);
```

$$\frac{1}{2}\, anything^2$$

which is not a valid type. If you put single quotes around the `int` command, the type checking works as intended.

```
> type( int(f(x), x), 'int'(anything, anything) );
```

true

The type `specfunc(type, f)` matches the function *f* with zero or more arguments of type *type*.

```
> type( exp(x), specfunc(name, exp) );
```

true

```
> type( f(), specfunc(name, f) );
```

true

The type `function(type)` matches any function with zero or more arguments of type *type*.

```
> type( f(1,2,3), function(integer) );
```

true

```
> type( f(1,x,Pi), function( {integer, name} ) );
```

true

You can also test the number (and types) of arguments. The type `anyfunc(t1, ..., tn)` matches any function with *n* arguments of the listed types.

```
> type( f(1,x), anyfunc(integer, name) );
```

true

```
> type( f(x,1), anyfunc(integer, name) );
```

false

Another useful variation is to use the **And**, **Or**, and **Not** type construtors to create Boolean combinations of types.

```
> type(Pi, 'And( constant, numeric)');
```

false

```
> type(Pi, 'And( constant, Not(numeric))');
```

true

See **?type,structured** for more information on structured types or **?type,definition** on how to define your own types.

4.5   Useful Looping Constructs

Section 4.3 describes the **for** loop and **while** loop. Many common kinds of loops appear so often that Maple provides special purpose commands for them. These commands help to make writing programs simpler and more efficient. They are the "bread and butter" commands in the Maple language. You can group the eight loop-like commands in Maple into three categories

1. **map**, **select**, **remove**, **selectremove**

2. **zip**

3. **seq**, **add**, **mul**

The map, select, remove, and selectremove Commands
The **map** command applies a function to every element of an aggregate object. The simplest form of the **map** command is

```
map( f, x )
```

where f is a function and x is an expression. The **map** command replaces each operand x_i of the expression x with $f(x\_i)$.[2]

```
> map( f, [a,b,c] );
```

$$[f(a),\ f(b),\ f(c)]$$

For example, if you have a list of integers, create a list of their absolute values and of their squares by using the **map** command.

```
> L := [ -1, 2, -3, -4, 5 ];
```

$$L := [-1,\ 2,\ -3,\ -4,\ 5]$$

```
> map(abs,L);
```

$$[1,\ 2,\ 3,\ 4,\ 5]$$

```
> map(x->x^2,L);
```

$$[1,\ 4,\ 9,\ 16,\ 25]$$

The general syntax of the **map** command is

```
map( f, x, y1, ..., yn )
```

where f is a function, x is any expression, and $y1, \ldots, yn$ are expressions. The action of **map** is to replace each operand x_i of x by $f(x\_i, y1, \ldots, yn)$.

```
> map( f, [a,b,c], x, y );
```

$$[f(a,\ x,\ y),\ f(b,\ x,\ y),\ f(c,\ x,\ y)]$$

```
> L := [ seq(x^i, i=0..5) ];
```

---

[2]Exception: for an rtable, table or array, Maple applies the function to the entries of the table or array, and not to the operands or indices.

$$L := [1,\, x,\, x^2,\, x^3,\, x^4,\, x^5]$$

```
> map( (x,y)->x^2+y, L, 1);
```

$$[2,\, x^2 + 1,\, x^4 + 1,\, x^6 + 1,\, x^8 + 1,\, x^{10} + 1]$$

The **select**, **remove**, and **selectremove** commands have the same syntax as the **map** command and they work in a similar way. The simplest forms are

```
select( f, x )
remove( f, x )
selectremove( f, x )
```

where f is a Boolean-valued function and x is an expression which must be one of a sum, product, list, set, function, or indexed name.

The **select** command selects the operands of x which satisfy the Boolean-valued function f, creating a new object of the same type as x. Maple discards those operands for which f does not return **true**.

The **remove** command does the opposite of **select**. It removes the operands of x that satisfy f.

```
> X := [seq(i,i=1..10)];
```

$$X := [1,\, 2,\, 3,\, 4,\, 5,\, 6,\, 7,\, 8,\, 9,\, 10]$$

```
> select(isprime,X);
```

$$[2,\, 3,\, 5,\, 7]$$

```
> remove(isprime,X);
```

$$[1,\, 4,\, 6,\, 8,\, 9,\, 10]$$

```
> selectremove(isprime,X);
```

$$[2,\, 3,\, 5,\, 7],\, [1,\, 4,\, 6,\, 8,\, 9,\, 10]$$

The general forms of the **select** and **remove** commands are

```
select( f, x, y1, ..., yn )
remove( f, x, y1, ..., yn )
selectremove( f, x, y1, ..., yn )
```

where f is a function, x is a sum, product, list, set, function or indexed name, and $y1, \ldots, yn$ are expressions. As with the general form of the map command the expressions $y1, \ldots, yn$ are passed to the function f.

```
> X := {2, sin(1), exp(2*x), x^(1/2)};
```

$$X := \{2,\, \sin(1),\, e^{(2\,x)},\, \sqrt{x}\}$$

```
> select(type, X, function);
```

$$\{\sin(1),\, e^{(2\,x)}\}$$

```
> remove(type, X, constant);
```

$$\{e^{(2\,x)},\, \sqrt{x}\}$$

```
> X := 2*x*y^2 - 3*y^4*z + 3*z*w + 2*y^3 - z^2*w*y;
```

$$X := 2\,x\,y^2 - 3\,y^4\,z + 3\,z\,w + 2\,y^3 - z^2\,w\,y$$

```
> select(has, X, z);
```

$$-3\,y^4\,z + 3\,z\,w - z^2\,w\,y$$

```
> remove( x -> degree(x)>3, X );
```

$$2\,x\,y^2 + 3\,z\,w + 2\,y^3$$

The zip Command

Use the zip command to merge two lists or vectors. The zip command has two forms

```
zip(f, u, v)
zip(f, u, v, d)
```

where f is a binary function, u and v are both lists or vectors, and d is a value. The action of `zip` is for each pair of operands u_i, v_i, to create a new list or vector out of $f(u\_i,v\_i)$. The following is an example of the action of `zip`.

```
> zip( (x,y)->x || y, [a,b,c,d,e,f], [1,2,3,4,5,6] );
```

$$[a1,\ b2,\ c3,\ d4,\ e5,\ f6]$$

If the lists or vectors are not the same length, the length of the result depends on whether you provide d. If you do not specify d, the length will be the length of the smaller of u and v.

```
> zip( (x,y)->x+y, [a,b,c,d,e,f], [1,2,3] );
```

$$[a+1,\ b+2,\ c+3]$$

If you do specify d, the length of the result of the `zip` command will be the length of the longer list (or vector) and Maple uses d for the missing value(s).

```
> zip( (x,y)->x+y, [a,b,c,d,e,f], [1,2,3], xi );
```

$$[a+1,\ b+2,\ c+3,\ d+\xi,\ e+\xi,\ f+\xi]$$

Note that Maple does *not* pass the extra argument, `xi`, to the function f as it does with the `map` command.

The `seq`, `add`, and `mul` Commands

The `seq`, `add`, and `mul` commands form sequences, sums, and products, respectively. Use the following syntax with these commands.

```
seq(f, i = a..b)
add(f, i = a..b)
mul(f, i = a..b)
```

where *f*, *a*, and *b* are expressions and *i* is a name. The expressions *a* and *b* must evaluate to numerical constants (except in the case of **seq**, where they may be single character strings).

The result of **seq** is the sequence that Maple produces by evaluating *f* after successively assigning the index name *i* the values *a*, *a+1*, ..., *b*, (or up to the last value not exceeding *b*). The result of **add** is the sum of the same sequence, and the result of **mul** is the product of the sequence. If the value *a* is greater than *b*, the result is the NULL sequence, 0, and 1, respectively.

```
> seq(i^2,i=1..4);
```

$$1, 4, 9, 16$$

```
> mul(i^2,i=1..4);
```

$$576$$

```
> add(x[i], i=1..4);
```

$$x_1 + x_2 + x_3 + x_4$$

```
> mul(i^2, i = 4..1);
```

$$1$$

```
> seq(i, i = 4.123 .. 6.1);
```

$$4.123, 5.123$$

You can also use the commands **seq**, **add**, and **mul** with the following syntax.

```
seq(f, i = X)
add(f, i = X)
mul(f, i = X)
```

where f is an expression, X is an expression (or string for **seq**), and i is a name.

The result of **seq** in this form is the sequence that Maple produces by evaluating f after successively assigning the operands of the expression X (or the characters of string X) to the index i. The result of **add** is the sum of the same sequence, and the result of **mul** is the product of the same sequence.

> a := x^3 + 3*x^2 + 3*x + 1;

$$a := x^3 + 3\,x^2 + 3\,x + 1$$

> seq(degree(i,x), i=a);

$$3,\ 2,\ 1,\ 0$$

> seq(i, i="square");

$$\text{``s''},\ \text{``q''},\ \text{``u''},\ \text{``a''},\ \text{``r''},\ \text{``e''}$$

> add(degree(i,x), i=a);

$$6$$

> a := [23,-42,11,-3];

$$a := [23,\ -42,\ 11,\ -3]$$

> mul(abs(i),i=a);

$$31878$$

> add(i^2,i=a);

$$2423$$

seq, add, **and** mul **Versus** $, sum, **and** product   Note that the dollar operator, $, and the sum and product commands are very similar to the seq, mul, and add commands. However, they differ in an important way. The index variable i and the end points a and b do not need to be integers. For example

```
> x[k] $ k=1..n;
```

$$x_k \, \$ \, (k = 1..n)$$

The design of these commands is for *symbolic* sequences, sums, and products. As with the int (integration) command, the index variable k is a global variable to which you must not assign a value.

When should you use $, sum, and product? versus seq, add, mul?

When you are computing a symbolic sum or product. For example, if the end points are unknowns, then clearly you must use $, sum, and product. When you are computing an explicit finite sequence, sum, or product, that is, you know that the range points a and b are integers, then use seq, add, or mul. These latter commands are more efficient than their symbolic counterparts $, sum, and product.

4.6   Substitution

The subs command does a *syntactic* substitution. It replaces subexpressions in an expression with a new value; the subexpressions must be operands in the sense of the op command.

```
> expr := x^3 + 3*x + 1;
```

$$expr := x^3 + 3x + 1$$

```
> subs(x=y, expr);
```

$$y^3 + 3y + 1$$

```
> subs(x=2, expr);
```

15

The syntax of the **subs** command is

```
subs( s, expr )
```

where *s* is either an equation, a list, or set of equations. Maple traverses the expression *expr* and compares each operand in *expr* with the left-hand side(s) of the equation(s) *s*. If an operand is equal to a left-hand side of an equation in *s*, then **subs** replaces the operand with the right-hand side of the equation. If *s* is a list or set of equations, then Maple makes the substitutions indicated by the equations simultaneously.

```
> f := x*y^2;
```

$$f := x\,y^2$$

```
> subs( {y=z, x=y, z=w}, f );
```

$$y\,z^2$$

The general syntax of the **subs** command is

```
subs( s1, s2, ..., sn, expr )
```

where *s1, s2, ..., sn* are equations or sets or lists of equations, $n > 0$, and *expr* is an expression. This is equivalent to the following sequence of substitutions.

```
subs( sn, ..., subs( s2, subs( s1, expr ) ) )
```

Thus, **subs** substitutes according to the given equations from left to right. Notice the difference between the previous example and the following one.

```
> subs( y=z, x=y, z=w, f );
```

$$y\,w^2$$

Maple does not evaluate the result of a substitution.

```
> subs( x=0, sin(x) + x^2 );
```

$$\sin(0)$$

If you want to combine the acts of substitution and evaluation, use the two-parameter version of the **eval** command instead of **subs**.

```
> eval(sin(x) + x^2, x=0);
```

$$0$$

Substitution only compares operands in the expression tree of *expr* with the left-hand side of an equation.

```
> subs(a*b=d, a*b*c);
```

$$a\,b\,c$$

The substitution did not result in **d*c** as intended because the operands of the product **a*b*c** are **a, b, c**. That is, the products **a*b**, **b*c**, and **a*c** do not appear explicitly as operands in the expression **a*b*c**; consequently, **subs** does not see them.

The easiest way to make such substitutions is to solve the equation for one unknown and substitute for that unknown, that is

```
> subs(a=d/b, a*b*c);
```

$$d\,c$$

You cannot always do this, and you may find that it does not always produce the results you expect. The **algsubs** routine provides a more powerful substitution facility.

```
> algsubs(a*b=d, a*b*c);
```

$$d\,c$$

Note also that operands of a rational power $x^{n/d}$ are x and n/d. Although in the following example

```
> subs( x^(1/2)=y, a/x^(1/2) );
```

$$\frac{a}{\sqrt{x}}$$

it looks as though the output has a $\sqrt{x}$ in it, the operands of this expression are a and $x^{-1/2}$. Think of the division as a negative power in a product, that is, $a \times x^{-1/2}$. Because the operands of $x^{-1/2}$ are x and $-1/2$, **subs** does not see $x^{1/2}$ in $x^{-1/2}$. The solution is to substitute for the negative power $x^{-1/2}$.

```
> subs( x^(-1/2)=1/y, a/x^(1/2) );
```

$$\frac{a}{y}$$

The reader should refer to the online help information under **?algsubs** for more details. Note that the **algsubs** command, as powerful as it is, is also much more computationally expensive than the **subs** command.

4.7   Conclusion

This chapter discusses the elements of Maple's language. Maple breaks your input into its smallest meaningful parts, called tokens. Its language statements include assignments, conditional, looping, and reading from and saving to files. Many types of expressions exist within Maple, and using its expression trees tells you of the type and operands in an expression. You have seen the efficient looping constructs **map**, **zip**, and **seq**, and how to make substitutions.

5 Procedures

The `proc` command defines procedures in Maple. This chapter describes the syntax and semantics of the `proc` command in the same manner as chapter 4 describes the rest of the Maple programming language. This chapter explains the concepts of local and global variables and how Maple passes arguments to procedures. The chapter also provides exercises to help extend your understanding of Maple procedures.

5.1 Procedure Definitions

A Maple procedure definition has the following general syntax.

```
proc( P )
    local L;
    global G;
    options O;
    description D;
    B
end proc
```

Here, B is a sequence of statements forming the body of the procedure. The formal parameters, P, along with the `local`, `global`, `options`, and `description` clauses are all optional.

The following is a simple Maple procedure definition. It has two *formal parameters*, x and y, no `local`, `global`, `options`, or `description` clauses, and only one statement in the body of the procedure.

```
> proc(x,y)
>      x^2 + y^2
> end proc;
```

$$\mathbf{proc}(x,\ y)\, x^2 + y^2\ \mathbf{end\ proc}$$

You can give a name to a procedure as to any other Maple object.

```
> F := proc(x,y) x^2 + y^2 end proc;
```

$$F := \mathbf{proc}(x,\ y)\, x^2 + y^2\ \mathbf{end\ proc}$$

You can then *execute* (invoke) it by using the function call,

> [!note]
> *F (A)*

When Maple executes the statements of the body of a procedure, it replaces the formal parameters, P, with the actual parameters, A, from the function call. Note that Maple evaluates the actual parameters, A, before substituting them for the formal parameters, P.

Normally, the result a procedure returns after executing is the value of the last executed statement from the body of the procedure.

```
> F(2,3);
```

$$13$$

Mapping Notation

You can also define simple one-line procedures by using an alternate syntax borrowed from algebra.

> [!note]
> *(P) -> B*

The sequence, P, of formal parameters may be empty and the body, B, of the procedure must be a single expression or an **if** statement.

```
> F := (x,y) -> x^2 + y^2;
```

$$F := (x,\ y) \to x^2 + y^2$$

If your procedure involves only one parameter, then you may omit the parentheses around the formal parameter.

```
> G := n -> if n<0 then 0 else 1 end if;
```

$$G := \mathbf{proc}(n)$$
$$\mathbf{option} \; operator, \; arrow;$$
$$\mathbf{if}\, n < 0 \, \mathbf{then}\, 0 \;\; \mathbf{else}\, 1 \, \mathbf{end\; if}$$
$$\mathbf{end\; proc}$$

```
> G(9), G(-2);
```

$$1, 0$$

The intended use for the *arrow notation* is solely for simple one-line function definitions. It does not provide a mechanism for specifying local or global variables, or options.

Unnamed Procedures and Their Combinations

Procedure definitions are valid Maple expressions. You can create, manipulate, and invoke all of them without assigning to a name.

```
> (x) -> x^2;
```

$$x \to x^2$$

You invoke an unnamed procedure in the following manner.

```
> ( x -> x^2 )( t );
```

$$t^2$$

```
> proc(x,y) x^2 + y^2 end proc(u,v);
```

$$u^2 + v^2$$

A common use of unnamed procedures occurs in conjunction with the `map` command.

```
> map( x -> x^2, [1,2,3,4] );
```

$$[1, 4, 9, 16]$$

You can add procedures together, or, if appropriate, you can process them by using commands, such as the differential operator , D.

```
> D(x -> x^2);
```

$$x \to 2\,x$$

```
> F := D(exp + 2*ln);
```

$$F := \exp + 2\left(a \to \frac{1}{a}\right)$$

You can apply the result, **F**, directly to arguments.

Procedure Simplification

When you create a procedure, Maple does not evaluate the procedure but it does *simplify* the body of the procedure.

```
> proc(x) local t;
>     t := x*x*x + 0*2;
>     if true then sqrt(t); else t^2 end if;
> end proc;
```

$$\mathbf{proc}(x)\,\mathbf{local}\,t;\ t := x^3\,;\ \mathrm{sqrt}(t)\,\mathbf{end\ proc}$$

Maple simplifies procedures with the **operator** option even further.

```
> x -> 3/4;
```

$$\frac{3}{4}$$

```
> (x,y,z) -> h(x,y,z);
```

$$h$$

Procedure simplification is a simple form of program optimization.

5.2   Parameter Passing

Consider what happens when Maple evaluates a function or procedure.

```
F( ArgumentSequence )
```

First, Maple evaluates F. Then it evaluates the *ArgumentSequence*. If any of the arguments evaluate to a sequence, Maple flattens the resulting sequence of sequences into a single sequence, the sequence of *actual parameters*. Suppose F evaluates to a procedure.

```
proc( FormalParameters )
    body
end proc
```

Maple then executes the statements in the *body* of the procedure, substituting the actual parameters for the formal parameters.

Consider the following example.

```
> s := a,b: t := c:
> F := proc(x,y,z) x + y + z end proc:
> F(s,t);
```

$$a + b + c$$

Here, s,t is the *argument sequence*, a,b,c is the *actual parameter sequence* and x,y,z is the *formal parameter sequence*.

The number of actual parameters, n, may differ from the number of formal parameters. If too few actual parameters exist, then an error occurs if (and only if) a missing parameter is actually used during the execution of the procedure body. Maple ignores extra parameters.

```
> f := proc(x,y,z) if x>y then x else z end if end proc:
> f(1,2,3,4);
```

$$3$$

```
> f(1,2);
```

```
Error, (in f) f uses a 3rd argument, z, which is
missing
```

```
> f(2,1);
```

$$2$$

Declared Parameters

You may write procedures that only work for certain types of input. Use *declared formal parameters* so that when you use the procedure with the wrong types of input Maple issues an informative standard error message. A type declaration has the following syntax.

```
parameter :: type
```

Maple knows many types of expressions; see **?type**.

When invoking the procedure, before executing the body of the procedure, Maple tests the types of the actual parameters from left to right. Any of these tests may generate an error message. If no type error occurs, the procedure executes.

```
> MAX := proc(x::numeric, y::numeric)
>    if x>y then x else y end if
> end proc:
> MAX(Pi,3);
```

```
Error, invalid input: MAX expects its 1st argument, x,
to be of type numeric, but received Pi
```

You can also use declared parameters with the **operator** option.

```
> G := (n::even) -> n! * (n/2)!;
```

$$G := n\text{::}even \to n! \, (\frac{1}{2}\,n)!$$

```
> G(6);
```

$$4320$$

```
> G(5);
```

```
Error, invalid input: G expects its 1st argument, n, to
be of type even, but received 5
```

If you do not declare the type of a parameter, it can have any type. Thus, **proc(x)** is equivalent to **proc(x::anything)**. If that is what you intend, you should use the latter form to inform other users that you intend your procedure to work for any input.

The Sequence of Arguments

You do not need to supply names for the formal parameters. You can access the entire sequence of actual arguments from within the procedure, by using the name **args** . The following procedure simply builds a list of its arguments.

```
> f := proc() [args] end proc;
```

$$f := \mathbf{proc}()\,[\text{args}]\,\mathbf{end\ proc}$$

```
> f(a,b,c);
```

$$[a,\ b,\ c]$$

```
> f(c);
```

$$[c]$$

```
> f();
```

$$[]$$

The ith argument is simply **args[i]**. Thus, the following two procedures are equivalent, provided you call them with at least two actual parameters of type **numeric**.

```
> MAX := proc(x::numeric,y::numeric)
>    if x > y then x else y end if;
> end proc;
```

$$MAX := \mathbf{proc}(x\text{::}numeric,\ y\text{::}numeric)$$
$$\mathbf{if}\,y < x\,\mathbf{then}\,x\ \mathbf{else}\,y\,\mathbf{end\ if}$$
$$\mathbf{end\ proc}$$

```
> MAX := proc()
>    if args[1] > args[2] then args[1] else args[2] end if;
> end proc;
```

$$MAX := \mathbf{proc}()$$
$$\mathbf{if}\,\text{args}_2 < \text{args}_1\,\mathbf{then}\,\text{args}_1\,\mathbf{else}\,\text{args}_2\,\mathbf{end\ if}$$
$$\mathbf{end\ proc}$$

The `nargs` command provides the total number of actual parameters. This allows you to easily write a procedure, **MAX**, which finds the maximum of any number of arguments.

```
> MAX := proc()
>    local i,m;
>    if nargs = 0 then return -infinity end if;
>    m := args[1];
>    for i from 2 to nargs do
>       if args[i] > m then m := args[i] end if;
>    end do;
>    m;
> end proc:
```

The maximum of the three values 2/3, 1/2, and 4/7 is

```
> MAX(2/3, 1/2, 4/7);
```

$$\frac{2}{3}$$

5.3   Local and Global Variables

Variables inside a procedure are either local to that procedure or global. Variables outside procedures are global. Maple considers local variables in different procedure invocations to be different variables, even if they have the same name. Thus, a procedure can change the value of a local variable without affecting variables of the same name in other procedures or a global variable of the same name. You should always declare which variables are local and which are global in the following manner.

```
local L1, L2, ..., Ln;
global G1, G2, ..., Gm;
```

In the procedure below, i and m are local variables.

```
> MAX := proc()
>    local i,m;
>    if nargs = 0 then return -infinity end if;
>    m := args[1];
>    for i from 2 to nargs do
>       if args[i] > m then m := args[i] end if;
>    end do;
>    m;
> end proc:
```

In the case of nested procedures, where one procedure is defined within the body of another, variables can also acquire local or global declaration from procedures which enclose them. See Section 2.2 for details and examples of nested procedures.

If no declaration is made of whether a variable is local or global, Maple decides. A variable is automatically made local in both of these cases:

- It appears on the left-hand side of an assignment statement. For example, A in `A := y` or `A[1] := y`.

- It appears as the index variable in a `for` loop, or in a `seq`, `add`, or `mul` command.

If neither of these two rules applies, the variable is a global variable.

```
> MAX := proc()
>    if nargs = 0 then return -infinity end if;
>    m := args[1];
>    for i from 2 to nargs do
>        if args[i] > m then m := args[i] end if;
>    end do;
>    m;
> end proc:
```

```
Warning, 'm' is implicitly declared local to procedure
'MAX'
Warning, 'i' is implicitly declared local to procedure
'MAX'
```

Maple declares m local because it appears on the left-hand side of the assignment `m:=args[1]`, and i local because it is the index variable of a `for` loop.

Do not rely on this facility to declare local variables. Declare all your local variables explicitly. Rely instead on the warning messages to help you identify variables that you have misspelled or have forgotten to declare.

The `newname` procedure below creates the next unused name in the sequence $C1, C2, \ldots$. The name that `newname` creates is a global variable since neither of the two rules above apply to `cat(C,N)`.

```
> newname := proc()
>    global N;
>    N := N+1;
>    while not assigned(cat(C,N)) do
>        N := N+1;
>    end do;
>    cat(C,N);
> end proc:
```

```
> N := 0;
```

$$N := 0$$

The **newname** procedure does not take any arguments.

```
> newname() * sin(x) + newname() * cos(x);
```

$$C1\sin(x) + C2\cos(x)$$

Assigning values to global variables inside procedures is generally a poor idea. Any change of the value of a global variable affects all uses of the variable, even any of which you were unaware. Thus, you should only use this technique judiciously.

Evaluation of Local Variables

Local variables are special in another very important way. During the execution of a procedure body, they evaluate exactly *one level*. Maple evaluates global variables fully, even inside a procedure.

This section should help to clarify this concept. Consider the following examples.

```
> f := x + y;
```

$$f := x + y$$

```
> x := z^2/ y;
```

$$x := \frac{z^2}{y}$$

```
> z := y^3 + 3;
```

$$z := y^3 + 3$$

The normal full recursive evaluation yields

```
> f;
```

$$\frac{(y^3 + 3)^2}{y} + y$$

You can control the actual level of evaluation by using `eval`. Using the following sequence of commands, you can evaluate to one level, two levels, and three levels.

```
> eval(f,1);
```

$$x + y$$

```
> eval(f,2);
```

$$\frac{z^2}{y} + y$$

```
> eval(f,3);
```

$$\frac{(y^3 + 3)^2}{y} + y$$

The notion of the use of *one-level evaluation*[1] is important for efficiency. It has very little effect on the behavior of programs because you tend to write code in an organized sequential fashion. In the rare case where a procedure body requires a full-recursive evaluation of a local variable, you may use the `eval` command.

```
> F := proc()
>    local x, y, z;
>    x := y^2;   y := z;   z := 3;
>    eval(x)
> end proc:
> F();
```

$$9$$

Without the call to `eval`, the answer would be y^2.

You can still use local variables as unknowns just like global variables. For example, in the following procedure, the local variable x does not have an assigned value. The procedure uses it as the variable in the polynomial $x^n - 1$.

---

[1]Such a concept of evaluation does not occur in traditional programming languages. However, here, you may assign to a variable a formula involving other variables, which in turn you may assign values and so on.

```
> RootsOfUnity := proc(n)
>    local x;
>    [solve( x^n - 1=0, x )];
> end proc:
> RootsOfUnity(5);
```

$$[1, -\frac{1}{4} + \frac{1}{4}\sqrt{5} + \frac{1}{4}I\sqrt{2}\sqrt{5+\sqrt{5}},$$

$$-\frac{1}{4} - \frac{1}{4}\sqrt{5} + \frac{1}{4}I\sqrt{2}\sqrt{5-\sqrt{5}}, -\frac{1}{4} - \frac{1}{4}\sqrt{5} - \frac{1}{4}I\sqrt{2}\sqrt{5-\sqrt{5}},$$

$$-\frac{1}{4} + \frac{1}{4}\sqrt{5} - \frac{1}{4}I\sqrt{2}\sqrt{5+\sqrt{5}}]$$

5.4   Procedure Options and the Description Field

Options

A procedure may have one or more options. You may specify options by using the **options** clause of a procedure definition.

```
options 01, 02, ..., Om;
```

You may use any symbol as an option but the following options have special meanings.

The remember and system Options   When you invoke a procedure with the **remember** option, Maple stores the result of the invocation in the *remember table* associated with the procedure. Whenever you invoke the procedure, Maple checks whether you have previously called the procedure with the same parameters. If so, Maple retrieves the previously calculated result from the remember table rather than executing the procedure again.

```
> fib := proc(n::nonnegint)
>    option remember;
>    fib(n-1) + fib(n-2);
> end proc;
```

$$\text{fib} := \mathbf{proc}(n\text{::}nonnegint)$$
$$\mathbf{option}\ remember;$$
$$\text{fib}(n-1) + \text{fib}(n-2)$$
$$\mathbf{end\ proc}$$

You may place entries in the remember table of a procedure by direct assignment; this method also works for procedures without the **remember** option.

> `fib(0) := 0;`

$$\mathrm{fib}(0) := 0$$

> `fib(1) := 1;`

$$\mathrm{fib}(1) := 1$$

The following is the **fib** procedure's remember table.

$$\mathrm{table}([0 = 0,\ 1 = 1])$$

Since **fib** has the **remember** option, invoking it places new values in its remember table.

> `fib(9);`

$$34$$

Below is the new remember table.

$$\mathrm{table}([0 = 0,\ 1 = 1,\ 2 = 1,\ 3 = 2,\ 4 = 3,\ 5 = 5,\ 6 = 8,\ 7 = 13,$$
$$8 = 21,$$
$$9 = 34$$
$$])$$

The use of remember tables can drastically improve the efficiency of recursively defined procedures.

The **system** option allows Maple to remove entries from a procedure's remember table. Such selective amnesia occurs during garbage collection, an important part of Maple's memory management scheme. See section 2.5 for more details and examples of remember tables.

The operator and arrow Options The **operator** option allows Maple to make additional simplifications to the procedure, and the **arrow** option indicates that the pretty-printer should display the procedure by using the arrow notation.

```
> proc(x)
>    option operator, arrow;
>    x^2;
> end proc;
```

$$x \to x^2$$

Section 5.1 describes procedures by using the arrow notation.

The `Copyright` Option Maple considers any option that begins with the word *Copyright* to be a `Copyright` option. Maple does not print the body of a procedure with a `Copyright` option unless the **interface** variable `verboseproc` is at least 2.

```
> f := proc(expr::anything, x::name)
>    option 'Copyright (c) 1684 by G. W. Leibnitz. All rights reserved';
>    Diff(expr, x);
> end proc;
```

$$f := \mathbf{proc}(expr\text{::}anything, x\text{::}name) \ldots \mathbf{end\ proc}$$

The `builtin` Option Maple has two main classes of procedures: those which are part of the Maple kernel, and those which the Maple language itself defines. The `builtin` option indicates the kernel procedures. You can see this when you fully evaluate a built-in procedure.

```
> eval(type);
```

$$\mathbf{proc}()\,\mathbf{option}\ \textit{builtin};\ 268\,\mathbf{end\ proc}$$

Each built-in procedure is uniquely identified by a number. Of course, you cannot create built-in procedures of your own.

The Description Field

The last part of the procedure header is the `description` field. It must appear after any `local` clause, `global` clause, or `options` clause, and before the body of the procedure. It takes the following form.

```
description symbol ;
```

The description field has no effect on the execution of the procedure. Its use is for documentation purposes. Unlike a comment, which Maple discards when you read in a procedure, the description field provides a way to attach a one line comment to a procedure.

```
> f := proc(x)
>    description 'computes the square of x';
>      x^2; # compute x^2
> end proc:
> print(f);
```

$$\mathbf{proc}(x)$$
$$\mathbf{description}\,{}^{\prime}computes\ the\ square\ of\ x{}^{\prime};$$
$$x^2$$
$$\mathbf{end\ proc}$$

Also, Maple prints the description field even if it does not print the body of a procedure due to a `Copyright` option.

```
> f := proc(x)
>    option 'Copyrighted ?';
>    description 'computes the square of x';
>      x^2; # compute x^2
> end proc:
> print(f);
```

$$\mathbf{proc}(x)$$
$$\mathbf{description}\,{}^{\prime}computes\ the\ square\ of\ x{}^{\prime}$$
$$\cdots$$
$$\mathbf{end\ proc}$$

5.5   The Value Returned by a Procedure

When you invoke a procedure, the value that Maple returns is normally the value of the last statement in the statement sequence of the body of the procedure. Three other types of returns from procedures are a return through a parameter, an *explicit* return, and an *error* return.

Assigning Values to Parameters

Sometimes you may want to write a procedure that returns a value through a parameter. Consider writing a Boolean procedure, MEMBER, which determines whether a list L contains an expression x. Moreover, if you call MEMBER with a third argument, p, then MEMBER should assign the position of x in L to p.

```
> MEMBER := proc(x::anything, L::list, p::evaln) local i;
>     for i to nops(L) do
>         if x=L[i] then
>             if nargs>2 then p := i end if;
>             return true
>         end if;
>     end do;
>     false
> end proc:
```

If you call **MEMBER** with two arguments, then **nargs** is two, so the body of **MEMBER** does not refer to the formal parameter, **p**. Therefore, Maple does not complain about a missing parameter.

```
> MEMBER( x, [a,b,c,d] );
```

$$false$$

If you call **MEMBER** with three arguments, then the type declaration **p::evaln** ensures that Maple evaluates the third actual parameter to a name[2] rather than by using full evaluation.

```
> q := 78;
```

$$q := 78$$

```
> MEMBER( c, [a,b,c,d], q );
```

$$true$$

```
> q;
```

$$3$$

Maple evaluates parameters only once. This means that you cannot use formal parameters freely like local variables within a procedure body. *Once you have made an assignment to a parameter you should not refer to that parameter again.* The only legitimate purpose for assigning to a parameter is so that on return from the procedure the corresponding actual parameter has an assigned value. The following procedure assigns the value -13 to its parameter, then returns the name of that parameter.

---

[2]If the third parameter has not been declared as **evaln**, then you should enclose the name q in single quotes ('q') to ensure that the name and not the value of q is passed to the procedure.

```
> f := proc(x::evaln)
>    x := -13;
>    x;
> end proc:
> f(q);
```

$$q$$

The value of q is now -13.

```
> q;
```

$$-13$$

The **count** procedure below is a more complicated illustration of this phenomenon. **count** should determine whether a product of factors, p, contains an expression, x. If p contains x, then **count** should return the number of factors that contain x in the third parameter, n.

```
> count := proc(p::'*', x::name, n::evaln)
>     local f;
>     n := 0;
>     for f in p do
>         if has(f,x) then n := n+1 end if;
>     end do;
>     evalb( n>0 );
> end proc:
```

The **count** procedure does not work as intended.

```
> count(2*x^2*exp(x)*y, x, m);
```

$$-m < 0$$

The value of the formal parameter **n** inside the procedure is always **m**, the actual parameter that Maple determines once and for all when you invoke the procedure. Thus, when execution reaches the **evalb** statement, the value of **n** is the name **m**, and not the value of **m**. Worse yet, the **n:=n+1** statement assigns to **m** the *name* **m+1**, as you can see if you evaluate **m** one level.

```
> eval(m, 1);
```

$$m + 1$$

The **m** in the above result also has the value **m+1**.

```
> eval(m, 2);
```

$$m + 2$$

Thus, if you were to evaluate m fully, Maple would enter an infinite loop.

A general solution to this type of problem is to use local variables and to view the assignment to a parameter as an operation which takes place just before returning from the procedure.

```
> count := proc(p::'*', x::name, n::evaln)
>     local f, m;
>     m := 0;
>     for f in p do
>         if has(f,x) then m := m + 1 fi;
>     od;
>     n := m;
>     evalb( m>0 );
> end:
```

The new version of count works as intended.

```
> count(2*x^2*exp(x)*y, x, m);
```

$$true$$

```
> m;
```

$$2$$

Explicit Returns

An *explicit return* occurs when you invoke the **return** statement, which has the following syntax.

```
return sequence
```

The **return** statement causes an immediate return from the procedure and the value of the *sequence* becomes the value of the procedure invocation.

For example, the following procedure computes the first position i of a value x in a list of values L. If x is not in the list L, the procedure returns 0.

```
> POSITION := proc(x::anything, L::list)
>    local i;
>    for i to nops(L) do
>        if x=L[i] then return i end if;
>    end do;
>    0;
> end proc:
```

In most applications of the **return** statement, it returns only a single expression. Returning a sequence, however, including the empty sequence, is quite legitimate. For example, the **GCD** procedure below computes the greatest common divisor g of two integers a and b. It returns the sequence $g, a/g, b/g$. **GCD** must treat the case $a = b = 0$ separately because that makes g zero.

```
> GCD := proc(a::integer, b::integer)
>    local g;
>    if a=0 and b=0 then return 0,0,0 end if;
>    g := igcd(a,b);
>    g, iquo(a,g), iquo(b,g);
> end proc:
> GCD(0,0);
```

$$0, 0, 0$$

```
> GCD(12,8);
```

$$4, 3, 2$$

Of course, instead of returning a sequence, you may also return a list or a set of values.

Error Returns

An *error return* occurs when you raise an exception by invoking the **error** statement, which has the following syntax:

```
error msgString
error msgString, msgParams
```

The *msgString* is a string value which is independent of any parameters that are to be part of the message (for instance, the string complaining about an unassigned variable should not mention the variable by name).

In the *msgString*, numbered parameters are used as placeholders for actual values. For example, the *error* "f has a 2nd argument, x, which is missing" is specified by the *msgString* "%1 has a %-2 argument, %3, which is missing", and the *msgParams* f, 2, and x.

Each numbered parameter consists of the percent symbol, "%", optionally followed by a minus sign, "-", followed by one or more digits, making up a single-digit integer n. At message display time, the nth *msgParam* will be substituted for the numbered parameter. A numbered parameter of the form %n will display the nth *msgParam* in lineprinted notation (i.e., as lprint would display it). A numbered parameter of the form %-n will display the nth *msgParam*, assumed to be an integer, in ordinal form. For example, the value 2 is displayed as "2nd". The special parameter, %0, will display all the *msgParams*, separated by a comma and space.

The *msgParams* are one or more arbitrary Maple objects that will be substituted into numbered parameter locations in the *msgString* in the event that the exception is ever printed as an error message.

The **error** statement will evaluate its arguments, and then create an exception object, which is an expression sequence with the following elements:

- The name of the procedure in which the exception was raised, or the constant 0 if the exception was raised at the top-level.

- The *msgString*.

- The *msgParams*, if any.

The created exception object is assigned to the global variable **lastexception** as an expression sequence. The actual arguments to the **error** statement are also assigned to **lasterror** for compatibility with older versions of Maple.

The **error** statement normally causes an immediate exit from the current procedure to the Maple session. Maple prints an error message of the form:

```
Error, (in procName) msgText
```

Here *msgText* is the text of the error message, which is constructed from the *msgString* and optional *msgParams* of the **error** statement. The procedure in which the error occurred is given by *procName*. If the procedure does not have a name, *procName* is "unknown". If the error occurs at the top-level, outside of any procedure, the entire "(in procName)" part is omitted from the message.

A common use of the **error** statement is to check that the actual parameters to a procedure are of the correct type, but parameter declarations are not sufficient for the job. The **pairup** procedure below takes a list L of the form $[x_1, y_1, x_2, y_2, \ldots, x_n, y_n]$ as input, and creates from it a listlist of the form $[[x_1, y_1], [x_2, y_2], \ldots, [x_n, y_n]]$. A simple type check cannot determine if the list L has an even number of elements, so you need to check that explicitly.

```
> pairup := proc(L::list)
>    local i, n;
>    n := nops(L);
>    if irem(n,2) = 1 then
>       error "list must have an even number of entries, but had %1", n
>    end if;
>    [seq( [L[2*i-1],L[2*i]], i=1..n/2 )]
> end proc:
> pairup([1, 2, 3, 4, 5]);

Error, (in pairup) list must have an even number of
entries, but had 5


> pairup([1, 2, 3, 4, 5, 6]);
```

$$[[1, 2], [3, 4], [5, 6]]$$

Trapping Exceptions

You can trap exceptions using the **try** statement. The syntax for the **try** statement is:

```
try tryStatSeq
catch catchStrings : catchStatSeq
end try
try tryStatSeq
catch catchStrings : catchStatSeq
finally finalStatSeq
end try
```

When execution enters a **try** statement, the *tryStatSeq* is executed. If no exceptions occur during the execution of *tryStatSeq*, execution continues with *finalStatSeq* if a **finally** clause was provided. After that, or if no **finally** clause was provided, execution continues with the statement after the **end try**.

If an exception does occur during the execution of *tryStatSeq*, execution of *tryStatSeq* terminates immediately. The exception object corresponding to the exception is compared against each *catchString* in turn until a match is found. Any number of **catch** clauses can be provided, and each can have any number of *catchStrings*, separated by commas. A `catch` clause can also have no catch string.

If a matching `catch` clause is found, or the `catch` clause contains no *catchStrings*, the *catchStatSeq* of that `catch` clause is executed, and the exception is considered to have been caught. If **no** matching `catch` clause is found, the exception is considered not-caught, and is re-raised outside the `try` construct.

A *catchStatSeq* can contain an `error` statement with no arguments, which also re-raises the exception. When an exception is re-raised, a new exception object is created that records the current procedure name, and the message and parameters from the original exception.

Under normal circumstances, the *finalStatSeq* of the `finally` clause, if there is one, is always executed before control leaves the `try` statement.[3] This is true even if a *catchStatSeq* re-raises the exception, raises a new one, or executes a `return`, `break`, or `next` statement.

Under certain abnormal circumstances, the *finalStatSeq* is **not** executed:

- If an exception is raised in a `catch` clause **and** this exception is caught by the debugger **and** the user exits the debugger, the user's command to stop execution overrides everything.

- If one of the following untrappable exceptions occurs, the exception is not caught, and the *finalStatSeq* is not executed:

  1. Computation timed out (this can only be caught by `timelimit`, which raises a `"time expired"` exception, which **can** be caught).

  2. Computation interrupted (i.e., user pressed Ctrl-C, Break, or equivalent).

  3. Internal system error (i.e., which indicates a bug in Maple itself).

  4. `ASSERT` or local variable type assertion failure (assertion failures are not trappable because they indicate a coding error, not an algorithmic failure).

  5. Stack overflow (when that happens, there's generally not enough stack space to do anything like run cleanup code).

If an exception occurs during the execution of a *catchStatSeq* or the *finalStatSeq*, it is treated in the same way as if it occurred outside the `try...end` statement entirely.

---

[3]This is true whether or not an exception occurs, and if one does occur, whether or not it is caught, and if it is caught, whether or not another exception occurs in the `catch` clause.

When looking for a matching catch clause, the following definition of "matching" is used:

- Neither the exception object nor the *catchStrings* are evaluated (the exception object will already have been evaluated by the error statement that produced it).

- The *catchStrings* are considered to be prefixes of the exception object's synmsgString. If a *catchString* has **n** characters, only the first **n** characters of the *msgString* need match the *catchString*. This allows one to define classes of exceptions.

- A missing *catchString* will match any exception.

- The "result" of a **try** statement (i.e., the value that **%** would return if evaluated immediately after execution of the **try** statement) is the result of the last statement executed within the **try** statement.

A given *catchString* (or a catch clause without one) can appear only once in a **try...end** construct.

A very useful application of the **try** and **error** statements is to abort an expensive computation as quickly and cleanly as possible. For example, suppose you are trying to compute an integral by using one of several methods, and in the middle of the first method, you determine that it will not succeed. You would like to abort that method and go on to try another method. The code that tries the different methods might look like this:

```
>   try
>   result := MethodA(f,x)
>   catch "FAIL":
>   result := MethodB(f,x)
>   end try;
```

MethodA can abort its computation at any time by executing the statement **error "FAIL"**. The catch clause will catch that exception, and proceed to try MethodB. If any other error occurs during the execution of MethodA, or if an error occurs during the execution of MethodB, it will not be caught.

Another useful application of the **try** statement is to make sure certain resources are freed when you are done with them, regardless of whether or not anything went wrong while you were using them. For example, you may wish to use the facilities of the I/O library (see Chapter 1) to read the lines of a file and process them in some way:

```
> f := fopen("myfile",TEXT,READ):
> try
>    line := readline(f);
>    while line < 0 do
>        ProcessContentsOfLine(line);
>        line := readline(f)
>    end do
> finally
>    fclose(f)
> end try;
```

In this example, if any exception occurs while reading or processing the lines of the file, it will **not** be caught, because there is no **catch** clause. However, the **fclose(f)** will be executed before execution leaves the **try** statement, regardless of whether or not there was an exception.

The final example makes use of both **catch** and **finally** clauses. In this example, we are writing to a file instead of reading from one.

```
> f := fopen("myfile",TEXT,WRITE):
> try
>    for i to 100 do
>        fprintf(f,"Result %d is %q\n",i,ComputeSomething(i))
>    end do
> catch:
>    fprintf(f,"Something went wrong: %q\n",lastexception);
>    error
> finally
>    fclose(f)
> end try;
```

If any exception occurs, we catch it with a **catch** clause with no *catchString*, and write the exception object into the file. We then re-raise the exception, by executing an **error** statement with no *msgString*. In all cases, we close the file by executing **fclose(f)** in the **finally** clause.

Returning Unevaluated

Maple often uses a particular form of return as a *fail return*, in the sense that it cannot carry out the computation and so returns the unevaluated function invocation as the result. The procedure **MAX**, below, calculates the maximum of two numbers, x and y.

```
> MAX := proc(x,y) if x>y then x else y end if end proc:
```

The above version of **MAX** is unacceptable for a symbolic computation system because it insists on its arguments being numerical values so that Maple can determine if $x > y$.

```
> MAX(3.2, 2);
```

3.2

```
> MAX(x, 2*y);
```

Error, (in MAX) cannot evaluate boolean: 2*y-x < 0

The absence of symbolic capabilities in **MAX** causes problems when you try to plot expressions involving **MAX**.

```
> plot( MAX(x, 1/x), x=1/2..2 );
```

Error, (in MAX) cannot evaluate boolean: 1/x-x < 0

The error occurs because Maple evaluates **MAX(x, 1/x)** before invoking the **plot** command.

The solution is to make **MAX** return unevaluated when its parameters, x and y, are not numeric. That is, in such cases **MAX** should return **'MAX'(x,y)**.

```
> MAX := proc(x, y)
>    if type(x, numeric) and type(y, numeric) then
>        if x>y then x else y end if;
>    else
>        'MAX'(x,y);
>    end if;
> end proc:
```

The new version of **MAX** handles both numeric and non-numeric input.

```
> MAX(3.2, 2);
```

3.2

```
> MAX(x, 2*y);
```

$$MAX(x, 2\,y)$$

```
> plot( MAX(x, 1/x), x=1/2..2 );
```

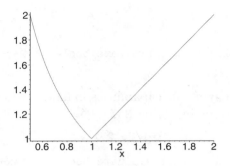

You can improve **MAX** so that it can find the maximum of any number of arguments. Inside a procedure, **args** is the sequence of actual parameters, **nargs** is the number of actual parameters, and **procname** is the name of the procedure.

```
> MAX := proc()
>    local m, i;
>    m := -infinity;
>    for i in (args) do
>        if not type(i, numeric) then
>            return 'procname'(args);
>        end if;
>        if i>m then m := i end if;
>    end do;
>    m;
> end proc:
> MAX(3,1,4);
```

$$4$$

```
> MAX(3,x,1,4);
```

$$MAX(3,\ x,\ 1,\ 4)$$

The **sin** function and the **int** integration command follow the same model as the **MAX** procedure above. If Maple can compute the result, it returns it; otherwise, **sin** and **int** return unevaluated.

Exercise

1. Improve the **MAX** procedure above so that **MAX(3,x,1,4)** returns **MAX(x,4)**; that is, the procedure returns the maximum numerical value along with all non-numerical values.

5.6   The Procedure Object

This section describes the procedure object, its type and operands, its special evaluation rule, and how to save it to a file and retrieve it again.

Last Name Evaluation

Maple evaluates ordinary expressions in a *full recursive evaluation* mode. All future references to a name that you assign a value return the computed value instead of the name.

```
> f := g;
```

$$f := g$$

```
> g := h;
```

$$g := h$$

```
> h := x^2;
```

$$h := x^2$$

Now f evaluates to x^2.

```
> f;
```

$$x^2$$

Names of procedures, modules, arrays, and tables are exceptions. For such names, Maple uses a *last name evaluation* model. This model avoids printing all the details forming the procedure definition.

```
> F := G;
```

$$F := G$$

```
> G := H;
```

$$G := H$$

```
> H := proc(x) x^2 end proc;
```

$$H := \mathbf{proc}(x)\, x^2 \,\mathbf{end\ proc}$$

Now F evaluates to H because H is the last name before the actual procedure.

```
> F;
```

$$H$$

You can use the `eval` command to evaluate a procedure fully.

```
> eval(F);
```

$$\mathbf{proc}(x)\, x^2 \,\mathbf{end\ proc}$$

See also section 2.1.

The Type and Operands of a Procedure

Maple recognizes all procedures (including those created by using the mapping notation) as being of type **procedure**, as are any names that you give to procedures.

```
> type(F,name);
```

$$true$$

```
> type(F,procedure);
```

$$true$$

```
> type(F,name(procedure));
```

$$true$$

```
> type(eval(F),procedure);
```

$$true$$

Thus, you can use the following test to ensure that F is the name of a procedure.

```
> if type(F, name(procedure)) then ... end if
```

A procedure has seven operands:

1. The sequence of formal parameters.

2. The sequence of local variables.

3. The sequence of options.

4. The remember table.

5. The description string.

6. The sequence of global variables.

7. The lexical table.

As an example of the structure of a procedure, consider the following.

```
> f := proc(x::name, n::posint)
>     local i;
>     global y;
>     option Copyright;
>     description "a summation";
>     sum( x[i] + y[i], i=1..n );
> end proc:
```

Place an entry in the procedure's remember table.

```
> f(t,3) := 12;
```

$$f(t, 3) := 12$$

You can see the various parts of f below.
The name of the procedure:

```
> f;
```

$$f$$

The procedure itself:

```
> eval(f);
```

$$\textbf{proc}(x\text{::}\textit{name},\ n\text{::}\textit{posint})$$
$$\textbf{description}\ \text{"a summation"}$$
$$\dots$$
$$\textbf{end proc}$$

The formal parameters:

```
> op(1, eval(f));
```

$$x\text{::}\textit{name},\ n\text{::}\textit{posint}$$

The local variables:

```
> op(2, eval(f));
```

$$i$$

The options:

```
> op(3, eval(f));
```

$$\textit{Copyright}$$

The remember table:

```
> op(4, eval(f));
```

$$\text{table}([(t,\ 3) = 12])$$

The description:

```
> op(5, eval(f));
```

$$\text{"a summation"}$$

The global variables:

```
> op(6, eval(f));
```

$$y$$

The body of a procedure is *not* one of its operands, so you cannot gain access to the body with the `op` command. If you need to manipulate the body of a procedure, see `?codegen`.

Saving and Retrieving Procedures

While you develop a new procedure, you can save your work by saving the whole worksheet. When you have finished, save the procedure.

```
> CMAX := proc(x::complex(numeric), y::complex(numeric))
>    if abs(x)>abs(y) then
>       x;
>    else
>       y;
>    end if;
> end proc:
```

Use the `save` command to save procedures in the same manner you save any other Maple object.

```
> save CMAX, "CMAX.mws":
```

The `read` command retrieves the objects stored in a .m file.

```
> read "CMAX.mws":
```

Some Maple users prefer to write Maple procedures with their favorite text editor. You can also use the `read` command to read in data from such files. Maple executes each line in the file as if you had typed it directly into your session.

If you make a number of related procedures, you may want to save them as a Maple package. Making a package allows you to load the procedures using the `with` command. See section 6.3.

5.7   Explorations

The purpose of the exercises in this section is to deepen your understanding of how Maple procedures work. In some cases you may wish to study the on-line help pages for the various Maple commands that you will need.

Exercises

1. Implement the function $f(x) = (\sqrt{1 - x^2})^3 - 1$, first as a procedure, then by using the mapping notation. Compute $f(1/2)$ and $f(0.5)$ and comment on the different results. Use the D operator to compute f', and then compute $f'(0)$.

2. Write a procedure, SPLIT, which on input of a product f and a variable x returns a list of two values. The first item in the list should be the product of the factors in f that are independent of x, and the second item should be the product of the factors that have an x in them. *Hint:* You may want to use the has, select, remove, and selectremove commands.

3. The following program tries to compute $1 - x^{|a|}$.

```
> f := proc(a::integer, x::anything)
> if a<0 then a := -a end if;
> 1-x^a;
> end proc:
```

What is wrong with this procedure? You may want to use the Maple debugger to isolate the error. See chapter 7.

4. ab/g gives the least common multiple of two integers, a and b, where g is the greatest common divisor of a and b. For example, the least common multiple of 4 and 6 is 12. Write a Maple procedure, LCM, which takes as input $n > 0$ integers $a_1, a_2, \ldots, a_n$ and computes their least common multiple. By convention, the least common multiple of zero and any other number is zero.

5. The following recurrence relation defines the Chebyshev polynomials of the first kind, $T_n(x)$.

$$T_0(x) = 1, \qquad T_1(x) = x, \qquad T_n(x) = 2xT_{n-1}(x) - T_{n-2}(x)$$

The following procedure computes $T_n(x)$ in a loop for any given integer n.

```
> T := proc(n::integer, x)
>    local t1, tn, t;
>    t1 := 1; tn := x;
>    for i from 2 to n do
>        t := expand(2*x*tn - t1);
>        t1 := tn; tn := t;
>    end do;
>    tn;
> end proc:
```

The procedure has several errors. Which variables should have been declared local? What happens if n is zero or negative? Identify and correct all errors, using the Maple debugger where appropriate. Modify the procedure so that it returns unevaluated if n is a symbolic value.

5.8   Conclusion

In this chapter, you have seen the details of the `proc` command. You have learned the finer points of the options at your disposal when defining procedures. You have learned about functional operators, unnamed procedures, and procedure simplification.

In addition, you have reviewed Maple's evaluation rules which chapter 2 introduced. For example, Maple generally evaluates local variables to one level and global variables fully. Maple evaluates the arguments to a procedure at the time you invoke it. How they are evaluated depends upon the environment in which the call occurs, and in some cases, the types specified within the procedure definition. Once evaluated, Maple substitutes the values into the procedure and then executes it. Maple does no further evaluation on the values which it substituted, unless you specifically use a command such as `eval`. This rule makes it impractical to use parameters to store temporary results, as you would use local variables.

This chapter extended the discussion of type declarations, which were introduced in chapters 1 and 2. Type declarations are particularly useful as a means of stating the intended purpose of your procedures and as a convenient means of supplying error messages to any user who might call them with inappropriate values.

This chapter concludes the formal review of the Maple language which began in chapter 4. The remaining chapters deal with specific areas of Maple programming. For example, chapter 7 discusses the Maple debugger, chapter 8 introduces you to the details of numerical programming in Maple, and chapter 9 shows how to extend Maple's extensive plotting facilities to suit your needs.

6 Programming with Modules

In the same way that procedures allow you to abstract a sequence of commands typed to the Maple interpreter, "modules" allow you to abstract collections of related procedures and data.

This chapter describes Maple's module system. Modules are a type of Maple expression, like numbers, equations, and procedures, that enable you to write generic algorithms, create packages, or simply use Pascal-style records in your programs.

Modules can be used a number of ways. In this chapter, we describe four broad categories of application for them.

1. Encapsulation

2. Packages

3. Modeling Objects

4. Generic Programming

Encapsulation refers to the provision of a guarantee that an abstraction is used only according to its specified interface. This provides the developer with the ability to write significant software systems that are transportable and reusable and that offer clean, well-defined user interfaces. This makes your code more maintainable and easier to understand—important properties for large software systems.

Packages are a vehicle for bundling together collections of related Maple procedures to address computations in some well-defined problem domain. Much of the functionality of the standard Maple library resides in packages.

Objects are easily represented using modules. An object is a representation, in software, of something that has both state and behavior. You compute with objects by sending them "messages", to which they respond by performing services.

Generic programs are written without knowledge of *how* the objects upon which they operate are represented. A generic program will work with any object that honors the "contract" against which the program is written, regardless of how the object satisfes that contract.

These are four very practical software engineering concepts, but they are all just different facets of the same underlying, abstract Maple language technology. We have devoted less space to the abstract language feature than to its practical implications.

Before we go into too many details about modules, it is helpful to examine a small example module to get an idea what they are all about.

A First Example Here is an example of a simple, but nontrivial module. When Maple evaluates the right-hand side of the assignment to **TempGenerator**, it creates a *module* using the *module definition* that begins with **module()**... and ends with **end module**.

```
> TempGenerator := module()
>         description "generator for temporary symbols";
>         export  gentemp;
>         local   count;
>
>         count := 0;
>         gentemp := proc()
>                 count := 1 + count;
>                 'tools/gensym'( T || count )
>         end proc;
> end module;
```

$$TempGenerator := \textbf{module}()$$
$$\textbf{local } count;$$
$$\textbf{export } gentemp;$$
$$\textbf{description } \text{"generator for temporary symbols"};$$
$$\textbf{end module}$$

The module definition that appears above resembles a procedure definition. The main differences visible here are the use of the keyword **module** instead of **proc** (and the corresponding terminator), and the **export** declaration following the description string.

We could do something quite similar using only procedures.

```
> TempGeneratorProc := proc()
>         description "generator for temporary symbols";
>         local   count, gentemp;
```

```
>        count := 0;
>        gentemp := proc()
>              count := 1 + count;
>              'tools/gensym'( T || count )
>        end proc;
>        eval( gentemp, 1 )
> end proc:
```

We can assign the procedure returned by **TempGeneratorProc**, and then use it to generate temporary symbols.

```
> f := TempGeneratorProc();
```

$$f := \mathbf{proc}()$$
$$\quad count := 1 + count\,; \text{ 'tools/gensym'}(T\|count)$$
$$\mathbf{end\ proc}$$

```
> f();
```

$$T1$$

```
> f();
```

$$T2$$

The module **TempGenerator** and the procedure **TempGeneratorProc** are similar. Understanding this similarity will take you a long way towards understanding how modules work.

In the procedure version, the local variable **gentemp** is assigned a little procedure that references another local variable **count**; the value of **gentemp** is returned by the procedure to its caller. The module version of the generator does much the same thing, except that its **gentemp** variable is declared as an *export*, not a *local*, and there is no explicit return. In fact, in both versions of the generator, the variables **count** and **gentemp** *are* local variables. The significant difference here is that, in the module version, one of those local variables is *exported*. This means that it is made available outside the scope in which it was created. Special syntax is used for accessing exported local variables. For example, to call the exported variable **gentemp** of the module, you can type

```
> TempGenerator:-gentemp();
```

$$T1$$

using the member selection operator : -. In a sense, a module definition "returns" a data structure (a module) that contains all of its exported local variables.

A second mechanism exists for conveniently accessing module exports — the **use** statement.

```
> use TempGenerator in
>       gentemp();
>       gentemp();
>       gentemp();
> end use;
```

$$T2$$

$$T3$$

$$T4$$

Within the body of a **use** statement, the exported local variables of the module that appears after the **use** keyword can be accessed directly, without the need for the member selection operator : -.

About This Chapter

This chapter provides many examples of the use of modules to help you understand the ideas presented. Some examples are very simple, designed to illustrate a very specific point. Others are more substantial, and can be used in your own programs. Many of the nontrivial examples are available as Maple source code in the **samples** directory of your Maple installation. You can load any of these into your private Maple library and experiment with them. You are encouraged to modify, extend, and improve on these code samples, and to use them in your own work.

6.1   Syntax and Semantics

The syntax of module definitions is very similar to that of procedures, given in Chapter 5. Here is an example of a very simple module definition.

```
> module()
>     export e1;
>     local a, b;
>
>     a := 2;
>     b := 3;
```

```
>    e1 := x -> a^x/b^x;
> end module:
```

Evaluating this expression results in a module with one "export", e1, and two local variables, a and b.

A template for a module definition looks like:

```
module()
    local L;
    export E;
    global G;
    options O;
    description D;
    B
end module
```

The simplest valid module definition is

```
> module() end;
```

$$\textbf{module() end module}$$

This module definition has no exported variables, no locals, no references, and no global variables. It does not even have a body of statements. The module to which this evaluates is not very useful.

Every module definition begins with the keyword **module**, followed by an empty pair of parentheses. Following that is an optional declaration section and the module body. The keyword combination `end module` (or just **end**) terminates a module definition.

The Module Body

The body of a module definition consists of zero or more Maple statements. The body is executed when the module definition is evaluated, producing a module as a result. Typically, a module body consists of a number of assignment statements that give values to the exported names of the module. It may also include assignments to local variables, and may, in fact, perform arbitrary computations. The body of a module may not contain a **break** or **next** statement outside a loop, but may contain a return statement. The effect of executing a `return` statement is to terminate the execution of the body of the module definition at the point at which the return statement occurs.

Module Parameters

Module definitions begin with the Maple keyword **module**, followed by an (empty) pair of parentheses. This is similar to the parentheses that follow the **proc** keyword in a procedure definition. Unlike procedures, however, module definitions do not have explicit parameters. This is because, unlike procedures (which result from the evaluation of procedure definitions), modules are not "called" (or "invoked") with arguments.

Instead, every module definition has an *implicit* parameter called **thismodule**. Within the body of a module definition, this special name evaluates to the module in which it occurs. This allows you to refer to a module within its own definition (before the result of evaluating it has been assigned to any name).

You have seen implicit parameters before; all procedure definitions may reference the implicit parameters **procname**, **args**, and **nargs**. The **args** and **nargs** currently have no meaning for modules, and the difference between **thismodule** and **procname** is that **procname** evaluates to a *name*, while **thismodule** evaluates to the module expression itself. This is because the "invocation" phase of evaluating a module definition is part of its normal evaluation, and it occurs immediately. Procedures, on the other hand, are not invoked until called with arguments. Normally, at least one name for a procedure is known by the time it is called; this is not the case for modules.

Named Modules

An optional symbol may appear after the **module** keyword in a module definition. Modules created with this variant on the syntax are called *named modules*. Semantically, named modules are nearly identical to normal modules, but the exported members of named modules are printed differently, in a way that allows the module from which it was exported to be identified visually.

```
> NormalModule := module() export e; end;
```

$$NormalModule := \textbf{module}() \, \textbf{export} \, e; \; \textbf{end module}$$

```
> NormalModule:-e;
```

$$e$$

```
> module NamedModule() export e; end module;
```

module *NamedModule* () **export** *e*; **end module**

```
> NamedModule:-e;
```

$$NamedModule : -e$$

When the definition of a named module is evaluated, the name (which appears immediately after the **module** keyword) is assigned the module as its value, *and the name is protected*. Therefore, a named module can, ordinarily, be created only once. For example, an attempt to execute the named module definition yields an error.

```
> module NamedModule() export e; end module;
```

```
Error, (in NamedModule) attempting to assign to
'NamedModule' which is protected
```

Executing the normal module definition again creates a *new* instance of the module, but does not result in an error. (It simply reassigns the variable `NormalModule` to the new module instance.)

```
> NormalModule := module() export e; end;
```

$$NormalModule := \textbf{module}() \, \textbf{export} \, e; \, \textbf{end module}$$

It is also important (if you expect sensible results) that you never assign a named module to another variable.

```
> SomeName := eval( NamedModule );
```

$$SomeName := $$
$$\textbf{module} \, NamedModule \, () \, \textbf{export} \, e; \, \textbf{end module}$$

```
> SomeName:-e;
```

$$NamedModule : -e$$

Exports of named modules are printed using the *distinguished* name that was given the module when it was created, regardless of any other names that you may refer to it by.

Whether a module has a name also affects the reporting of errors that occur during its evaluation. When the second attempt to evaluate the named module definition above failed, the error message reported the location of the error by name. By contrast, when an error occurs during the evaluation of a normal module definition, the name **unknown** is used instead.

```
> NormalModule := module() export e; error "oops"; end;
```

```
Error, (in unknown) oops
```

This differs from the way error reporting works with procedures. You cannot report the name of a normal module (where, by "the name", we mean the name of the variable to which the module is assigned), because the evaluation of the right side of an assignment occurs *before* the assignment to the name takes place. So the error occurs *before* any association between a variable and the module has occurred.

Declarations

The declarations section of the module must appear immediately after the parentheses. All statements in the declarations section are optional, but at most one of each kind may appear. Most module declarations are the same as those for procedures.

Description Strings   Many modules constitute a nontrivial body of software. When you write a module, you should provide a brief description so that users who encounter it will be able to recognize what it is or what it does. Use the **description** keyword to do this, just as you would in a procedure definition.

```
> Hello := module()
>     description "my first module";
>     export say;
>     say := proc()
>         print( "HELLO WORLD" )
>     end proc;
> end module:
```

When the module is printed, its description string is displayed.

```
> eval( Hello );
```

> **module()**
> **export** *say*;
> **description** "my first module";
>
> **end module**

The **export** declaration that appears in this example is explained later in this chapter.

Global Variables Global variables referenced within a module definition should be declared with the **global** declaration. Following the keyword **global** is a sequence of one or more symbols. These symbols are bound to their global instances. In certain cases you must declare a name as a global to prevent implicit scoping rules from making it a local variable.

```
> Hello := module()
>     export say;
>     global message;
>     say := proc()
>         message := "HELLO WORLD!"
>     end proc;
> end module:
> message;
```

message

```
> Hello:-say();
```

"HELLO WORLD!"

```
> message;
```

"HELLO WORLD!"

Local Variables You can refer to variables that are local to the module definition by using the **local** declaration. Its format is exactly the same as for procedures. Here is a variant on our `Hello` module above which makes (gratuitous) use of a local variable.

```
> Hello := module()
>     local loc;
>     export say;
>     loc := "HELLO WORLD!";
>     say := proc()
>         print( loc )
>     end proc;
> end module:
```

Local variables are not visible outside the definition of the module in which they occur. They are "private" to the module, and are exactly analogous to local variables of procedures.

A local variable `foo` in a module (or procedure) is a distinct object from a global variable with the same name `foo`. Local variables are normally "short-lived" variables; the normal lifetime of a local variable is the execution time of the body of code (a module or procedure body) to which it is local. (Local variables may persist once execution of the scope in which they occur has completed, but they are normally inaccessable and will eventually be recycled by Maple's automatic storage management system.)

Exported Local Variables

Procedures and modules both support local variables. Only modules support *exported* local variables, often referred to simply as "exports".

Module exports are declared using the **export** declaration. It begins with the keyword **export**, after which follows a (nonempty) sequence of symbols. A name is never exported "implicitly"; exports *must* be declared.

The result of evaluating a module definition is a module. You can view a module as a collection of its exports, which are also referred to as "members" of the module. These are simply names that may (but need not) be assigned values. You can establish initial values for the exports by assigning to them in the body of the module definition.

The word "export" is short for "exported local variable". In most respects, a module export is a local variable (such as those declared via the **local** declaration.) The crucial difference is that you can access the exported local variables of a module after it has been created.

To access an export of a module, use the :- member selection operator. Its general syntax is:

```
modexpr :- membername
```

Here, `modexpr` must be an expression that evaluates to a module, and `membername` must be the name of an export of the module to which `modexpr` evaluates. Anything else signals an exception. You cannot access local variables of an instantiated module by using this syntax.

Local variables of a procedure are created when the procedure is called (or invoked). Normally, the locals persist only during the execution of the statements that form the body of the procedure. Sometimes, however, local variables persist beyond the procedure activation that instantiated them. For example:

```
> gen := proc()
>     local s, p;
>     s := 2;
>     p := x -> s * x;
>     p
> end proc:
> g := gen();
```

$$g := p$$

```
> g( 3 );
```

6

The local variable **s** of **gen** persists after **gen** has returned. It is "captured" in the closure of the procedure **p**, whose name is returned by **gen**. Thus, both local variables **p** and **s** of **gen** "escape", but in different ways. The local name **p** is accessible because it is the assigned value of the global variable **g**. However, there is no way to refer to **s** once **gen** has returned. No Maple syntax exists for that purpose. What the member selection operator `:-` does is provide a syntax for referencing certain local variables of modules–those declared as exports.

Our most recent **Hello** example has one export, named **say**. In this case, **say** is assigned a procedure. To call it, you can type

```
> Hello:-say();
```

"HELLO WORLD!"

Whereas the following expression raises an exception, because the name **noSuchModule** is not assigned a module expression.

```
> noSuchModule:-e;
```

```
Error, `noSuchModule` does not evaluate to a module
```

Here, a module expression is assigned to the name **m**, and the member selection expression `m:-e` evaluates to the value of the exported variable **e** of **m**.

```
> m := module() export e; e := 2 end module:
> m:-e;
```

2

Since **m** does not export a variable named **noSuchExport**, the following expression raises an exception.

```
> m:-noSuchExport;
```

```
Error, module does not export `noSuchExport`
```

Important! Suppose that we construct a module that exports an unassigned name.

```
> m := module() export e; end:
```
References to the exported name e in m evaluate to the name e.

```
> m:-e;
```

$$e$$

Note, however, that this is a *local* name e, not the global instance of the name.

```
> evalb( e = m:-e );
```

$$false$$

The first e in the expression above refers to the global e, while the expression m:-e evaluates to the e that is local to the module m. This means that you can have a special version of sin, for instance, that is private to your module, and that assigning to it will not affect the value of the global name sin.

The Procedure exports You can determine the names of the exports of a module by using the procedure exports.

```
> exports( Hello );
```

$$say$$

```
> exports( VerifyImplementation );
```

```
Error, wrong number (or type) of parameters in function
exports
```

This returns the *global* instances of the export names.

```
> exports( m );
```

$$e$$

```
> evalb( % = e );
```

$$true$$

You can also obtain the local instances of those names by passing the option **instance**.

```
> exports( m, 'instance' );
```

$$e$$

```
> evalb( % = e );
```

false

```
> evalb( %% = m:-e );
```

true

For this reason, you cannot have the same name declared both as a local and an export.

```
> module() export e; local e; end;
```

```
Error, export and local 'e' have the same name
```

(The declared exports and locals really form a partition of the names that are local to a module.)

The Procedure member You have already seen the built-in procedure **member** that is used to test for membership in a set or list.

```
> member( 4, { 1, 2, 3 } );
```

false

This procedure can be used for membership tests in modules as well.

```
> member( say, Hello );
```

true

```
> member( cry, Hello );
```

false

The first argument is a (global) name whose membership is to be tested, and the second argument is a module. It returns the value **true** if the module has an export whose name is the same as the first argument.

The procedure **member** also has a three argument form that can be used with lists to determine the (first) position at which an item occurs.

```
> member( b, [ a, b, c ], 'pos' );
```

$$true$$

The name **pos** is now assigned the value 2 because **b** occurs at the second position of the list [a, b, c].

```
> pos;
```

$$2$$

When used with modules, the third argument is assigned the *local instance* of the name whose membership is being tested, provided that the return value is **true**.

```
> member( say, Hello, 'which' );
```

$$true$$

```
> which;
```

$$say$$

```
> eval( which );
```

$$\textbf{proc}()\,\text{print}(loc)\,\textbf{end proc}$$

If the return value from **member** is **false**, then the name remains unassigned (or maintains its previously assigned value).

```
> unassign( 'which' ):
> member( cry, Hello, 'which' );
```

$$false$$

```
> eval( which );
```

which

Module Options

As with procedures, a module definition may declare options. The options that Maple recognizes as being meaningful for modules are different from those for procedures. Only the options `trace`, `package`, and `'Copyright...'` are meaningful (and have the same meaning) for both procedures and modules.

A special module option `load` takes the form `load = thunk`, where `thunk` is the name of an exported or local module member. `thunk` must be a procedure that is invoked when the (instantiated) module is first created or read from a Maple repository. This option may be used for any per-session initialization required.

Implicit Scoping Rules

The bindings of names that appear within a module definition are determined when the module definition is simplified. Module definitions are subject to the same implicit scoping rules that procedure definitions are. Under no circumstances is a name ever "implicitly" determined to be exported by a module; implicitly scoped names can resolve only to locals or globals.

Lexical Scoping Rules

Module definitions, along with procedure definitions, obey standard lexical scoping rules. Modules may be nested, in the sense that a module may have any of its exports assigned to a module whose definition occurs within the body of the outer module.

Here is a simple example of a submodule.

```
> m := module()
>     export s;
>     s := module()
>         export e;
>         e := proc()
>             print( "HELLO WORLD!" )
>         end proc;
>     end module
> end module:
```

The global name `m` is assigned a module that exports the name `s`. Within the body of `m`, the export `s` is assigned a module that exports the name `e`. We call `s` a *submodule* of `m`. The `Shapes` package, described later, illustrates a nontrivial use of submodules.

Modules and procedures can be mutually nested to an arbitrary depth. The rules for the "visibility" of local variables (including exported locals of modules) and procedure parameters are exactly the same as the rules for nested procedures.

Parameterized Modules   We have already remarked that modules do not take explicit parameters. It could be useful, however, to be able to write a "generic" module that could then be specialized by providing one or more parameters.

For example, here is a module for arithmetic modulo 6.

```
> z6 := module()
>     export add, mul;
>     add := ( a, b ) -> a + b mod 6;
>     mul := ( a, b ) -> a * b mod 6;
> end module:
> z6:-add( 5, 4 );
```

$$3$$

```
> z6:-mul( 2, 3 );
```

$$0$$

It would be nice to write a *generic* module for arithmetic modulo any positive integer n, and then specialize it for each integer that you want to use. This is already possible because of the standard lexical scoping rules. So to do this, write a *constructor* procedure for the module that accepts the value of n as an argument. Here is a generic version of the z6 example above.

```
> MakeZn := proc( n::posint )
>     module()
>         export add, mul;
>         add := ( a, b ) -> a + b mod n;
>         mul := ( a, b ) -> a * b mod n;
>     end module
> end proc:
```

To generate a module that does arithmetic modulo 7, simply call the constructor MakeZn with the number 7 as its argument.

```
> z7 := MakeZn( 7 );
```

$$z7 := \mathbf{module}()\,\mathbf{export}\ add,\ mul;\ \mathbf{end\ module}$$

```
> z7:-add( 3, 4 );
```

$$0$$

Modules and Types

Two Maple types are associated with modules. First, the name **module** is a type name. Naturally, an expression is of type **module** only if it is a module. When used as a type name, the name **module** must be enclosed in name quotes (`).

```
> type( module() end, ''module'' );
```

true

```
> type( LinearAlgebra, ''module'' );
```

true

Secondly, a type called `moduledefinition` identifies expressions that are module definitions. In the first example above, the module definition

```
> module() end:
```

was evaluated before being passed to `type`, so the expression that was tested was not the definition, but the module to which it evaluates. We must use unevaluation quotes (') to delay the evaluation of a module definition.

```
> type( 'module() end', 'moduledefinition' );
```

true

Other important type tests satisfied by modules are the types `atomic` and `last_name_eval`.

```
> type( module() end, 'atomic' );
```

true

The procedure `map` has no effect on modules; they pass through unchanged.

```
> map( print, module() export a, b, c; end );
```

$$\text{module}()\,\text{export}\,a,\,b,\,c;\quad\text{end module}$$

Modules also suffer last name evaluation rules.

```
> m := module() end:
> m;
```

$$m$$

```
> type( m, 'last_name_eval' );
```

$$true$$

Although type `module` is a surface type, it acts also as a structured type. Parameters passed as arguments to the unevaluated name **module** are taken to be the names of exports. For example, the module

```
> m := module() export a, b; end:
```

has type structured module type `module`(a, b):

```
> type( m, ''module'( a, b )' );
```

$$true$$

It also has type type `module`(a)

```
> type( m, ''module'( a )' );
```

$$true$$

because any module that exports symbols a and b is a module that exports the symbol a.

Example: A Symbolic Differentiator

In this section we will illustrate the various module concepts discussed so far by writing a simple symbolic differentiator. Maple already provides a built-in differentiator `diff`, so we will call our differentiator `differentiate`. Its (final) implementation is hidden in a module `DiffImpl`, which holds all the local states for the program. Much of the code for the differentiator is designed to implement either a standard "rule" (such as the rule that the derivative of a sum is the sum of the derivatives of the summands), or special case rules for mathematical functions such as `sin` and `exp`. Our simple differentiator will handle only real valued functions of a single real variable.

We will show several steps in the development of the module, from a very simple "first try" to the final, fully functional program. The final form of the differentiator is a good illustration of a very common Maple "design pattern". This pattern arises when you have a single top-level routine that has to dispatch to a number of subroutines to handle special cases using special purpose algorithms.

The First Attempt   Initially, we will present the differentiator as an ordinary procedure, not yet involving modules. The first version of the differentiator is shown below.

```
> differentiate := proc( expr, var )
>     local a, b;
>
>     if type( expr, 'constant' ) then
>         0
>     elif expr = var then
>         1
>     elif type( expr, '`+`' ) then
>         map( procname, args )
>     elif type( expr, '`^`' ) then
>         a, b := op( expr );
>         if a = var and not has( b, var ) then
>             b * a ^ ( b - 1 )
>         else
>             'procname( args )'
>         end if
>     elif type( expr, '`*`' ) then
>         a, b := op( 1, expr ), subsop( 1 = 1, expr );
>         procname( a, var ) * b + a * procname( b, var )
>     else
>         'procname( args )'
>     end if
> end proc:
```

Trivial cases are handled first: The derivative of a constant expression is equal to 0, and the derivative of the variable with respect to which we are differentiating is equal to 1. The additivity of the derivative operator is expressed by mapping the procedure over sums, using the idiom

```
> map( procname, args );
```

This is commonly used to map a procedure over its first argument, passing along all the remaining arguments. Only the simple case of powers of the differentiation variable is handled so far, provided also that the power is independent of the differentiation variable. The product rule for derivatives is expressed by splitting expressions of type product into two "pieces":

- the first factor in the product, and

- the product of all the remaining factors.

This is achieved by the double assignment of

```
> a, b := op( 1, expr ), subsop( 1 = 1, expr );
```

so the input expression `expr` is expressed as `expr = a * b`. The standard technique of returning "unevaluated" is used so that computation may proceed symbolically on expressions that the differentiator is unable to do anything meaningful with.

This first version is quite simple, but it is already able to handle polynomials with numeric coefficients.

```
> differentiate( 2 - x + x^2 + 3*x^9, x );
```

$$-1 + 2\,x + 27\,x^8$$

However, it fails on expressions containing calls to standard mathematical functions.

```
> differentiate( sin( x ), x );
```

$$\mathrm{differentiate}(\sin(x),\ x)$$

It is also unable to deal successfully with symbolic coefficients.

```
> differentiate( a*x^2 + b*x + c, x );
```

$$\mathrm{differentiate}(a,\ x)\,x^2 + 2\,a\,x + \mathrm{differentiate}(b,\ x)\,x + b$$
$$+\ \mathrm{differentiate}(c,\ x)$$

Adding Missing Functionality   To add the missing functionality, we can add a case for expressions of type `function`.

```
> differentiate := proc( expr, var )
>     local a, b;
>
>     if not has( expr, var ) then
>         0
>     elif expr = var then
>         1
>     elif type( expr, ''+'' ) then
>         map( procname, args )
>     elif type( expr, ''^'' ) then
>         a, b := op( expr );
>         if not has( b, var ) then
>             b * a ^ ( b - 1 ) * procname( a, var )
>         else
>             'procname( args )'
>         end if
>     elif type( expr, ''*'' ) then
>         a, b := op( 1, expr ), subsop( 1 = 1, expr );
>         procname( a, var ) * b + a * procname( b, var )
>     elif type( expr, 'function' ) and nops( expr ) = 1 then
>         # functions of a single variable; chain rule
>         b := op( 0, expr ); # the name of the function
>         a := op( 1, expr ); # the argument
>         if b = 'sin' then
>             cos( a ) * procname( a, var )
>         elif b = 'cos' then
>             -sin( a ) * procname( a, var )
>         elif b = 'exp' then
>             exp( a ) * procname( a, var )
>         elif b = 'ln' then
>             ( 1 / a ) * procname( a, var )
>         else
>             'procname( args )'
>         end if
>     else
>         'procname( args )'
>     end if
> end proc:
```

This uses the chain rule to compute the derivatives of calls to "known" functions.

```
> differentiate( sin( x ) + cos( exp( x ) ), x );
```

$$\cos(x) - \sin(e^x)\, e^x$$

```
> differentiate( sin( x^2 ) + cos( x^2 ), x );
```

$$2\cos(x^2)\, x - 2\sin(x^2)\, x$$

```
> differentiate( sin( x )^2 + cos( x )^3, x );
```

$$2\sin(x)\cos(x) - 3\cos(x)^2\sin(x)$$

At the same time, we have also improved the handling of expressions independent of the variable of differentiation.

```
> differentiate( a*x^2 + b*x + c, x );
```

$$2\,a\,x + b$$

This is effected by using the expression **has(expr, var)** instead of the weaker test **type(expr, 'constant')**. The "power rule" now handles more than just powers of **var**.

```
> differentiate( sin( x )^2, x );
```

$$2\sin(x)\cos(x)$$

However, adding new functions to our differentiator is tedious and error-prone, and the job of handling the chain rule has to be repeated for each function "known" to it.

Introducing a Function Table A better way to deal with the many functions that we should eventually want to add is to store them, and the rules used for their differentiation, in a table.

```
> differentiate := proc( expr, var )
>       local a, b, functab;
>
>       functab := table();
>       functab[ 'sin' ] := 'cos';
>       functab[ 'cos' ] := x -> -sin( x );
>       functab[ 'exp' ] := exp;
>       functab[ 'ln' ] := x -> 1 / x;
>
>       if not has( expr, var ) then
>           0
>       elif expr = var then
>           1
>       elif type( expr, '+' ) then
>           map( procname, args )
>       elif type( expr, '^' ) then
>           a, b := op( expr );
>           if a = var and not has( b, var ) then
>               b * a ^ ( b - 1 ) * procname( a, var )
>           else
>               'procname( args )'
```

```
>        end if
>    elif type( expr, ''*'' ) then
>        a, b := op( 1, expr ), subsop( 1 = 1, expr );
>        procname( a, var ) * b + a * procname( b, var )
>    elif type( expr, 'function' ) and nops( expr ) = 1 then
>        # functions of a single variable; chain rule
>        b := op( 0, expr ); # the name of the function
>        a := op( 1, expr ); # the argument
>        if assigned( functab[ b ] ) then
>            # This is a ''known'' function
>            functab[ b ]( a ) * procname( a, var )
>        else
>            # This function is not known; return unevaluated
>            'procname( args )'
>        end if
>    else
>        'procname( args )'
>    end if
> end proc:
```

This not only simplifies the code used for the **function** case, but also makes it very easy to add new functions.

Unfortunately, this implementation suffers from a serious drawback. It is not extensible. The known functions are hardcoded as part of the procedure definition for **differentiate**.

New functions cannot be added without editing this source code.

A second problem relates to performance. A complete implementation would require a table of dozens or hundreds of functions. That large table would have to be created and initialized each time **differentiate** was invoked.

Encapsulation and Extensibility   One way to fix both problems is to make the table of functions a global variable. However, using global variables can be dangerous, because they pollute the user namespace and are subject to unwanted inspection and tampering.

A better solution is to put the **differentiate** procedure, along with its table of functions, into a module. The table is then initialized only once–when the module is created–and can be saved to a Maple repository along with the rest of the module by using a **savelib** call. By making the table a local variable of the module, we prevent users from modifying the table, or otherwise inspecting it in unwanted ways.

This does not prevent us from making the differentiator user-extensible, however. We can add an access procedure **addFunc** that allows users to add their own rules for differentiating new functions. For instance, we can use the call

```
> addFunc( 'cos', x -> -sin(x) );
```

to add the derivative of the **sin** function. The export **addFunc** of the **DiffImpl** module is a procedure that requires two arguments. The first is the name of a function whose derivative is to be made known to the differentiator. The second is a Maple procedure of one argument that expresses the derivative of the function being added.

With this strategy in mind, we will create a module **DiffImpl**, with principal export **differentiate**. At the same time, we will also take the opportunity to make the basic differentiation rules extensible.

Here is the complete source code for the differentiator with these improvements.

```
> DiffImpl := module()
>     description "a symbolic differentiator";
>     local      functab, ruletab, diffPower;
>     export     differentiate, addFunc, addRule, rule;
>
>     addFunc := proc( fname::symbol, impl )
>         functab[ fname ] := impl
>     end proc;
>
>     addRule := proc( T, impl )
>         if type( T, '{ set, list }' ) then
>             map( procname, args )
>         elif type( T, 'And( name, type )' ) then
>             ruletab[ T ] := impl
>         else
>             error "expecting a type name, but got %1", T
>         end if
>     end proc;
>
>     rule := proc( T )
>         if type( T, 'And( name, type )' ) then
>             if assigned( ruletab[ T ] ) then
>                 eval( ruletab[ T ], 1 )
>             else
>                 error "no rule for expressions of type %1", T
>             end if
>         else
>             error "expecting a type symbol, but got %1", T
>         end if
>     end proc;
>
>     differentiate := proc( expr, var )
>         local a, b, e;
>         if not has( expr, var ) then
>             0
>         elif expr = var then
>                     1
>         elif type( expr, 'function' ) and nops( expr ) = 1 then
>             e := op( 0, expr );
```

```
>                       a := op( expr );
>                       if assigned( functab[ e ] ) then
>                           functab[ e ]( a ) * procname( a, var )
>                       else
>                           'procname( args )'
>                       end if
>               else
>                   b := whattype( expr );
>                   if assigned( ruletab[ b ] ) then
>                       ruletab[ b ]( expr, var )
>                   else
>                       'procname( args )'
>                   end if
>               end if
>       end proc;
>
>       addRule( '{list,set,tabular}',
>               () -> map( differentiate, args ) );
>       addRule( '`+`',
>               () -> map( differentiate, args ) );
>       addRule( '`*`',
>           (expr,var) ->
>           op(1,expr)*differentiate(subsop(1=1,expr),var)
>               + differentiate(op(1,expr),var)*subsop(1=1,expr) );
>       diffPower := proc( expr, var )
>           local    b, e;
>           Assert( type( expr, '`^`' ) );
>           b, e := op( expr );
>           if has( e, var ) then
>               expr * ( differentiate( e, var ) * ln( b )
>                   + e * differentiate( b, var ) / b )
>           else # simpler formula
>               e * b^(e - 1) * differentiate( b, var )
>           end if;
>       end proc;
>       addRule( '`^`', eval( diffPower ) );
>
>       addFunc( 'sin', cos );
>       addFunc( 'cos', x -> -sin(x) );
>       addFunc( 'exp', exp );
>       addFunc( 'ln', x -> 1/x );
>       # ... etc.
>
> end module:
> differentiate := DiffImpl:-differentiate:
```

To give our set of rules for nonfunctional expressions a similar kind of extensibility, we will store those rules in a table as well. The table will be indexed by the primary (or basic) type name for the expression type, as given by the Maple procedure whattype.

```
> whattype( a + 2 );
```

$$+$$

```
> whattype( a / b );
```

$$*$$

```
> whattype( a^sqrt(2) );
```

$$\hat{}$$

```
> whattype( [ f( x ), g( x ) ] );
```

list

A "rule" is expressed by a procedure of two arguments, **expr** and **var**, in which **expr** is the expression to be differentiated, and **var** is the variable of differentiation. For instance, we would like the differentiator to handle items such as sets and lists by differentiating their individual components. So we add the rule

```
> addRule( '{ list, set, tabular }', () -> map( differentiate,
>     args ) );
```

The first version of our differentiator dealt with sums by mapping itself over the sum expression. In the new scheme, this is expressed by the statement

```
> addRule( ''+'', () -> map( differentiate, args ) );
```

in the module body. Now, the advantage of using this scheme is that, not only can the author of the differentiator extend the system, but so can users of the system. Having instantiated the module **DiffImpl**, any user can add rules or new functions, simply by issuing appropriate calls to **addRule** and **addFunc**.

The differentiator cannot handle the procedure **tan**

```
> differentiate( tan( x )/exp( x ), x );
```

$$-\frac{\tan(x)}{e^x} + \frac{\text{differentiate}(\tan(x), x)}{e^x}$$

so we will add it to the database of known functions.

```
> DiffImpl:-addFunc( 'tan', x -> 1 + tan(x)^2 );
```

$$x \rightarrow 1 + \tan(x)^2$$

```
> differentiate( tan( x )/exp( x ), x );
```

$$-\frac{\tan(x)}{e^x} + \frac{1 + \tan(x)^2}{e^x}$$

Similarly, there is not yet any rule for handling equations and other relations.

```
> differentiate( y( x ) = sin( x^2 ) - cos( x^3 ), x );
```

$$\text{differentiate}(y(x) = \sin(x^2) - \cos(x^3),\, x)$$

```
> DiffImpl:-addRule( '{ '=', '<', '<=' }',
>                    () -> map( differentiate, args ) );
```

$$\{() \rightarrow \text{map}(\textit{differentiate}, \text{args})\}$$

```
> differentiate( y( x ) = sin( x^2 ) - cos( x^3 ), x );
```

$$\text{differentiate}(y(x),\, x) = 2\cos(x^2)\,x + 3\sin(x^3)\,x^2$$

The Extension Mechanism is "Module Aware" Take care not to confuse the extension mechanism proposed above for our differentiator with the extension mechanism used by the built-in Maple command **diff**. **diff** uses a traditional string concatenation mechanism for adding knowledge of the derivatives of functions, and all its rules are built-in, so they cannot be extended. For instance, to add a new function **F** to Maple's built-in **diff** command, you can define a procedure `diff/F` that computes the derivative of **F**.

By contrast, the extension mechanism used in our **differentiate** example is "module aware". Suppose that you want to add knowledge of the derivative of some top-level function F. You can simply issue a command, such as

```
> DiffImpl:-addFunc( 'F', x -> sin( x ) + cos( x ) );
```

$$x \to \sin(x) + \cos(x)$$

(We are supposing that, in fact, the derivative of F(x) is sin(x) + cos(x).) Now suppose that you have defined a module with some special functions, one of which is also called F.

```
> SpecFuncs := module()
>     export F; # etc.
>     # definition of F() and others
> end module:
```

You can now add this new F to the known functions.

```
> DiffImpl:-addFunc( SpecFuncs:-F, x -> exp( 2 * x ) );
```

$$x \to e^{(2\,x)}$$

```
> differentiate( F( x ), x );
```

$$\sin(x) + \cos(x)$$

```
> use SpecFuncs in
>     differentiate( F( x ), x );
> end use;
```

$$e^{(2\,x)}$$

With the traditional mechanism, this does not work.

```
> `diff/` || F := x -> sin( x ) + cos( x );
```

$$diff/F := x \to \sin(x) + \cos(x)$$

```
> diff( F( x ), x );
```

$$\sin(x) + \cos(x)$$

```
> use SpecFuncs in
>     `diff/` || F := x -> exp( 2 * x );
>     diff( F( x ), x );
> end use;
```

$$diff/F := x \to e^{(2\,x)}$$

$$e^{(2\,x)}$$

The definition for the global **F** has been lost.

```
> diff( F( 2 * x ), x );
```

$$e^{(4\,x)}$$

(We use a different argument to `diff` to avoid recalling the answer from its remember table.) The traditional mechanism fails because it relies on the *external representation* of names, and not upon their bindings, so each attempt to define an extension to `diff` in fact added a definition for the derivative of *all* functions whose names are spelled `"F"`.

A commented version of the differentiator module is available in the sample source code of your Maple installation. The implementation shown in the text has been somewhat simplified.

6.2   Records

The simplest way in which to use modules is as Pascal-style records (or "structures", as in C and C++). A record is a data structure that has some number of named "slots" or "fields". In Maple, these slots can be assigned arbitrary values.

Instantiating Records   To create a record, use the **Record** constructor. It takes the slot names as arguments.

```
> rec := Record( 'a', 'b', 'c' );
```

$$rec :=$$
module() **export** a, b, c; **option** *record*; **end module**

The name `rec` is now assigned a record with slots named `a`, `b`, and `c`. These are the slot names for the record `rec`. You can access, and assign, these slots by using the expressions `rec:-a`, `rec:-b`, and `rec:-c`.

```
> rec:-a := 2;
```

$$a := 2$$

```
> rec:-a;
```

$$2$$

If not assigned, the record slot evaluates to the *local* instance of the slot name.

```
> rec:-b;
```

$$b$$

```
> evalb( % = b );
```

false

The usefulness of this is that the entire record may be passed around as an *aggregate* data structure.

The record constructor accepts initializers for record slots. That is, you may specify an initial value for any among the slots of a newly created record by passing an equation with the slot name on the left side and the initial value on the right.

```
> r := Record( 'a' = 2, 'b' = sqrt( 3 ) );
```

$$r := \mathbf{module}()\, \mathbf{export}\, a,\, b;\ \ \mathbf{option}\, record;\ \mathbf{end\ module}$$

```
> r:-b;
```

$$\sqrt{3}$$

Record Types   Expressions created with the `Record` constructor are of type `record`.

```
> type( rec, 'record' );
```

true

This is a structured type that works the same way that type `module` does but recognizes records specifically.

Using Records to Represent Quaternions   Records are useful for implementing simple aggregate data structures for which named access to slots is wanted. For example, four real numbers can be combined to form a quaternion, and we can represent this using a record structure, as follows.

```
> MakeQuaternion := proc( a, b, c, d )
>     Record( 're' = a, 'i' = b, 'j' = c, 'k' = d )
> end proc:
> z := MakeQuaternion( 2, 3, 2, sqrt( 5 ) );
```

$$z := \mathbf{module}()$$
$$\mathbf{export}\ re,\ i,\ j,\ k;$$
$$\mathbf{option}\ record;$$
$$\mathbf{end\ module}$$

In this example, z represents the quaternion $2 + 3i + 2j + \sqrt{5}k$ (where i, j, and k are the nonreal quaternion basis units). The quaternion records can now be manipulated as single quantities. The following procedure accepts a quaternion record as its sole argument and computes the Euclidean length of the quaternion that the record represents.

```
> qnorm := proc( q )
>     use re = q:-re, i = q:-i, j = q:-j, k = q:-k in
>         sqrt( re * re + i * i + j * j + k * k )
>     end use
> end proc:
> qnorm( z );
```

$$\sqrt{22}$$

A Maple type for quaternions can be introduced as a structured record type.

```
> 'type/quaternion' := 'record( re, i, j, k )':
> type( z, 'quaternion' );
```

$$true$$

6.3   Packages

Modules are ideal for writing Maple packages. They provide facilities that are better equipped for large software projects than are the older table- and procedure-based methods.

What Is a Package?

A *package* is a collection of procedures, and other data, that can be treated as a whole. Packages typically gather a number of procedures that enable you to perform computations in some well-defined problem domain. Packages may contain data other than procedures, and may even contain other packages ("subpackages").

Packages in the Standard Library   A number of packages are shipped with the standard Maple library. For example, the **group**, **numtheory**, **codegen**, and **LinearAlgebra** packages are all provided with Maple, along with several dozen others. The **group** package provides procedures that allow you to compute with groups that have a finite representation in terms of permutations, or of generators and defining relations. The **LinearAlgebra** package has a large number of procedures available for computational linear algebra.

Table-Based Packages   Many packages are implemented as tables. The essential idea underlying this implementation scheme is that the name of a package routine is used as the index into a table of procedures. The table itself is the concrete representation of the package.

Use Modules for New Packages   Modules are the new implementation vehicle for packages. A module represents a package by its exported names. The exported names can be assigned arbitrary Maple expressions, typically procedures, and these names form the package.

Package Exports   Some of the data in a package is normally made accessible to the user as an "export" of the package. For packages implemented as modules, the package exports are the same as the exports of the underlying module. For packages implemented as tables, the package exports are the names used to index the underlying table.

Accessing the exports of a package is a fundamental operation that is supported by all packages. If P is a Maple package, and e is one among its exports, you can access e by using the fully qualified reference P[e]. If it happens that P is a module, then you can also use the syntax P:-e.

These methods of accessing the exports of a module are normally used when programming with a package.

Note that `:-` is a left-associative operator. If S is a submodule of a module P, and the name e is exported by S, then the notation `P:-S:-e` is parsed as `(P:-S):-e`, and so it refers to the instance of e local to S. This fact is important to reference members of subpackages. For example,

```
> m := Matrix(2,2,[[1-x,2-x],[3-x,4-x]],
>               'datatype' = 'polynom(integer)' );
```

$$m := \begin{bmatrix} 1-x & 2-x \\ 3-x & 4-x \end{bmatrix}$$

```
> LinearAlgebra:-LA_Main:-Norm( m, 1, conjugate = false );
```

$$\max(|x-1| + |x-3|, \ |x-2| + |x-4|)$$

calls the procedure Norm in the subpackage LA_Main of the LinearAlgebra package. (You cannot use indexed notation for this.)

Using Packages Interactively   For interactive use, it is inconvenient to have to type fully qualified references to all the exports of a package. To ease this burden, the Maple procedure with is provided for the interactive management of package namespaces. Using with, you can globally impose the exported names of a package. This allows you to access the package exports, without typing the package prefix, by making the names of the exports visible at the top-level of your Maple session. For example, to use the numtheory package, you can issue the command

```
> with( numtheory );
```

```
Warning, the protected name order has been redefined
and unprotected
```

[*GIgcd, bigomega, cfrac, cfracpol, cyclotomic, divisors, factorEQ, factorset, fermat, imagunit, index, integral_basis, invcfrac, invphi, issqrfree, jacobi, kronecker, λ, legendre, mcombine, mersenne, minkowski, mipolys, mlog, mobius, mroot, msqrt, nearestp, nthconver, nthdenom, nthnumer, nthpow, order, pdexpand, φ, π, pprimroot, primroot, quadres, rootsunity, safeprime, σ, sq2factor, sum2sqr, τ, thue*]

The effect of this command is to make the names exported by tne **numtheory** package (a list of which is returned by the call to **with**) available temporarily as top-level Maple commands.

```
> cfrac( ( 1 + x )^k, x, 5, 'subdiagonal', 'simregular' );
```

$$
\cfrac{1}{1 - \cfrac{k\,x}{1 + \cfrac{1}{2}\cfrac{(k+1)\,x}{1 - \cfrac{1}{6}\cfrac{(k-1)\,x}{1 + \cfrac{1}{6}\cfrac{(k+2)\,x}{1 + \ldots}}}}}
$$

In this section, we are concerned primarily with how to write Maple packages by using modules. The following subsections present several examples that illustrate how to do this.

Example: The LinkedList Package

The first example package is a small package called **LinkedList**. This example illustrates the basic structure of a package implemented by using modules.

Background Linked lists are a basic data structure used in programs for many different purposes. There are many different kinds of linked lists, with variations on the basic idea intended to deal with various issues involving performance and functionality. The example package shown in this subsection provides a few operations on the simplest possible form of linked lists.

The "links" in a linked list are formed from a very simple data structured called a "pair". A pair is essentially a container with space for exactly two elements. Pairs can be modeled by fixed length records with two slots. When used to implement linked lists, the first slot holds the data for the list entry, and the second slot stores a pointer to the next pair in the list.

The `LinkedList` package implements an abstract data definition for the pair data structure, and adds some higher level operations on pairs to effect the list abstraction. A linked list is effectively represented by its first pair.

The "pair" abstract data structure is very simple. It consists of a constructor "pair", and two accessors called "head" and "tail" that satisfy the algebraic specification

$$p = \mathrm{pair}(\mathrm{head}(p), \mathrm{tail}(p))$$

for each pair p. In addition, there is a distinguished "pair" nil, satisfying this algebraic relation, that is unequal to any other pair, and satisfies

$$\mathrm{head}(\mathrm{nil}) = \mathrm{nil}, \mathrm{tail}(\mathrm{nil}) = \mathrm{nil}.$$

Note that linked lists are quite different from Maple's builtin list structures, which are really immutable arrays. Linked lists are best suited for applications in which you want to incrementally build up the list from its members.[1]

Package Implementation   The `LinkedList` package is implemented as a module containing the primitive operations on pairs, and higher level operations that implement the list abstraction.

```
> macro( _PAIR = `` ): # for nice printing
> LinkedList := module()
>     description "routines for simple linked lists";
>     export
>         nil,
>         nullp,
>         pair,
>         head,
>         tail,
>         list,
>         length,
>         member,
>         reverse,
>         append,
>         map;
>     local
```

---

[1]Lisp programmers will recognise the pair, head and tail operations as the more traditional operations known as "cons", "car" and "cdr".

```
>          setup,
>          cleanup,
>          map1,
>          reverse1,
>          _PAIR;
>     option
>          package,
>          load = setup,
>          unload = cleanup;
>
>     setup := proc()
>          global 'type/Pair', 'type/LinkedList';
>          'type/Pair' := '{ _PAIR( anything, anything ),
>                            identical( nil ) }';
>          'type/LinkedList' := proc( expr )
>              if expr = nil then
>                   true
>              elif type( expr, Pair ) then
>                   type( tail( expr ), 'LinkedList' )
>              else
>                   false
>              end if
>          end proc;
>          userinfo( 1, 'LinkedList',
>              "new types 'Pair' and 'LinkedList' defined" );
>          NULL
>     end proc;
>
>     cleanup := proc()
>          global 'type/Pair', 'type/LinkedList';
>          userinfo( 1, 'LinkedList',
>              "cleaning up global types" );
>          'type/Pair' := evaln( 'type/Pair' );
>          'type/LinkedList' := evaln( 'type/LinkedList' );
>          NULL
>     end proc;
>
>     pair := ( a, b )
>          -> setattribute( '_PAIR'( a, b ), 'inert' );
>     head := ( c::Pair )
>          -> 'if'( c = nil, nil, op( 1, c ) );
>     tail := ( c::Pair )
>          -> 'if'( c = nil, nil, op( 2, c ) );
>     nullp := ( pair )
>          -> evalb( pair = nil );
>
>     list := proc()
>          local   a, L;
>          L := nil;
>          for a in args do
>              L := pair( a, L )
>          end do
>     end proc;
>
```

```
>       length := proc( lst )
>           if nullp( lst ) then
>               0
>           else
>               1 + length( tail( lst ) )
>           end if
>       end proc;
>
>       member := proc( item, lst )
>           if nullp( lst ) then
>               false
>           elif item = head( lst ) then
>               true
>           else
>               procname( item, tail( lst ) )
>           end if
>       end proc;
>
>       map := proc( p, lst )
>           if nullp( lst ) then
>               nil
>           else
>               pair( p( head( lst ) ),
>                   procname( p, tail( lst ) ) )
>           end if
>       end proc;
>
>       append := proc( lst1, lst2 )
>           if nullp( lst1 ) then
>               lst2
>           else
>               pair( head( lst1 ),
>                   procname( tail( lst1 ), lst2 ) )
>           end if
>       end proc;
>
>       reverse1 := proc( sofar, todo )
>           if nullp( todo ) then
>               sofar
>           else
>               procname( pair( head( todo ), sofar ),
>                   tail( todo ) )
>           end if
>       end proc;
>
>       reverse := lst -> reverse1( nil, lst );
>
>       setup();
>
> end module:
```

Normally, a package definition like this would be entered into a Maple source file using a text editor, or in a worksheet using Maple's GUI interface. In either case, the definition would then be followed by a call to the `savelib` procedure using the name of the module as its sole argument:

```
> savelib( 'LinkedList' );
```

Evaluating the `savelib` call saves the module to the first repository found in the global variable `libname`, or the repository named with the global variable `savelibname`, if it is defined. (At least one of these must be defined.) **You should always ensure that your standard Maple library is write-protected to avoid saving your own expressions in it.** If you accidentally save something to the standard Maple library, you may need to restore the original from the media on which you obtained your copy of Maple.

The package exports are listed as the exports of the module. A few local variables are used to implement the package. The local procedures `map1` and `reverse1` are part of the package implementation that is not available to users of the package. They are visible only within the module definition. This allows the package author to make improvements to the package without disturbing any code that uses it. If the local procedures `reverse1` and `map1` were exported (thus, available to users), it would be difficult for the author to replace these routines without breaking existing code that relies upon them.

The package includes two special (local) procedures, `setup` and `cleanup`. These are executed, respectively, when the module is first read from a repository, and when the package is either garbage collected or when Maple is about to exit.

Using the Package   The package exports can always be accessed by using the long form of their names.

```
> LinkedList:-pair( a, b );
```

$$(a, b)$$

For consistency with the older table-based package implementations, an indexed notation may also be used.

```
> LinkedList[ 'pair' ]( a, b );
```

$$(a, b)$$

This form requires that the index (in this case, the symbol **pair**) be protected from evaluation, and the notation does not extend to packages with nested subpackages.

To access the package exports interactively, use the **with** command.

```
> with( LinkedList );
```

```
Warning, the protected names length, map and member
have been redefined and unprotected
```

[*append, head, length, list, map, member, nil, nullp, pair,*
reverse, tail]

Note that, since some of the package exports shadow global procedures with the same name, **with** issues warnings. These warnings are normal and merely serve to remind you that these names will now refer to expressions other than the expressions to which they referred prior to issuing the command. Once the exports of the package **LinkedList** have been bound, you can call them as you would global Maple routines with those names. Note that you can still access the global version of **member**, for example, by using the syntax **:-member**.

```
> use LinkedList in
>     member( a, %% );
>     :-member( a, [ a, b, c, d ] )
> end use;
```

$$true$$

$$true$$

This is one of the principal advantages of using modules and binding, rather than assignment, to implement packages.

Lists are either built up incrementally using the **pair** export of the package, or by calling the **list** export.

```
> L := nil:
> for i from 1 to 10 do
>     L := pair( i, L )
> end do;
```

$$L := (1, \ nil)$$

$$L := (2, \ (1, \ nil))$$

$$L := (3, \ (2, \ (1, \ nil)))$$

$$L := (4, \ (3, \ (2, \ (1, \ nil))))$$

$$L := (5, \ (4, \ (3, \ (2, \ (1, \ nil)))))$$

$$L := (6, \ (5, \ (4, \ (3, \ (2, \ (1, \ nil))))))$$

$$L := (7, \ (6, \ (5, \ (4, \ (3, \ (2, \ (1, \ nil)))))))$$

$$L := (8, \ (7, \ (6, \ (5, \ (4, \ (3, \ (2, \ (1, \ nil))))))))$$

$$L := (9, \ (8, \ (7, \ (6, \ (5, \ (4, \ (3, \ (2, \ (1, \ nil)))))))))$$

$$L := (10, \ (9, \ (8, \ (7, \ (6, \ (5, \ (4, \ (3, \ (2, \ (1, \ nil))))))))))$$

```
> length( L );
```

$$10$$

```
> member( 3, L );
```

true

```
> member( 100, L );
```

false

```
> reverse( L );
```

$$(1, \ (2, \ (3, \ (4, \ (5, \ (6, \ (7, \ (8, \ (9, \ (10, \ nil))))))))))$$

```
> map( x -> x^2, L );
```

$$(100, \ (81, \ (64, \ (49, \ (36, \ (25, \ (16, \ (9, \ (4, \ (1, \ nil))))))))))$$

```
> member( 100, % );
```

true

```
> L2 := list( a, b, c, d );
```

$$L2 := (d, \ (c, \ (b, \ (a, \ nil))))$$

```
> map( sin, L2 );
```

$$(\sin(d), \ (\sin(c), \ (\sin(b), \ (\sin(a), \ nil))))$$

```
> eval( L2, { a = 1, b = 2, c = 3, d = 4 } );
```

$$(4, \ (3, \ (2, \ (1, \ nil))))$$

```
> map( evalf[ 10 ], % );
```

$$(4., \ (3., \ (2., \ (1., \ nil))))$$

The Maple source code for this package is available in the 'samples' directory of your Maple installation as the file 'samples/ch06/11.mpl'. The source code in the 'samples' directory may differ slightly from that shown in this book.

Example: A Code Coverage Profiling Package

Our next example is a package called coverage. It instruments procedures and modules for coverage profiling. Besides serving as an example of a small package, it also illustrates some of the ways in which modules can be manipulated.

Design When you have written some Maple code, you will want to write tests that exercise each part of the program to ensure that it works correctly, and that it continues to work when it, or other programs on which it depends, change over time. It is important to be able to determine whether each statement in a procedure is executed by some test case. The traceproc option of the Maple command debugopts provides that capability. It takes the name p of a procedure, using the syntax

```
debugopts( 'traceproc' = p );
```

and instruments the procedure assigned to p for coverage profiling. Here is an example.

```
> p := proc( x )
>       if x < 0 then
>           2 * x
>       else
>           1 + 2 * x
>       end if
> end proc:
> debugopts( 'traceproc' = p ):
```

Once the procedure has been instrumented, then each time it is executed, profiling information at the statement level is stored. To view the profiling information, use the procedure showstat.

```
> p( 2 );
```

                                5

```
> showstat( p );
```

```
p := proc(x)
        |Calls Seconds  Words|
  PROC |    1   0.000      12|
     1 |    1   0.000      12| if x < 0 then
     2 |    0   0.000       0|    2*x
                                else
     3 |    1   0.000       0|    1+2*x
                                end if
end proc
```

The display shows that only one branch of the **if** statement that forms the body of p was taken so far. This is because only a non-negative argument has been supplied as an argument to p. To get complete coverage, a negative argument must also be supplied.

```
> p( -1 );
```

                               −2

```
> showstat( p );
```

```
p := proc(x)
     |Calls Seconds  Words|
PROC |   2   0.000     24|
   1 |   2   0.000     24| if x < 0 then
   2 |   1   0.000      0|   2*x
                             else
   3 |   1   0.000      0|   1+2*x
                             end if
end proc
```

Now the display shows that each statement in the body of **p** has been reached.

The profiling information is stored in an rtable assigned to a name that is formed by concatenating the name **TRACE** with the name of the procedure (the one used in the call to **debugopts**), separated by a **/** character.

```
> eval( 'TRACE/p' );
```

$$\begin{bmatrix} 2 & 0 & 24 \\ 2 & 0 & 24 \\ 1 & 0 & 0 \\ 1 & 0 & 0 \end{bmatrix}$$

The little package illustrated in this section helps to extend this functionality to modules, and acts as a front end to the **debugopts** with the **traceproc** option.

The **coverage** package has two exports: **profile** and **covered**. Two private procedures, **rprofile** and **traced**, are used as subroutines. They are stored in local variables of the underlying module of the package.

The Package Source   Here is the source code for the package.

```
> coverage := module()
>     description "a package of utilities for "
>                 "code coverage profiling";
>     option package;
>     export profile, covered;
>     local rprofile, traced;
>
>     # Instrument a procedure or module
>     # for coverage profiling. Return the
>     # number of procedures instrumented.
>     profile := proc()
>         local arg;
```

```
>            add( rprofile( arg ), arg = [ args ] )
>        end proc;
>
>    rprofile := proc( s::name )
>        local e;
>        if type( s, 'procedure' ) then
>            debugopts( 'traceproc' = s );
>            1
>        elif type( s, ''module'' ) then
>            add( procname( e ),
>                e = select( type,
>                        [ exports( s, 'instance' ) ],
>                        '{ 'module', procedure }' ) )
>        else
>            error "only procedures and modules can be profiled"
>        end if
>    end proc;
>
>    # Subroutine to recognize an rtable that
>    # is used to store profiling information,
>    # based on its name.
>    traced := proc( s )
>        evalb( substring( convert( s, 'string' ),
>                        1 .. 6 ) = "TRACE/" )
>    end proc;
>
>    # Determine which procedures have
>    # coverage information.
>    covered := proc()
>        local S;
>        S := [ anames( 'rtable' ) ];
>        S := select( traced, S );
>        if nargs > 0 and args[ 1 ] = 'nonzero' then
>            S := select( s -> evalb( s[1,1] <> 0 ), S )
>        elif nargs > 0 then
>            error "optional argument is the name nonzero"
>        end if;
>        map( parse, map( substring,
>                map( convert, S, 'string' ), 7 .. -1 ) )
>    end proc;
> end module:
```

How the Package Works The export profile is an interface to the package's principal facility: instrumenting procedures and modules for coverage profiling. It returns the number of procedures instrumented, and calls the private subroutine rprofile to do most of the work.

The procedure rprofile accepts a name s as an argument. If s is the name of a procedure, rprofile simply calls debugopts to instrument the procedure assigned to that name. Otherwise, if s is the name of a module, rprofile picks out any exports of the module that are procedures or modules and calls itself recursively to instrument them. If the parameter s is assigned a value of any other type, then an exception is raised.

The expression [exports(s, 'instance')] evaluates to a list of all the exported variables of the module that are assigned to s. It is important to pass the instance option to exports, because when those names are passed to rprofile in a recursive call, rprofile must test the type of their assigned values. This list contains *all* the module exports, so those that are of type procedure, or of type module, are picked out by using a call to select. The recursion is effected in the call to add, which sums the return values of all the recursive calls to rprofile.

The exported procedure covered is used to determine which procedures have been instrumented and called, with profiling information stored. One possible design would store this information in a private table in the coverage package. With this design, covered could simply query that internal table for the names of the procedures that have been instrumented and that have profiling information stored. However, a user may have instrumented the procedure "manually" by calling debugopts directly, or historical profiling data may have been read from a Maple repository. Therefore, we have adopted a design that queries the system directly, without regard to how a procedure came to be instrumented initially.

The procedure covered queries Maple for all the names currently assigned values of type rtable, using the Maple command anames ("assigned names"). Names beginning with the character string "TRACE/" are selected, by using the subroutine traced, as there may be other rtables in the system. If the nonzero option is passed to covered, then only those which have actually been called are chosen. The final statement

```
> map( parse, map( substring,
>                  map( convert, S, 'string' ),
>                  7 .. -1 ) )
```

first converts the names to strings, then removes the "TRACE/" prefix by forming the substring from the seventh position to the end of the string, and finally calls parse on each string to convert it to the procedure for which profiling data is stored.

Using the Package   As with all packages, you can access the coverage package interactively by using the with command.

```
> with( coverage );
```

```
Warning, the protected name profile has been redefined
and unprotected
```

[*covered, profile*]

A list of the package exports is returned. Alternatively, the package exports can always be accessed by using the long forms `coverage:-profile` and `coverage:-covered`.

Suppose that we want to test the procedure `copy` (chosen because it is short). This procedure produces a new copy of a table, array, or rtable. Now that the `coverage` package has been globally imposed by using `with`, we can simply call

```
> profile( copy );
```

$$1$$

The return value of 1 indicates that, as expected, one procedure was instrumented. Next we call `copy` with a few arguments (output suppressed):

```
> copy( table() ):
> copy( array( 1 .. 3 ) ):
```

Using **covered**, we see that `copy` has indeed had its profiling information stored.

```
> covered( 'nonzero' );
```

[*copy*]

From the output of **showstat**,

```
> showstat( copy );
```

```
copy := proc(A)
      |Calls Seconds  Words|
PROC  |   2   0.000    640|
   1  |   2   0.000    640| if type(A,rtable) then
   2  |   0   0.000      0|    return rtable(rtable_indfns(A),
                                   rtable_dims(A),A,rtable_options(A),
                                   readonly = false)
                                elif type(A,{array, table}) then
   3  |   2   0.000    582|    if type(A,name) then
   4  |   0   0.000      0|       return map(proc () args end proc,
                                      eval(A))
                                   else
   5  |   2   0.000    574|       return map(proc () args end proc,A)
                                   end if
```

```
                               else
  6 |     0    0.000      0|     return A
                               end if
end proc
```

we see that we have missed the rtable case (statement 2), so we
add a test for that.

```
> copy( rtable() ):
> showstat( copy );
```

```
copy := proc(A)
     |Calls Seconds  Words|
PROC |   3   0.000    828|
  1 |   3   0.000    828| if type(A,rtable) then
  2 |   1   0.000    176|    return rtable(rtable_indfns(A),
                               rtable_dims(A),A,rtable_options(A),
                               readonly = false)
                             elif type(A,{array, table}) then
  3 |   2   0.000    582|    if type(A,name) then
  4 |   0   0.000      0|      return map(proc () args end proc,
                                 eval(A))
                               else
  5 |   2   0.000    574|      return map(proc () args end proc,A)
                               end if
                             else
  6 |   0   0.000      0|    return A
                             end if
end proc
```

Statement 4 is still missing. This statement can be reached by
assigning an array or table to a name and by calling copy with that name
as argument.

```
> t := table():
> copy( t ):
> showstat( copy );
```

```
copy := proc(A)
     |Calls Seconds  Words|
PROC |   4   0.000   1127|
  1 |   4   0.000   1127| if type(A,rtable) then
  2 |   1   0.000    176|    return rtable(rtable_indfns(A),
                               rtable_dims(A),A,rtable_options(A),
                               readonly = false)
                             elif type(A,{array, table}) then
  3 |   3   0.000    873|    if type(A,name) then
  4 |   1   0.000    287|      return map(proc () args end proc,
                                 eval(A))
                               else
```

```
  5 |    2   0.000    574|        return map(proc () args end proc,A)
                                 end if
                               else
  6 |    0   0.000      0|       return A
                               end if
end proc
```

The only missing case now is the one in which the argument to copy is something other than an rtable, array, or table.

```
> copy( 2 ):
> showstat( copy );
```

```
copy := proc(A)
      |Calls Seconds  Words|
PROC |    5   0.000    1153|
   1 |    5   0.000    1153|  if type(A,rtable) then
   2 |    1   0.000     176|     return rtable(rtable_indfns(A),
                                    rtable_dims(A),A,rtable_options(A),
                                    readonly = false)
                               elif type(A,{array, table}) then
   3 |    3   0.000     873|     if type(A,name) then
   4 |    1   0.000     287|       return map(proc () args end proc,
                                      eval(A))
                                  else
   5 |    2   0.000     574|        return map(proc () args end proc,A)
                                  end if
                               else
   6 |    1   0.000      10|     return A
                               end if
end proc
```

The final output shows that every statement has been reached by our test cases. This functionality is very useful for interactively developing unit tests for Maple programs.

The source presented here for the **coverage** package has been simplified for presentation in printed form. The full source code is available in the **samples** directory of your Maple installation.

Example: The Shapes Package

Modules permit the construction of packages with hierarchical structure. This cannot be done with table-based implementations of packages.

This section presents a detailed look at how you can organize your source code for a (potentially) large package that has nontrivial substructure. A package **Shapes** is described, and the details of its design and implementation are provided. We also give some "hints" related to source code organization.

The mathematical functionality of this package is trivial. It provides the means to compute areas and circumferences of various planar figures, which are called "shapes".

Only portions of the source code for this package are shown here. The fully commented source code can be found in the **samples** directory of your Maple installation.

Source Code Organization The Shapes package is organized into several source files:

```
shapes.mpl

   point.mpl

   segment.mpl

   circle.mpl

   square.mpl

   triangle.mpl
```

To avoid platform-specific differences, a flat directory structure is used. (All the source files reside in the same directory or folder.)

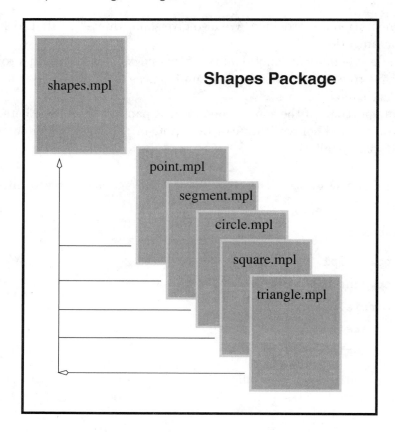

To define the module that implements this package, we use the Maple preprocessor to include the remaining source files at the appropriate point in the "master" source file `shapes.mpl`. A number of `$include` directives are included in `shapes.mpl`, such as

```
$include        "point.mpl"
$include        "segment.mpl"
...
```

Splitting a large project into a number of source files makes it easier to manage, and allows several developers to work on a project simultaneously. The source file is divided into shape-specific functionality. Most of the functionality for points, for instance, is implemented by source code stored in the file `point.mpl`.

Package Architecture The `Shapes` package is structured as a module with a number of exported procedures. Individual submodules provide shape-specific functionality for each shape type supported by the package.

Each of these shape-specific submodules is stored in its own source file; these are the files included into the main package source file, `shapes.mpl`.

The shape-specific submodules are submodules of another submodule, called `Shapes`. That is, the package module is called `Shapes`; it has a submodule, *also* called `Shapes`; and the module `Shapes:-Shapes` contains one submodule for each kind of shape supported. This submodule hierarchy is illustrated below.

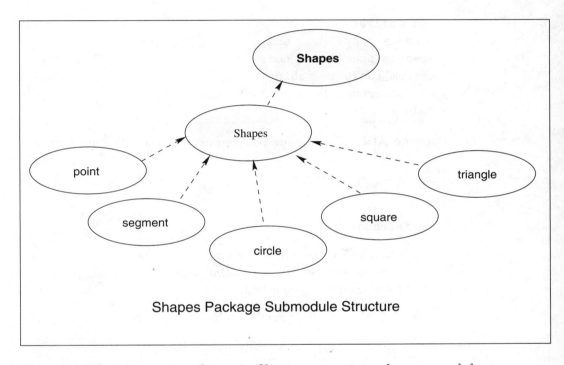

Shapes Package Submodule Structure

The result of preprocessing the main file `shapes.mpl` produces a module whose source has the following general outline.

```
Shapes := module()
    export make, area, circumference;
    local Shapes, circum_table;
    Shapes := module()
        export point, segment, circle, square, triangle;
        point := module() ... end;
        segment := module() ... end;
        .....
    end module;
    make := proc() ... end;
    area := proc() ... end;
    circum_table := table(); ...
    circumference := proc() ... end;
end module:
```

The Package API   The Shapes package exports the following routines:

1. make

2. area

3. circumference

The exported procedure make is a constructor for shapes. It is used to create a shape expression from the input data. For example, points are constructed from their x and y coordinates.

> org := make('point', 0, 0);

$$org := \mathrm{make}(point, 0, 0)$$

A circle is constructed from its center and radius.

> circ := make('circle', org, 2);

$$circ := \mathrm{make}(circle, \mathrm{make}(point, 0, 0), 2)$$

In each case, the name of the shape is passed as the first argument, to tell make what kind of shape to return.

To compute the area of a shape, call the exported procedure area with the shape as its argument.

> area(circ);

$$\text{area}(\text{make}(circle, \text{make}(point, 0, 0), 2))$$

Similarly, the exported procedure `circumference` computes the circumference of a given shape.

```
> circumference( circ );
```

$$\text{circumference}(\text{make}(circle, \text{make}(point, 0, 0), 2))$$

Shape Representation Shapes are represented as unevaluated function calls. The arguments to the call are the instance-specific data for the shape. For example, a point with coordinates $(2,3)$ is represented by the unevaluated function call `POINT( 2, 3 )`. Some instance data may be shapes themselves. For instance, a segment is represented, using its endpoints, as an unevaluated function call of the form `SEGMENT( start_point, end_point )`. The start and end points of the segment can be obtained by calls to the point constructor.

Procedure Dispatch The `Shapes` package illustrates three types of procedure dispatching:

1. dispatching on submodule exports

2. conditional dispatching

3. table-based dispatching

1. Dispatching on Submodule Exports The procedure `makei`, which is exported from the `Shapes` package, uses its submodule `Shapes:-Shapes` to effect procedure dispatching. To test whether a method for a given shape is available, the procedure `make` tests whether there is a submodule by that name in the `Shapes:-Shapes` submodule. If no such submodule is found, an exception is raised. Otherwise, the export `make` *from the submodule* is passed the arguments that were given to the top-level `Shapes:-make` procedure. Here is the `make` source code.

```
> make := proc( what::symbol )
>         description "constructor for shapes";
>         local   ctor,     # the shape constructor,
>                           # if found
>                 theShape; # the submodule for the
>                           # kind of shape requested
>
>         if not member( what, Shapes, 'theShape' ) then
```

```
>                    error "shape '%1' not available", what
>            end if;
>            if member( ':-make', theShape, 'ctor' ) then
>                    ctor( args[ 2 .. nargs ] )
>            else
>                    error "no constructor provided for "
>                        "shape %1", what
>            end if
> end proc:
```

The first argument to **make** is a symbol that denotes the kind of shape to construct (**point**, **circle**, **triangle**). This symbol is used as an "index" into the **Shapes:-Shapes** submodule. The first statement uses **member** to test whether the symbol passed in the parameter **what** is exported by the submodule **Shapes:-Shapes**. If it is not found, an appropriate diagnostic is issued, and an exception raised. If **member** returns the value **true**, then its third argument, the local variable **theShape**, is assigned the export found in the submodule.

For example, if **what** is the symbol **circle**, then the local variable **theShape** is assigned the submodule **Shapes:-Shapes:-circle** that implements operations on circles. The same idea is used to pick out the shape-specific constructor; it is the value assigned to the local variable **ctor** upon a **true** value being returned from the second call to **member**. Any remaining arguments are taken to be data used to construct the shape. These are passed on to the **make** export in a shape-specific submodule, if found, and are not checked further at this level. This design keeps the knowledge of each kind of shape localized to the submodule responsible for it.

2. Conditional Dispatching The procedure **area** uses a simple conditional dispatching mechanism. The "tag" of the input shape is extracted and is used in direct comparisons with hard-coded values to determine which shape-specific **area** subroutine to call to perform the area computation.

```
> area := proc( shape )
>        description "compute the area of a shape";
>        local    tag;
>
>        if not type( shape, 'function' ) then
>                error "expecting a shape expression, "
>                    "but got %1", shape
>        end if;
>
>        # Extract the "tag" information from the shape
>        tag := op( 0, shape );
>
```

```
>                 # Dispatch on the "tag" value
>                 if tag = ':-POINT' then
>                         Shapes:-point:-area( shape )
>                 elif tag = ':-SEGMENT' then
>                         Shapes:-segment:-area( shape )
>                 elif tag = ':-CIRCLE' then
>                         Shapes:-circle:-area( shape )
>                 elif tag = ':-SQUARE' then
>                         Shapes:-square:-area( shape )
>                 elif tag = ':-TRIANGLE' then
>                         Shapes:-triangle:-area( shape )
>                 else
>                         error "not a recognized shape: %1", tag
>                 end if
> end proc:
```

3. Table-based Dispatching The third dispatch method illustrated in
the Shapes package is table-based. This technique is used by the exported
procedure circumference, which references the table circum_table to
look up the appropriate routine to call. This table is built simply by
assigning its entries in the body of the Shapes package.

```
> circum_table := table();
> circum_table[ 'POINT' ] := Shapes:-point:-circumference;
> circum_table[ 'SEGMENT' ] := Shapes:-segment:-circumference;
> circum_table[ 'CIRCLE' ] := Shapes:-circle:-circumference;
> circum_table[ 'SQUARE' ] := Shapes:-square:-circumference;
> circum_table[ 'TRIANGLE' ] := Shapes:-triangle:-circumference;
```

The source code for the procedure circumference follows.

```
> circumference := proc( shape )
>         description "compute the circumference of a "
>                 "shape expression";
>         if not type( shape, 'function' ) then
>                 error "expecting a shape, but got %1", shape
>         end if;
>         if assigned( circum_table[ op( 0, shape ) ] ) then
>                 circum_table[ op( 0, shape ) ]( shape )
>         else
>                 error "no circumference method available "
>                     "for shape %1. Supported shapes "
>                     "are: %2", tag,
>                         sprintf( "%q", op( ALL_SHAPES ) ) )
>         end if
> end proc:
```

Minimal checking is done to ensure that the input has the right structure. If an entry is found in the table circum_table for the shape "tag"
(as with the area routine), then the corresponding procedure is called

with the given shape as argument. (The shape must be passed as an argument, so that the shape-specific subroutine can extract the instance data from it.) Otherwise, a diagnostic is issued, and an exception raised.

Shape-specific Submodules   As already noted, each shape is implemented in a shape-specific submodule. The set of exports of each module varies, but each supports at least the "required" exports `make`, `area`, and `circumference`. Particular shapes may support other operations. Only two of these submodules are described here. You can see the source for the other submodules in the sample source code.

The `point` Submodule   The submodule that implements points is fairly simple. In fact, it makes no reference to any lexically scoped variables in any of its parent modules (either **Shapes** or **Shapes:-Shapes**).

```
> point := module()
>     description "support routines for points";
>     export make, area, circumference, xcoord, ycoord;
>     option package;
>
>     make := ( x, y ) -> 'POINT'( x, y );
>     area := () -> 0;
>     circumference := () -> 0;
>     xcoord := p -> op( 1, p );
>     ycoord := p -> op( 2, p );
> end module:
```

Since the area and circumference of a point are both 0, these procedures are trivial to implement. In addition to the "required" exports, the **point** submodule also exports two utility routines, `xcoord` and `ycoord` for retrieving the x and y coordinates of a point. Providing these makes it possible for clients of this submodule to use it without knowing anything about the concrete representation of points. This makes it easier to change the representation later should that be required.

Within this submodule, the names `make`, `area`, and `circumference` shadow the names with the same external representation at the top-level **Shapes** module.

The `circle` Submodule   `circle` submodule provides the circle-specific subroutines for the **Shapes** package.

```
> circle := module()
>     export  make, center, radius, diameter,
>             area, circumference;
>     option package;
>
>     make := proc( cntrPt, radius )
```

```
>            'CIRCLE'( cntrPt, radius )
>       end proc;
>
>       center := circ -> op( 1, circ );
>       radius := circ -> op( 2, circ );
>       diameter := circ -> 2 * radius( circ );
>       circumference := circ ->  Pi * diameter( circ );
>       area := circ -> Pi * radius( circ )^2;
> end module:
```

Again, a few "extra" routines are provided beyond those required at the top-level of the **Shapes** package. The exported procedure **radius** is used to define some of the other routines. It could have been made local to this submodule.

6.4   The use Statement

The **use** statement is formally unrelated to modules, but is expressly designed to complement them and to make programming with modules easier in some circumstances.

Syntax and Semantics   The keyword **use** introduces the **use** statement, which has the following syntax template:

```
use env in
    body
end use;
```

Here, *env* is an expression sequence of *binding equations*, each of which is either a module or an equation whose left-hand side is a symbol; and *body* is a sequence of Maple statements. The right-hand side of a binding equation may be any Maple expression.

Executing a **use** statement executes the body of the statement. Each occurrence of a name that appears on the left-hand side of any of the binding equations is replaced by the right-hand side of the corresponding equation.

For example,

```
> use f = sin, g = cos in
>     f( x )^2 + g( x )^2
> end use;
```

$$\sin(x)^2 + \cos(x)^2$$

Characteristics of use   The **use** statement can be nested.

```
> use f = sin in
>       use g = cos in
>               simplify( f(x)^2 + g(x)^2 )
>       end use
> end use;
```

$$1$$

When nested **use** statements are encountered, the name bindings established by the inner **use** statement take precedence over those of the outer one.

```
> use a = 2, b = 3 in
>       use a = 3 in a + b end
> end use;
```

$$6$$

In this example, the inner binding of the name **a** to the value **3** takes precedence, so the value of the expression **a + b** (and hence of the entire statement) is the number **6**. The inner binding of **a** to **3** has an effect only within the body of the inner **use** statement. Once the execution has exited the inner **use** statement, the binding of **a** to **2** is restored.

```
> use a = 2, b = 3 in
>       # here a is bound to 2 and b to 3
>       use a = 3 in
>           # here, b is still bound to 3, but a is bound to 3
>           a + b
>       end use;
>       # binding of a to 2 is restored
>       a + b
> end use;
```

$$6$$

$$5$$

The **use** statement is unique in the Maple language because it is fully resolved during automatic simplification. It is not possible to *evaluate* a **use** statement. (Recall that Maple uses a modified "read-eval-print" loop, which actually involves the four stages: parsing (reading), *automatic simplification*, evaluation and printing.)

To see how this works, consider an example in which the **use** statement appears inside a procedure.

```
> f := proc( a, b )
>      use x = a + b, y = a - b in
>          x * y
>      end use
> end proc;
```

$$f := \mathbf{proc}(a, b) \, (a + b) * (a - b) \ \mathbf{end \ proc}$$

Note that the body of the procedure f contains no **use** statement. During automatic simplification, the **use** statement that formed the body of f was "expanded", yielding the expression that involves only the parameters a and b.

Modules and use Statements As a special case, a module m may appear in the binding sequence of a **use** statement. The module is regarded as an abbreviation for the sequence of equations a = m:-a, b = m:-b, ..., where a,b,... are the exports of the module m.

For example,

```
> m := module() export a, b; a := 2; b := 3; end:
> use m in a + b end;
```

$$5$$

This is useful for programming with packages.

```
> m := Matrix( 4, 4, [[ 26, 0,   0,    30 ],
>                      [ 0,  -41, -90, 0],
>                      [ 0,  -7,  -56, 0 ],
>                      [ 0,  0,   0,    0]] );
```

$$m := \begin{bmatrix} 26 & 0 & 0 & 30 \\ 0 & -41 & -90 & 0 \\ 0 & -7 & -56 & 0 \\ 0 & 0 & 0 & 0 \end{bmatrix}$$

```
> use LinearAlgebra in
>      Determinant( m );
>      Rank( m );
>      CharacteristicPolynomial( m, 'lambda' )
> end use;
```

$$0$$

$$3$$

$$(26 - \lambda)\,(-1666\,\lambda - 97\,\lambda^2 - \lambda^3)$$

Please note that a name that appears in a binding list for a **use** statement that is intended to be a module must evaluate to a module *at the time the **use** statement is simplified.* This is necessary because the simplification of the **use** statement must be able to determine the exports of the module. In particular, the following attempt to pass a module as a parameter to a procedure does *not* work, and yields an error during the simplification of the procedure.

```
> proc( m, a, b )
>      use m in e( a, b ) end
> end proc;
```

```
Error, no bindings were specified or implied
```

The correct way to use a module as a parameter is to specify the names to be bound explicitly, such as in this example:

```
> proc( m, a, b )
>      use e = m:-e in a + b end
> end proc;
```

$$\mathbf{proc}(m,\, a,\, b)\, a + b\,\mathbf{end\ proc}$$

This is necessary because, until the procedure is called with a module expression as first argument, Maple does not know whether the **e** refers to a module export or to something else (such as a global name). To expand the **use** statement, this must be known at the time the procedure is simplified.

Operator Rebinding

An additional feature of the **use** statement is that it allows most infix and prefix operators in the Maple language to be rebound. This is not really the same thing as the "operator overloading" found in some programming languages (such as **C++**), because the rebinding occurs during automatic simplification in Maple.

If an operator name appears on the left-hand side of a binding equation for a **use** statement (consequently, if it is an exported name of a module that is bound via **use**), then the corresponding operator expressions in the body of the **use** statement are transformed into function calls. For example:

```
> use '+' = F in a + b end;
```

$$F(a, b)$$

```
> m := module()
>     export '*', '+';
>     '+' := ( a, b ) -> a + b - 1;
>     '*' := ( a, b ) -> a / b;
> end module:
> s * ( s + t );
```

$$s(s + t)$$

```
> use m in s * ( s + t ) end;
```

$$\frac{s}{s + t - 1}$$

The operators that can be rebound are summarized in the following table.

Operator	Arity	Position	Description
Arithmetic Operators			
+	binary	infix	addition
*	binary	infix	multiplication
.	binary	infix	multiplication
^	binary	infix	exponentiation
-	unary	prefix	negation
/	unary	prefix	inversion (reciprocal)
Logical Operators			
and	binary	infix	logical and
or	binary	infix	logical or
not	unary	prefix	logical negation
Relational Operators			
<	binary	infix	less than
<=	binary	infix	less than or equal
>	binary	infix	greater than
>=	binary	infix	greater than or equal
=	binary	infix	equality
<>	binary	infix	not equal
Other Operators			
@	binary	infix	composition
@@	binary	infix	power composition
!	unary	postfix	factorial

Please note that the operators - and / are treated as *unary* operators (that represent negation and inversion, respectively). Subtraction is represented internally in Maple by composing addition and negation: a - b = a + (-b). Similarly for division. Therefore, it is not necessary to override the *binary* infix operators - and /.

Note also that an expression such as a + b + c + d is treated as though it were parenthesized as ((a + b) + c) + d, so that each + operator is binary. For example,

```
> use '+' = F in
>     a + b + c + d;
>     a + ( ( b + c ) + d )
> end use;
```

$$F(F(F(a, b), c), d)$$

$$F(a, F(F(b, c), d))$$

6.5   Modeling Objects

A principle application of modules is modeling objects. An *object* is something that has both state and behavior. Many programming languages provide support for programming with objects. Some of these are called "object-oriented"; popular examples include Smalltalk, CLOS, Java, and C++.

Maple is not an object-oriented programming language, but it does support programming with objects. In Maple, an object can be represented by a module. The state of the object (module) is stored in the local and exported data variables. The behavior of the object is represented by procedures assigned to the exported variables. Since, in Maple, procedures stand on an equal footing with all other values in the language, this distinction between state and behavior is somewhat artificial and exists only as a convention.

The essential idea behind programming with objects is that the "objects" carry their behavior around with them. Clients of an object can elicit behavior by sending the object "messages". Objects respond to these messages by performing some prescribed computation that is determined by both the recipient of the message (the object) and the message itself (which may be parameterized by other arguments). This is in contrast to non-object-oriented approaches to programming, in which the objects in a software system merely contain static data and serve as inputs and outputs of the algorithms, which are represented separately from the objects by procedures or other routines.

Objects and Constructors   Objects are usually created by invoking a "constructor". A *constructor* is a procedure that builds the object expression from some (possibly empty) set of inputs. Maple uses constructors for a number of its native expression types. For example, the procedure `table` is a constructor for Maple tables, and `series` is a constructor for Maple series expressions. Here we are interested in constructors for objects represented by modules.

A constructor *must* be used to create objects that have no input syntax (such as series and tables, in Maple), but may also be used for expressions that do have an input syntax (the `Float` constructor is an example of the latter case). Therefore, most user-defined objects must be created by using a constructor. So most of our object examples will be defined by specifying a constructor for the object.

Example: a Complex Number Constructor A simple example of an object is the following representation of a complex number.

```
> MakeComplex := proc( real, imag )
>     if nargs <> 2 then
>         error "real and imaginary parts are required"
>     end if;
>     module()
>         description "a complex number";
>         local real_part, imag_part;
>         export re, im, abs, arg;
>
>         real_part, imag_part := real, imag;
>         re := () -> real_part;
>         im := () -> imag_part;
>         abs := () -> sqrt( re()^2 + im()^2 );
>         arg := () -> arctan( im(), re() );
>     end module
> end proc:
```

To create the complex number $1 + i$, we call the constructor as follows.

```
> z := MakeComplex( 1, 1 );
```

$$z := \textbf{module}()$$
$$\textbf{local } real\_part, imag\_part;$$
$$\textbf{export } re, im, abs, arg;$$
$$\textbf{description } \text{“a complex number”};$$
$$\textbf{end module}$$

The procedure `MakeComplex` is a constructor for complex number objects. The value returned by the procedure is the instantiation of the module whose definition appears in the body of `MakeComplex`.

The local state of the complex number is represented by the local variables of the module, `real_part` and `imag_part`. The behavior is represented by the exported procedures `re`, `im`, `abs`, and `arg`.

The exports of a module that represents an object are sometimes viewed also as *messages*. Objects respond to these messages by exhibiting the behavior that the messages elicit.

```
> z:-re(), z:-im();
```

$$1, 1$$

```
> z:-abs();
```

$$\sqrt{2}$$

```
> z:-arg();
```

$$\frac{1}{4}\,\pi$$

For instance, the expression `z:-abs()` is viewed as sending the `abs` "message" to the complex number object `z`. The object responds by computing its absolute value.

Note that each time the procedure `MakeComplex` is invoked, a new module is created using the module definition that is visible within the procedure body. Thus, complex numbers created by different calls to the constructor are distinct, even if the arguments `real` and `imag` are the same. Whether a constructor should produce distinct objects for the same input (instance) data depends on the nature of the objects being modeled. For complex number objects, we would likely want to have the same object produced for multiple calls with the same inputs. This can be easily achieved by using the `remember` option in the constructor.

Effect of Immutable Local States   The `MakeComplex` constructor above represented the local state of complex number objects by using two local variables `real_part` and `imag_part`. For many object constructors, some or all of the local state of the object is expected to be immutable. In these cases, local variables do not have to be allocated in the module to store the local state of the object. The state can instead be represented by the parameters to the constructor, which are visible within the module because of Maple's lexical scoping rules. Using this idea, the constructor above can be simplified as follows.

```
> MakeComplex := proc( real, imag )
>     if nargs <> 2 then
>         error "real and imaginary parts are required"
>     end if;
>     module()
>         description "a complex number";
>         export re, im, abs, arg;
>
>         re := () -> real;
>         im := () -> imag;
>         abs := () -> sqrt( real^2 + imag^2 );
>         arg := () -> arctan( imag, real );
>     end module
> end proc:
```

Example: Priority Queues

A very useful data structure that can be implemented in an object-oriented way with modules is the priority queue. A *priority queue* is a container data structure that admits the following operations:

- test for an empty priority queue

- insert a prioritized item into a priority queue

- return (non-destructively) the highest-priority item on the priority queue

- delete the highest priority item from a priority queue

Design An object representation of priority queues will have the following methods.

empty	test for an empty priority queue
top	return the highest-priority item
insert	insert a prioritized item
delete	remove (and return) the highest priority item

This representation leads directly to the following Maple type, which can be used to identify priority queues.

```
> 'type/PriorityQueue' := ''module'( empty, top, insert,
>                                    delete )':
```

Constructor Implementation We can implement priority queues as Maple objects satisfying this interface by writing a constructor for the objects.

```
> PriorityQueue := proc( priority::procedure )
>     description "priority queue constructor";
>     local largs, lnargs;
>
>     lnargs := nargs;
>     if lnargs > 1 then
>         largs := [ args[ 2 .. -1 ] ]
>     else
>         largs := []
>     end if;
>
>     module()
```

```
>       description "a priority queue";
>       export empty, top, insert,
>               size, delete, init;
>       local  heap, nitems,
>               bubbleup, bubbledown;
>
>       nitems := 0;
>       heap := table();
>
>       bubbleup := proc( child::posint )
>           local parent;
>           parent := iquo( child, 2 );
>           if child > 1
>             and priority( heap[ child ] ) > priority( heap[
>             parent ] ) then
>                 heap[ parent ], heap[ child ] := heap[ child ],
>                   heap[ parent ];
>                 procname( parent ) # recurse
>           end if
>       end proc;
>
>       bubbledown := proc( parent::posint )
>           local child;
>           child := 2 * parent;
>           if child < nitems
>             and priority( heap[ 1 + child ] ) > priority(
>             heap[ child ] ) then
>                 child := 1 + child
>           end if;
>           if child <= nitems
>             and priority( heap[ parent ] ) < priority( heap[
>             child ] ) then
>                 heap[ parent ], heap[ child ] := heap[ child ],
>                   heap[ parent ];
>                 procname( child ) # recurse (new parent)
>           end if
>       end proc;
>
>       # Initialize the priority queue.
>       init := proc()
>           heap := table();
>           nitems := 0
>       end proc;
>
>       # Test whether the priority queue is empty.
>       empty := () -> evalb( nitems < 1 );
>
>       # Return the number of items on the priority queue.
>       size := () -> nitems;
>
>       # Query the highest priority item.
>       top := proc()
>           if empty() then
>               error "priority queue is empty"
```

```
>                    else
>                        heap[ 1 ]
>                    end if
>            end proc;
>
>            # Delete the highest priority item from the
>            # priority queue.
>            delete := proc()
>                local val;
>                val := heap[ 1 ]; # val := top()
>                # move bottom to the top
>                heap[ 1 ] := heap[ nitems ];
>                # allow expression to be collected
>                heap[ nitems ] := evaln( heap[ nitems ] );
>                # decrement the bottom of heap counter
>                nitems := nitems - 1;
>                # heapify the array
>                bubbledown( 1 );
>                # return the value
>                val
>            end proc;
>
>            # Insert an item into the priority queue.
>            insert := proc( v )
>                if nargs > 1 then
>                    op( map( procname, [ args ] ) )
>                else
>                    nitems := 1 + nitems;
>                    heap[ nitems ] := v;
>                    bubbleup( nitems )
>                end if
>            end proc;
>
>            # Insert any intially specified items.
>            if lnargs > 1 then
>                insert( op( largs ) )
>            end if
>        end module
> end proc:
```

The constructor takes a Maple procedure **priority** as its argument. For each expression that may be placed on the queue, this procedure should return a numeric measure of its "priority". Items on the queue are maintained in a prioritized order so that the highest priority items are removed first.

In this sample computation with a priority queue, we use the Maple built-in procedure **length** as the "priority" of an expression. Here, the randomly generated expressions are all polynomials.

```
> pq := PriorityQueue( x -> length( x ) );
```

$$pq := \textbf{module}()$$

$$\textbf{local } heap, \; nitems, \; bubbleup, \; bubbledown;$$

$$\textbf{export } empty, \; top, \; insert, \; size, \; delete, \; init;$$

$$\textbf{description } \text{“a priority queue”};$$

$$\textbf{end module}$$

```
> for i from 1 to 10 do
>     pq:-insert( randpoly( x ) );
> end do:
> while not pq:-empty() do
>     pq:-delete()
> end do;
```

$$-85\,x^5 - 55\,x^4 - 37\,x^3 - 35\,x^2 + 97\,x + 50$$

$$-99\,x^5 - 85\,x^4 - 86\,x^3 + 30\,x^2 + 80\,x + 72$$

$$-53\,x^5 + 85\,x^4 + 49\,x^3 + 78\,x^2 + 17\,x + 72$$

$$79\,x^5 + 56\,x^4 + 49\,x^3 + 63\,x^2 + 57\,x - 59$$

$$-86\,x^5 + 23\,x^4 - 84\,x^3 + 19\,x^2 - 50\,x + 88$$

$$-50\,x^5 - 12\,x^4 - 18\,x^3 + 31\,x^2 - 26\,x - 62$$

$$-58\,x^5 - 90\,x^4 + 53\,x^3 - x^2 + 94\,x + 83$$

$$77\,x^5 + 66\,x^4 + 54\,x^3 - 5\,x^2 + 99\,x - 61$$

$$45\,x^5 - 8\,x^4 - 93\,x^3 + 92\,x^2 + 43\,x - 62$$

$$x^5 - 47\,x^4 - 91\,x^3 - 47\,x^2 - 61\,x + 41$$

Priority Queue Usage   Priority queues can be used to implement a heapsort algorithm.

```
> HeapSort := proc( L::list(numeric) )
>     local pq, t, count;
>     pq := PriorityQueue( x -> -x, op( L ) );
>     t := array( 1 .. nops( L ) );
>     count := 0;
>     while not pq:-empty() do
>         count := 1 + count;
>         t[ count ] := pq:-delete()
>     end do;
>     ASSERT( count = nops( L ) );
>     [ seq( t[ count ], count = 1 .. nops( L ) ) ]
> end proc:
> r := rand(100):
```

```
> L := [ seq( r(), i = 1 .. 20 ) ]:
> HeapSort( L );
```

$$[7, 7, 15, 25, 27, 27, 28, 29, 42, 51, 52, 55, 62, 74, 82,$$
$$88, 94, 97, 97, 98]$$

The fully commented source code for the Priority Queue constructor is available in the sample source code of your Maple installation.

An Object-oriented Shapes Package

In this subsection, we will demonstrate an object-oriented approach to the Shapes package described earlier. The earlier revision of the package used unevaluated function calls as the concrete representation of shapes. In this section we will demonstrate how to put together a package that offers the same functionality, but which represents shapes as "objects". Each shape will use a module as its concrete representation. The "package" itself does not export the area and circumference features of the traditional style package, because these features are available as part of each shape object. Instead, the package is merely a collection of constructors for the various kinds of shapes. You could use the object representation at a lower level, and present exactly the same interface as the first Shapes package, but we have not done so here, choosing instead to make the object-oriented nature of shape expressions more apparent to the user.

The point Constructor   Points are quite simple shapes, so the corresponding constructor is similarly simple.

```
> point := proc( x, y )
>     module()
>         export  area, circumference, xcoord, ycoord;
>         xcoord := () -> x;
>         ycoord := () -> y;
>         area := () -> 0;
>         circumference := () -> 0;
>     end module
> end proc:
```

The module returned by this constructor uses the lexically scoped parameters x and y, representing the abscissa and ordinate of the point. These values are part of the local state, or instance data, of each point constructed. These points are captured in the closures of the exported methods, so that variables local to the module in which to store these values are not necessary.

The segment Constructor Segments are represented using the start and end points of the segment. These are the points returned by the `point` constructor.

```
> segment := proc( pt1, pt2 )
>     module()
>         export area,
>                 circumference,
>                 length,
>                 start_point,
>                 end_point;
>         local mymidpoint;
>
>         start_point := () -> pt1;
>         end_point := () -> pt2;
>         area := () -> 0;
>         circumference := () -> 0;
>         length := proc()
>             local   x, y;
>             x := pt1:-xcoord() - pt2:-xcoord();
>             y := pt1:-ycoord() - pt2:-ycoord();
>             sqrt( x^2 + y^2 )
>         end proc;
>         midpoint := proc()
>             local   x, y;
>             if assigned( mymidpoint ) then
>                 mymidpoint
>             else
>                 y := (pt1:-ycoord() + pt2:-ycoord())/2;
>                 x := (pt1:-xcoord() + pt2:-xcoord())/2;
>                 point( x, y )
>             end if
>         end proc;
>     end module
> end proc:
```

The segment objects implement methods in addition to the required `area` and `circumference` methods. Apart from the trivial syntax methods `start_point` and `end_point`, there are methods for computing the length of a segment and its midpoint.

The circle Constructor Circles are represented by using the center and radius of the circle as instance data.

```
> circle := proc( ctr, rad )
>     module()
>         export area, circumference, diameter,
>                 center, centre, radius;
>         radius := () -> rad;
>         center := () -> ctr;
>         centre := eval( center ); # UK spelling
>         diameter := () -> 2 * radius();
```

```
>              circumference := () -> Pi * diameter();
>              area := () -> Pi * rad * rad;
>         end module
> end proc:
```

Again, the lexically scoped parameters `ctr` and `rad` encode the instance data of the circle object.

The remainder of the object oriented version of the `Shapes` package can be read in the sample source code file `ShapeObj.mpl`.

6.6   Interfaces and Implementations

Generic programming is a programming style and a software engineering methodology for software reuse. In this sense, many Maple builtin operations are generic. The addition operator + is able to compute sums of integers, rational numbers, complex numbers, polynomials, special functions, and so on. It is not necessary for + to know how an expression is represented to do its job. (The automatic simplifier, on the other hand, knows a very great deal about how Maple expressions are represented.) As with any dynamically typed language, Maple provides much genericity without you having to do anything special. Most built-in Maple operations (including many standard library routines) are naturally *polymorphic* in that they are able to perform successfully with a large variety of data formats.

Genericity as Good Software Engineering Practice   On any large project, it is important to write *reusable* code; that is, code that can perform a well-defined function in a wide variety of situations. Generic programs do not rely on the details of how their inputs are represented. They are able to perform their function on *any* inputs that satisfy a specified set of constraints. Normally, these constraints are described in terms of the *behavior* of the inputs in response to various "messages" rather than on their physical representation or the storage layout of their concrete representation. This behavior is sometimes called a "contract". The idea is that an object makes a "promise" to behave a certain way, and anything which uses that object knows that the "promised" behavior can be relied upon. Generic programs rely *only* on the "promises" made by an object's "contract". They do *not* rely on knowledge of how an object is implemented. So, generic software *separates* "interfaces" from implementations.

With this discussion, we are finally able to see the real meaning behind the distinction between local and exported variables in a module. A module's exports are part of its "promise" to those who would use it. Whatever is expressed through its local variables is the business only of the module, and is not to be relied upon, or even known, by clients of the module. (Client access is, in fact, the only technical difference between module locals and exports.)

Before the introduction of the module system, Maple's "design by contract" was enforced only by convention. Maple routines whose names had to be enclosed in name quotes (') were considered "private", and not for client use. But this was only a convention. Moreover, it was necessary to use global variables to communicate information and state between the various routines that made up a subsystem (such as `solve` or `assume`). Now, using modules, it is possible to design software systems that enforce their contracts by a mechanism embedded in the Maple language itself.

Interfaces

The "contracts" discussed above are represented formally in Maple by an *interface*. An interface is a special kind of structured type. It has the form

```
'module'( symseq );
```

in which **symseq** is a sequence of symbols or of typed symbols (expressions of the form **symbol::type**). For example, an interface for a ring might be written as

```
> 'type/ring' := ''module'( '+', '*', '-', zero, one )':
```
while that for an (additive) abelian group could take the form

```
> 'type/abgroup' := ''module'( '+', '-', zero )':
```

These symbols are the ones that clients are "allowed" to access as module exports.

A module is said to *satisfy*, or to *implement*, an interface if it is of the type defined by the interface.

```
> z5 := module()
>     description "the integers modulo 5";
>     export '+', '*', '-', zero, one;
>     '+' := (a,b) -> a+b mod 5;
>     '*' := (a,b) -> a*b mod 5;
>     '-' := s -> 5-s mod 5;
>     zero := 0;
>     one := 1;
> end module:
```

```
> type( z5, 'ring' );
```

$$true$$

A module may satisfy more than one interface.

```
> type( z5, 'abgroup' );
```

$$true$$

Interfaces are an abstraction that form part of Maple's type system. They provide a form of *constrained* polymorphism. Not every Maple type is an interface; only those that have the form just described are. We can define a Maple type (that, as it happens, is not itself an interface) to describe interfaces.

```
> 'type/interface' := 'specfunc( {symbol,symbol::type},
>                         'module' )':
```

This is a structured type that describes expressions that are themselves structured types that have the form of an unevaluated function call with operator the symbol 'module' and all arguments of type symbol, or of type symbol::type. In the two examples at the start of this section, the types type/ring and type/abgroup are the interface expressions, and the names ring and abgroup are the respective names of those interfaces.

A Package for Manipulating Interfaces Interfaces are sufficiently important that it is worthwhile to develop a package for manipulating them. The package is small enough that it can be reproduced here, in full, but it is also available in the **samples/** directory of your Maple installation.

```
> Interface := module()
>     description "a package for manipulating interfaces";
>     global 'type/interface';
>     export define,       # define an interface
>            extend,        # extend an interface
>            extends,       # test for an extension
>            equivalent,#   test equivalence
>            savelib,       # save an interface
>            satisfies;     # test whether a module satisfies
>                           # an interface
>     local  gassign,       # assign to a global variable
>            totype,        # convert from interface name to type
>            toset,         # convert from interface name to a set
>            setup;         # install 'type/interface' globally
>     option load = setup;
>
>     # Define a global type for interfaces.
```

```
>       # This assignment takes care of installing the type
>       # in the Maple session in which this module definition
>       # is evaluated. Calling 'setup()' ensures that this also
>       # happens when the instantiated module is read from a
>       # repository.
>       'type/interface'
>               := 'specfunc( {symbol, '::'}, 'module' )';
>
>       # Ensure that 'type/interface' is defined. This thunk is
>       # called when the instantiated 'Interface' module is read
>       # from a Maple repository.
>       setup := proc()
>           global 'type/interface';
>           'type/interface'
>               := 'specfunc( {symbol, '::'}, 'module' )';
>           NULL # quiet return
>       end proc;
>
>       # Assign to the global instance of a name
>       gassign := proc( nom::symbol, val )
>           option inline;
>           eval( subs( _X = nom,
>                       proc()
>                           global _X;
>                           _X := val
>                       end ) )()
>       end proc;
>
>       # Convert an interface name to the corresponding type.
>       totype := ( ifc::symbol ) -> ( 'type/' || ifc );
>
>       # Convert an interface name to a set of symbols.
>       toset := ( ifc::symbol ) -> { op( ( 'type/' || ifc ) ) };
>
>       # Install a new interface into the type system.
>       define := proc( ifc )
>           description "define an interface";
>           if map( type, {args}, 'symbol' ) <> { true } then
>               error "arguments must all be symbols"
>           end if;
>           gassign( 'type/' || ifc,
>               ''module''( args[ 2 .. nargs ] ) );
>           ifc # return the interface name
>       end proc;
>
>       # Implement subtyping.
>       extend := proc( new, old )
>           description "extend an existing inteface";
>           if map( type, {args}, 'symbol' ) <> { true } then
>               error "arguments must all be symbols"
>           end if;
>           if not type( totype( old ), 'interface' ) then
>               error "cannot find an interface named %1", old
>           end if;
```

```
>            define( new, op( totype( old ) ), args[3..nargs] )
>        end proc;
>
>        # Test whether ifc2 is an extension of ifc1.
>        extends := proc( ifc1, ifc2 )
>            description "test whether the second interface "
>                        "extends the first";
>            local t1, t2;
>            t1, t2 := op( map( totype, [ ifc1, ifc2 ] ) );
>            if not type( [t1,t2], '[interface,interface]' ) then
>                if not type( t1, 'interface' ) then
>                    error "arguments must be interface names, "
>                          "but got %1", ifc1
>                else
>                    error "arguments must be interface names, "
>                          "but got %1", ifc1
>                end if
>            end if;
>            toset( ifc1 ) subset toset( ifc2 )
>        end proc;
>
>        # Save an interface to the repository.
>        savelib := proc()
>            description "save a named interface to a "
>                        "repository";
>            local ifc;
>            for ifc in map( totype, [ args ] ) do
>                if not type( ifc, 'interface' ) then
>                    error "arguments must be interfaces, "
>                          "but got %1", ifc
>                end if;
>                :-savelib( totype( ifc ) )
>            end do
>        end proc;
>
>        # Test whether a module satisfies an interface.
>        # This is simply an alternative to a call
>        # to 'type()'.
>        satisfies := proc( m, ifc )
>            description "test whether a module satisfies an interface";
>            if not type( totype( ifc ), 'interface' ) then
>                error "second argument must be an interface name, "
>                      "but got %1", ifc
>            end if;
>            type( m, ifc )
>        end proc;
>
>        # Test whether two interfaces are equivalent.
>        # Since unevaluated function calls compare
>        # differently if their arguments are in a
>        # different order, we convert them to sets first,
>        # and then test for equality.
>        equivalent := proc( ifc1, ifc2 )
>            description "test whether two interfaces "
```

```
>                        "are equivalent";
>           local t1, t2;
>           t1, t2 := totype( ifc1 ), totype( ifc2 );
>           if not type( t1, 'interface' ) then
>               error "expecting an interface name, "
>                       "but got %1", ifc1
>           elif not type( t2, 'interface' ) then
>               error "expecting an interface name, "
>                       "but got %1", ifc2
>           end if;
>           evalb( { op( t1 ) } = { op( t2 ) } )
>       end proc;
> end module:
```

This little package implements the interface abstraction. It allows you to manipulate interfaces without having to worry about how they fit into Maple's type system.

```
> with( Interface );
```

```
Warning, the protected names define and savelib have
been redefined and unprotected
```

$$[define,\ equivalent,\ extend,\ extends,\ satisfies,\ savelib]$$

```
> define( 'abgroup', ''+'', ''-'', 'zero' );
```

$$abgroup$$

```
> type( 'type/abgroup', 'interface' );
```

$$true$$

```
> type( z5, 'abgroup' );
```

$$true$$

```
> satisfies( z5, 'abgroup' );
```

$$true$$

```
> extend( 'ring', 'abgroup', ''*'', 'one' );
```

$$ring$$

```
> type( 'type/ring', 'interface' );
```

$$true$$

```
> extends( abgroup, ring );
```

$$true$$

```
> satisfies( z5, 'ring' );
```

$$true$$

```
> type( z5, 'ring' );
```

$$true$$

The `load=` Option Besides providing a nice abstraction of the interface concept in Maple, this package also serves to illustrate a module feature not demonstrated earlier. This is the `load=thunk` option. In the `Interface` package, this option is used in a fairly typical way. The declaration

```
option load = setup;
```

that appears in the module definition instructs Maple that, when the instantiated module is read from a repository, it is to call the procedure `setup`. The procedure named must be a local or an exported local of the module. The local procedure `setup` in this module simply ensures that the global variable `type/interface` is assigned an appropriate value. This assignment is also made in the body of the module so that the assignment is also executed in the session in which the module is instantiated. This was done for illustrative purposes. A better scheme would simply have invoked `setup` at some point in the body of the module definition.

Example: Generic Graph Algorithms

We use (simple) graph algorithms as an example of generic programming with a computer science orientation.

Mathematical Description A directed graph may be thought of as an object that consists of a set V of vertices and a set $E \subseteq V \times V$ of ordered pairs of vertices, called "edges". Graphs may be visualized by diagrams like the following.

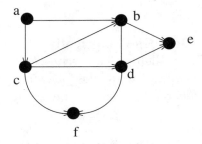

This diagram represents a graph with vertex set $V = \{a, b, c, d, e, f\}$, and edge set $E = \{(a, b), (a, c), (b, d), (c, f), (f, d), (b, e), (d, e), (c, b), (c, d)\}$.

Software Models Graphs may be represented in software in a variety of ways. The choice of storage mechanism depends on the expected applications of the graph. Three possibilities for representing graphs in software are:

1. store the set V of vertices and the set E of edges explicitly;

2. store the "adjacency matrix" of the graph;

3. store, for each vertex of the graph, the set of all its neighbours.

(The *adjacency matrix* is a square matrix whose rows are columns are indexed by the vertices of the graph; the (i, j)-entry is equal to 1 if there is an edge from i to j, and is equal to 0 otherwise.) We would like to be able to write software that can manipulate a graph regardless of which of the above (or other) representations is chosen.

Designing a Graph Interface To demonstrate how this can be achieved, let us consider graphs as objects that implement the following methods:

vertices	returns the set of vertices of the graph
edges	returns the set of edges of the graph
addedge	allows one to add a new edge to a graph
order	returns the number of vertices of the graph
size	returns the number of edges of the graph

Then, we can represent the *abstract interface* of a graph by a Maple type.

```
> `type/Graph` := ''module'( vertices, edges, addedge, order,
>                                   size )':
```

We say that an object *implements* the Graph interface if it is of type **Graph**.

Computing Vertex Degrees Generically   If we have an object that implements this interface, then we can write generic code based on that interface. For example, we can write the following procedure to compute the in-degree and out-degree of a vertex of a given graph.

```
> vdeg := proc( G::Graph, v )
>     local vs, vt;
>     description "compute the in- and out-degrees "
>                 "of a vertex in a graph";
>     if member( v, G:-vertices() ) then
>         vs := select( e -> evalb( v = e:-source() ),
>                           G:-edges() );
>         vt := select( e -> evalb( v = e:-target() ),
>                           G:-edges() );
>         nops( vs ), nops( vt )
>     else
>         0, 0
>     end if
> end proc:
```

We could write this procedure even though we have, as yet, no idea how graphs are going to be implemented. Although this is but a tiny example, this capability is very important when you are designing a large software system.

Edge Object Representation   We are tacitly assuming that edges will also be represented as objects that implement, at least, the interface `module'( source, target )`, which provides methods for extracting the source and target vertices from an edge. Writing a constructor **Edge** for edges is easy.

```
> Edge := proc( src, targ )
>     module()
>         local the_source, the_target;
>         export source, target, setsource, settarget;
>         the_source := src;
>         the_target := targ;
>         source := () -> the_source;
>         target := () -> the_target;
>         setsource := proc( v )
>             the_source := v
>         end proc;
>         settarget := proc( v )
```

```
>                  the_target := v
>             end proc;
>        end module
> end proc:
```

First Graph Constructor At first, we might choose to adopt a graph representation that is simple to implement. Here is a graph constructor that produces graphs represented by storing the vertex and edge sets explicitly as part of the state of a module.

```
> Graph1 := proc()
>     local vertex_set, edge_set;
>     description "graph constructor";
>
>     edge_set := { args };
>     if map( type, edge_set, '[ anything, anything ]' )
>        <> { true } then
>          error "graph must be specified by a sequence of edges"
>     end if;
>     if map( nops, edge_set ) <> { 2 } then
>             error "each edge must be specified "
>                   "as a [ source, target ] pair"
>     end if;
>     vertex_set := map( op, edge_set );
>     edge_set := map( Edge@op, edge_set );
>     module()
>         export order, size,
>                vertices, edges,
>                addedge; # required exports
>         vertices := () -> vertex_set;
>         edges := () -> edge_set;
>         addedge := proc( src, targ )
>             edge_set := { Edge( src, targ ) }
>                         union edge_set;
>             vertex_set := { src, targ }
>                         union vertex_set;
>             NULL
>         end proc;
>         order := () -> nops( vertices() );
>         size := () -> nops( edges() );
>     end module
> end proc:
```
If we now create a small graph using this constructor

```
> g1 := Graph1( [ a, b ], [ a, c ], [ b, c ] ):
> type( g1, 'Graph' );
```

$$true$$

we can use the routine **vdeg** with the graph **g1**, since graphs produced by **Graph1** implement the **Graph** interface.

```
>  vdeg( g1, a );
```

$$2, 0$$

```
>  vdeg( g1, b );
```

$$1, 1$$

```
>  vdeg( g1, c );
```

$$0, 2$$

The important feature of the procedure **vdeg** is its genericity. It can be used with *any* implementation of graphs that implements the **Graph** interface specified above.

Second Graph Constructor Here is another, different implementation of the **Graph** interface. The graph is represented by using a table **N** in which the neighbors of each vertex are stored.

```
>  Graph2 := proc()
>      local    vertex_set, edge_set;
>      description "graph constructor";
>
>      edge_set := { args };
>      vertex_set := map( op, edge_set );
>      if map( type, edge_set, 'list' ) <> { true } then
>          error "graph must be specified by a sequence of edges"
>      end if;
>      if map( nops, edge_set ) <> { 2 } then
>          error "each edge must be specified "
>                "as a [ source, target ] pair"
>      end if;
>      module()
>          export order, size,
>                  vertices, edges,
>                  addedge;
>          local  N, e, v, n, edge_pairs;
>          N := table();
>          edge_pairs := () -> { seq(
>                  seq( [ v, n ], n = N[ v ] ),
>                  v = map( op, { indices( N ) } )
>              ) };
>          vertices := () -> map( op, edge_pairs() );
```

```
>         edges := () -> map( Edge@op, edge_pairs() );
>         addedge := proc( src, targ )
>             if assigned( N[ src ] )
>               and not member( targ, N[ src ] ) then
>                 N[ src ] := { op( N[ src ] ), targ }
>             else
>                 N[ src ] := { targ };
>             end if;
>             NULL
>         end proc;
>         order := () -> nops( vertices() );
>         size := () -> nops( edges() );
>         for e in edge_set do
>             addedge( op( 1, e ), op( 2, e ) )
>         end do
>     end module
> end proc:
```

A graph returned by the constructor **Graph2** also satisfies the **Graph** interface.

```
> g2 := Graph2( [ a, b ], [ a, c ], [ b, c ] ):
> type( g2, 'Graph' );
```

$$true$$

Because of this, the *generic* procedure **vdeg** works equally well with it.

```
> vdeg( g2, a );
```

$$2, 0$$

```
> vdeg( g2, b );
```

$$1, 1$$

```
> vdeg( g2, c );
```

$$0, 2$$

Generic Computation of Adjacency Matrices   Another example of a procedure generic over the **Graph** interface is the following routine for computing the adjacency matrix of a graph.

```
> AdjacencyMatrix := proc( g::Graph )
>     local  a,   # the adjacency matrix; returned
>            n,   # the order of the graph g
>            V,   # the vertex set of the graph
>            E,   # the edge set of the graph
>            row, # row index for matrix
>            col, # column index for matrix
>            e;   # induction variable for loop
>
>     n := g:-order();
>     a := Matrix( n, n, 'storage' = 'sparse' );
>     V := sort( convert( g:-vertices(), 'list' ) );
>     E := g:-edges();
>     for e in E do
>         if not member( e:-source(), V, 'row' )
>            or not member( e:-target(), V, 'col' ) then
>             error "inconsistent graph structure detected"
>         end if;
>         a[ row, col ] := 1
>     end do;
>     a
> end proc:
> AdjacencyMatrix( g1 );
```

$$
\begin{bmatrix}
0 & 1 & 1 \\
0 & 0 & 1 \\
0 & 0 & 0
\end{bmatrix}
$$

```
> AdjacencyMatrix( g2 );
```

$$
\begin{bmatrix}
0 & 1 & 1 \\
0 & 0 & 1 \\
0 & 0 & 0
\end{bmatrix}
$$

Example: Quotient Fields

As an example of generic programming, we will discuss a generic quotient field (or "field of fractions") construction algorithm.

Mathematical Description   Given an integral domain D, its quotient field is (up to isomorphism) the unique field k, paired with a nonzero ring homomorphism $\eta : D \longrightarrow k$, with the property that, for any nonzero ring homomorphism $\varphi : D \longrightarrow F$, in which F is a field, is a unique ring homomorphism σ for which the diagram

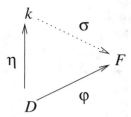

commutes. Because a nonzero ring homomorphism into a field must be injective, this says that every field F that contains D as a subring must also contain an isomorphic copy of k.

Concretely, the quotient field of an integral domain D can be thought of as the set of "reduced fractions" n/d, with $n, d \in D$. A formal construction can be produced by defining an equivalence relation on the set $D \times (D \setminus \{0\})$, according to which two pairs $(n1, d1)$ and $(n2, d2)$ are equivalent only if,

$$n1 \cdot d2 = n2 \cdot d1.$$

A representative from each equivalence class is chosen to represent the field element defined by that class. This understanding guides the computer representation of the quotient field.

Unit Normal Representatives If R is a commutative ring with multiplicative identity, then

$$U(R) \times R \longrightarrow R : (u, r) \to u \cdot r$$

is a natural action of the group $U(R)$ of units of R on R. Each orbit of this action has a representative called the *unit normal* representative of the class, and we will suppose the existence of an effective mapping $R \longrightarrow R$ that selects the unit normal representative of each class. For instance, for the ring $\mathbb{Z}$ of integers, the group $U(\mathbb{Z})$ of units is the set $\{1, -1\}$, the orbits are the sets $\{n, -n\}$ for $n \in \mathbb{Z} \setminus \{0\}$ together with $\{0\}$, and we take the unit normal representative to be the positive member of each orbit, or 0 for the orbit $\{0\}$. (Thus, the unit normal mapping simply computes the sign and absolute value of an integer.) The unit normal mapping on the ring $k[T]$ of polynomials in an indeterminate T over a field k is

$$p(T) \to \frac{1}{\mathrm{lc}(p(T))} \cdot p(T),$$

in which $\mathrm{lc}(p(T))$ denotes the leading coefficient of the polynomial $p(T)$. (The group of units in $k[T]$ is the set $k^* = k \setminus \{0\}$, of nonzero members of k, and each orbit of $k[T]$ under the action of k^* contains an unique monic polynomial that is its representative.)

Designing the Ring Interfaces The first step in representing these ideas in software is to devise an interface that describes the rings we are to work with. We will suppose that our rings are equipped with the basic ring operations, as well as several methods that implement the kind of computations we want to do.

```
> 'type/Ring' := ''module'(
>       '+'::procedure,
>       '*'::procedure,
>       '-'::procedure,
>       iszero::procedure,
>       isone::procedure,
>       zero, one
> )':
```

This interface corresponds quite naturally with a formal mathematical characterization of the ring as a tuple

$$\langle S, +, *, 0, 1 \rangle$$

that satisfies a number of properties, and to which we have added some computational capabilities. We have added unary negation (−) because of the way operator overrides work in Maple. (In a more tightly integrated system, we might also specify the number and types of arguments to each of the procedures.)

For the kind of computations that we want to do, we will need a slightly richer structure.

```
> 'type/GcdRing' := ''module'(
>       '+'::procedure,
>       '*'::procedure,
>       '-'::procedure,
>       quo::procedure,
>       rem::procedure,
>       gcd::procedure,
>       unormal::procedure,
>       iszero::procedure,
>       isone::procedure,
>       zero, one
> )':
```

This interface extends the **Ring** interface defined previously. Note that nothing in the signature enforces any ring-theoretic properties (such as being an integral domain, or having unique factorization). It merely specifies the admissible operations. Since we want to be able to compute with infinite rings (and even large finite ones), we avoid requiring an enumeration of the elements of the ring, but focus entirely on the effectively computable operations that the ring must support.

Representing the ring ℤ of Integers One of the simplest examples of a ring that supports the computations we require is the ring ℤ of integers in its native Maple representation.

```
> MapleIntegers := module()
>     description "the ring of integers";
>     export '+', '*', '-',
>             gcd, unormal, iszero,
>             isone, zero, one, rem, quo;
>     '+' := ( a, b ) -> a + b;
>     '*' := ( a, b ) -> a * b;
>     '-' := i -> -i;
>     quo := ( a, b ) -> :-iquo( a, b );
>     rem := ( a, b ) -> :-irem( a, b );
>     gcd := ( a, b ) -> :-igcd( a, b );
>     unormal := proc( i::integer )
>         if i < 0 then
>             -1, -i
>         else
>             1, i # includes 0
>         end if
>     end proc;
>     iszero := i -> evalb( i = 0 );
>     isone := i -> evalb( i = 1 );
>     zero := 0;
>     one := 1;
> end module:
```

This is a software representation of the ring of integers. The unit normal mapping is represented by the exported procedure **unormal**. It returns an expression sequence of length two, whose first member is a unit, and whose second member is the unit normal form of its argument. The product of the output values yields the input ring element. The other methods just invoke the corresponding, built-in Maple operations.

```
> type( MapleIntegers, 'Ring' );
```

$$true$$

```
> type( MapleIntegers, 'GcdRing' );
```

$$true$$

An Interface for Fields Our quotient field constructor produces a field. An interface that describes fields differs from the one for integral domains by the absence of a **gcd** method (since they are trivial) and the addition of the (unary) **/** operator that computes inverses. The methods **rem** and **quo** are also not included in the signature for fields, because those too are trivial in a field. We do include two new methods: **make** for constructing field elements from their numerators and denominators, and **embed**, the natural embedding of the integral domain D into its field k of fractions. Additionally, the two methods **numer** and **denom** allow the user to extract the components of a fraction.

```
> 'type/Field' := ''module'(
>       '+'::procedure,
>       '*'::procedure,
>       '-'::procedure,
>       '/'::procedure,
>     normal::procedure,
>     iszero::procedure,
>     isone::procedure,
>     zero, one,
>     make::procedure,
>     embed::procedure
> )':
```

Naturally, the ring $\mathbb{Z}$ of integers is not a field.

```
> type( MapleIntegers, 'Field' );
```

$$false$$

Fields produced by the quotient field constructor will satisfy this interface.

The Quotient Field Functor   Here is the generic constructor for quotient fields.

```
> QuotientField := proc( R::GcdRing )
>       description "quotient field functor";
>       module()
>           description "a quotient field";
>           export '+', '*', '-', '/',
>                   zero, one,
>                   iszero, isone,
>                   make,
>                   numer, denom,
>                   normal, embed;
>       make := proc( n, d )
>           local u, nd;
>           if R:-iszero( d ) then
>               error "division by zero"
>           end if;
>           u, nd := R:-unormal( d );
>           'FRACTION'( u*n, nd )
>       end proc;
>       embed := d -> make( d, R:-one );
>       numer := f -> op( 1, f );
```

```
>        denom := f -> op( 2, f );
>        zero := embed( R:-zero );
>        one := embed( R:-one );
>        iszero := f -> evalb( normal( f ) = zero );
>        isone := f -> evalb( normal( f ) = one );
>        normal := proc( f )
>            local g, a, b;
>            g := R:-gcd( numer( f ), denom( f ) );
>            if R:-isone( g ) then
>                f
>            else
>                a := R:-quo( numer( f ), g );
>                b := R:-quo( denom( f ), g );
>                make( a, b )
>            end if
>        end proc;
>        '-' := f -> normal( R:-'-'( numer( f ) ), denom( f ) );
>        '/' := f -> normal( make( denom( f ), numer( f ) ) );
>        '+' := proc( a, b )
>            use '+' = R:-'+', '*' = R:-'*' in
>                normal( make( numer( a ) * denom( b )
>                            + denom( a ) * numer( b ),
>                        denom( a ) * denom( b ) ) )
>            end use
>        end proc;
>        '*' := proc( a, b )
>            use '*' = R:-'*' in
>                normal( make( numer( a ) * numer( b ),
>                        denom( a ) * denom( b ) ) )
>            end use
>        end proc;
>    end module
> end proc:
```

Most of the exported routines are quite straightforward. The fraction constructor **make** accepts two members of the ring R as arguments and returns the constructed fraction, which we represent by an unevaluated function call of the form

FRACTION(numerator, denominator)

The exported procedure **embed** is the canonical embedding η of the integral domain into its quotient field, described previously. This makes the constructor functorial. The arithmetic operators are simple implementations of the familiar rules for fraction arithmetic:

$$\frac{a}{b} + \frac{c}{d} = \frac{ad + bc}{bd}$$
$$\frac{a}{b} \times \frac{c}{d} = \frac{ac}{bd}$$
$$\left(\frac{a}{b}\right)^{-1} = \frac{b}{a}$$

$$-\left(\frac{a}{b}\right) = \frac{-a}{b}$$

After applying these simple formulae, the result is normalized by using a call to the *local* routine `normal` (not `:-normal`). `normal` does most of the interesting work in the ring generated by this constructor. It uses the manifestation of the division algorithm in the ring R via the exported procedures `quo` and `gcd` to reduce each fraction to the "lowest terms". Together, the fraction constructor `make` and the method `normal` ensure that field elements are represented by the normal form representative of the equivalence class that is the field element. Preventing division by zero, and forcing denominators to be unit normal representatives, is performed by `make`. Ensuring that fractions are reduced to "lowest terms" is handled by `normal`.

The most important property of the `QuotientField` functor is that it is *generic*. It relies solely on the `GcdRing` interface to do its job. No knowledge of the concrete representation of the input integral domain `R` (other than that it is a module that satisfies the required interface) is used anywhere in the construction. Therefore, it will work with *any* implementation of the `GcdRing` interface that implements the correct semantics for its public operations and that satisfies the abstract constraint that it be a software representation of an integral domain. (The latter constraint is required to ensure that the arithmetic operations are well defined.)

Constructing the Rationals as the Quotient Field of $\mathbb{Z}$ To construct the quotient ring of the ring `MapleIntegers` defined previously, we will proceed as follows.

```
> FF := QuotientField( MapleIntegers );
```

> FF := **module**()
> **export**' + ', ' * ', ' − ', '/', *zero, one, iszero, isone, make,*
> *numer, denom, normal, embed;*
> **description** "a quotient field";
>
> **end module**

```
> type( FF, 'Field' );
```

$$true$$

```
> a := FF:-make( 2, 3 );
```

$$a := \text{FRACTION}(2, 3)$$

```
> b := FF:-make( 2, 4 );
```

$$b := \text{FRACTION}(2, 4)$$

```
> use FF in
>     a + b;
>     a * b;
>     a / b
> end use;
```

$$\text{FRACTION}(7, 6)$$

$$\text{FRACTION}(1, 3)$$

$$\text{FRACTION}(4, 3)$$

The Quotient Field of the Polynomial Ring $\mathbb{Q}[T]$ To illustrate the genericity of this constructor, we will construct the field $\mathbb{Q}[T]$ of rational functions in a single indeterminate T from a concrete representation of Maple rational polynomials.

```
> MaplePoly := module()
>        description "the ring of rational polynomials";
>        export '+', '*', '-',
>               zero, one,
>               iszero, isone,
>               gcd, unormal,
>               quo, rem;
>        '+' := ( a, b ) -> expand( a + b );
>        '*' := ( a, b ) -> expand( a * b );
>        '-' := p -> -p;
>        gcd := ( a, b ) -> :-gcd( a, b );
>        unormal := proc( p )
>             local lc;
>             if iszero( p ) then
>                  one, zero
>             else
>                  use lc = lcoeff( p ) in
>                       lc, :-normal( p / lc )
>                  end use
>             end if
>        end proc;
>        iszero := p -> Testzero( p );
>        isone := p -> Testzero( p - 1 );
>        zero := 0;
>        one := 1;
```

```
>          rem := ( a, b ) -> :-rem( a, b );
>          quo := ( a, b ) -> :-quo( a, b );
> end module:
```

The **unormal** method produces the leading coefficient and monic associate of a given polynomial in $\mathbb{Q}[T]$. The remaining exports simply capture built-in Maple operations on univariate rational polynomials.

```
> RR := QuotientField( MaplePoly );
```

$RR :=$ **module**$()$
export$` + `, ` * `, ` - `, `/`,$ *zero, one, iszero, isone, make,*
numer, denom, normal, embed;
description "a quotient field";

end module

```
> type( RR, 'Field' );
```

$$true$$

To make printed fractions more readable, we introduce the following extension to the **print** command.

```
> 'print/FRACTION' := ( n, d ) -> sort( n ) / sort( d ):
```

Finally, we will construct a few examples, and test the arithmetic.

```
> a := RR:-make( randpoly( 'T', 'degree' = 4, 'terms' = 3 ),
>               randpoly( 'T', 'degree' = 4, 'terms' = 3 ) );
```

$$a := \frac{-2072\,T^2 - 1960\,T + 5432}{T^3 + \dfrac{7}{8}\,T^2 + \dfrac{9}{8}}$$

```
> b := RR:-make( randpoly( 'T', 'degree' = 4, 'terms' = 3 ),
>               randpoly( 'T', 'degree' = 4, 'terms' = 3 ) );
```

$$b := \frac{-2790\,T^3 + 496\,T^2 + 5766}{T^2 - \dfrac{77}{62}\,T - \dfrac{33}{31}}$$

```
> use RR in
>      a + b,
>      a * b,
>      a / b
> end use;
```

$$\left(-2790\,T^6 - \frac{7781}{4}\,T^5 - 1638\,T^4 + \frac{401827}{124}\,T^3\right.$$

$$\left.+ \frac{1943715}{124}\,T^2 - \frac{144452}{31}\,T + \frac{87333}{124}\right)\Big/\Big($$

$$T^5 - \frac{91}{248}\,T^4 - \frac{1067}{496}\,T^3 + \frac{6}{31}\,T^2 - \frac{693}{496}\,T - \frac{297}{248}\Big),\Big($$

$$5780880\,T^5 + 4440688\,T^4 - 16127440\,T^3 - 9252880\,T^2$$

$$- 11301360\,T + 31320912)/\Big($$

$$T^5 - \frac{91}{248}\,T^4 - \frac{1067}{496}\,T^3 + \frac{6}{31}\,T^2 - \frac{693}{496}\,T - \frac{297}{248}\Big),\Big($$

$$5780880\,T^4 - 1711080\,T^3 - 28100520\,T^2 + 13000680\,T$$

$$+ 16133040)/\Big($$

$$T^6 + \frac{251}{360}\,T^5 - \frac{7}{45}\,T^4 - \frac{113}{120}\,T^3 - \frac{241}{120}\,T^2 - \frac{93}{40}\Big)$$

Example: A Generic Group Implementation

In this section, we illustrate how to develop a moderately complex software system based on the use of features of Maple's module system. Generic programming is at the heart of the design. Only a fraction of the complete system from which the examples are taken is shown. The examples that follow comprise a system for computing with finite groups. Recall that a *group* is a set of objects together with an associative binary operation, for which there is an unique two-sided identity element, and with respect to which each member of the underlying set possesses an unique inverse. Examples of groups include systems of numbers, using addition, closed sets of invertible matrices (all of the same size, with a common ground field) using multiplication ("linear groups"), closed sets of permutations (bijective mappings on a set) using composition ("permutation groups"), and groups of points on elliptic curves. We are concerned here only with finite groups.

An Interface for Finite Groups First, we must decide how to represent the generic group interface. This is, in large measure, determined by the use to which the group objects will be put. Once again, our design takes a group to be a repository of data and computational services that we may query or invoke.

The `Group` signature that we will use in our examples describes a computational model of abstract groups that supports the following methods.

id	the group identity
` . `	the binary operation on the group
mul	n-ary version of ` . `
inv	unary inversion operation
pow	computes integral powers of group elements
eq	tests whether two group elements are equal
member	tests membership in the group and in sets
gens	a generating set for the group
order	returns the order of the group
elements	returns an enumeration of the group's members

```
> 'type/Group' := ''module'(
>     id, '.', mul, inv,
>     eq, member,
>     gens,
>     order, elements
> )':
```

A corresponding constructor for groups is easily written using the **Record** constructor introduced earlier. For the examples in this section, we will not need to introduce any default methods.

```
> Group := proc()
>     Record( op( 'type/Group' ) );
> end proc:
```

This constructor does very little work on its own. It relies on more specialized constructors to establish useful values or defaults for the methods exported.

We can begin to write generic algorithms using this interface immediately. A few simple examples are these routines for computing conjugates and commutators of group elements. The *conjugate* of a group member a by a group member b is $b^{-1}ab$. This routine computes the conjugate of an element a by an element b in a group G.

```
> Conjugate := proc( G, a, b )
>     description "compute the conjugate of a "
>                 "group element by another";
>     use '/' = G:-inv, '.' = G:-'.' in
>         b^(-1) . a . b
>     end use
> end proc:
```

Since the group operations ` . ` and **inv** in a generic group remain unassigned, the following computation is done symbolically.

```
> Conjugate( Group(), 'x', 'y' );
```

$$(\mathrm{inv}(y)) \cdot x \cdot y$$

Similarly, we can compute the commutator $[a, b] = a^{(-1)}b^{(-1)}ab$, generically, as follows.

```
> Commutator := proc( G, a, b )
>     description "compute the commutator of "
>                 "two group elements";
>     use '/' = G:-inv, mul = G:-mul in
>         mul( inv( a ), inv( b ), a, b )
>     end use
> end proc:
```

Again, this computation is done symbolically, so the group operations return unevaluated.

```
> Commutator( Group(), 'x', 'y' );
```

$$\mathrm{mul}(\mathrm{inv}(x), \mathrm{inv}(y), x, y)$$

The ability to write algorithms generic over a given interface is important for the management of large software projects involving many developers. Here, one developer can be assigned the task of implementing particular group constructors along with the attendant arithmetic, while another developer can begin coding generic routines like those above. The two developers can work independently, provided each ensures that their work conforms to some agreed-upon interface and semantics.

Permutation Groups   Before attempting to develop any complicated algorithms, it is helpful to have available a few constructors for specific kinds of groups. These can then be used to validate generic algorithms in specific instances. For this reason, we develop a straight-forward implementation of permutation groups.

Permutations are represented using Maple lists. For example, the list [2,1,3] represents the permutation that maps $1 \to 2$, maps $2 \to 1$, and leaves 3 fixed. (In cycle notation, this is written as the transposition (12).) The constructor takes a positive integer as its first argument, indicating the degree of the permutation group. The remaining arguments are expected to be permutations (represented as lists) of the stated degree. These are used to form the generating set of the group returned by the constructor.

```
> PermutationGroup := proc( deg::posint )
>     description "permutation group constructor";
>     local G, gens;
>     gens := { args[ 2 .. -1 ] };
>     G := Group();
>     G:-id := [ $ 1 .. deg ];
>     G:-'.' := proc( a, b )
```

```
>             local i;
>             [ seq( b[ i ], i = a ) ]
>         end proc;
>         G:-mul := () -> foldl( G:-'.', G:-id, args );
>         G:-inv := proc( g )
>             local i, a;
>             a := array( 1 .. deg );
>             for i from 1 to deg do
>                 a[ g[ i ] ] := i
>             end do;
>             [ seq( a[ i ], i = 1 .. deg ) ]
>         end proc;
>         G:-member := proc( g, S, pos::name )
>             if nargs = 1 then
>                 type( g, 'list( posint )' )
>                     and { op( g ) } = { $ 1 .. deg }
>             else
>                     :-member( args )
>             end if
>         end proc;
>         G:-eq := ( a, b ) -> evalb( a = b );
>         G:-gens := gens;
>         eval( G, 1 )
> end proc:
```

For example, to construct the group $\langle (12), (123) \rangle$ in the symmetric group S_4, we use the `PermutationGroup` constructor as follows.

```
> G := PermutationGroup( 4, { [2,1,3,4], [2,3,1,4] } );
```

$G :=$ **module()**

export

$id, \text{'.'}, mul, inv, eq, member, gens, order, elements;$

option *record*;

end module

We can now call upon the "services" provided by the methods exported by the instantiated group G to compute with its elements.

```
> use G in
>     inv( [ 2,1,3,4 ] ) . [2,3,1,4];
> end use;
```

$$[3, 2, 1, 4]$$

It is useful to provide more specialized permutation group constructors for special kinds of groups. Using the general constructor `PermutationGroup`, and over-riding some of the exported methods, we can define several of these specialized constructors as follows.

The full symmetric group S_n on the n points $\{1, 2, 3, \ldots, n\}$ is produced by specifying a particular set of generators for a given degree (which must be specified as an argument to the constructor).

```
> Symmetric := proc( n::posint )
>     description "symmetric group constructor";
>     if n < 2 then
>         error "argument must be an integer larger than 1"
>     elif n = 2 then
>         PermutationGroup( 2, [2,1] );
>     else
>         PermutationGroup( n, [2,1,$3..n], [$2..n,1] );
>     end if
> end proc:
```

This uses the fact that S_n is the two-generator group

$$S_n = \langle (12), (123 \cdots n) \rangle,$$

for any integers $n \geq 3$.

A second special case worth considering is the class of dihedral groups. We can think of these as the groups of symmetries of regular plane polygons. The symmetry group of the regular n-gon is the dihedral group of degree n and order $2n$; it is denoted by D_n.

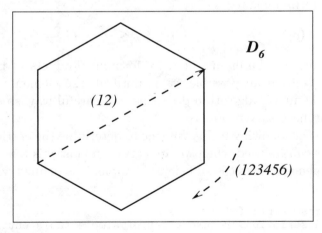

We'll use the following little utility for reversing a list.

```
> lreverse := proc( L::list )
>     description "reverse a list";
>     option inline;
>     [ seq( L[ -i ], i = 1 .. nops( L ) ) ]
> end proc:
> Dihedral := proc( n::posint )
>     description "dihedral group constructor";
>     local a, b, D;
>     if n = 2 or n = 3 then
```

```
>            return Symmetric( n )
>        end if;
>        a := [ $ 2 .. n, 1 ];
>        b := [ 1, op( lreverse( [ $ 2 .. n ] ) ) ];
>        D := PermutationGroup( n, { a, b } );
>        D:-order := () -> 2*n;
>        eval( D, 1 )
> end proc:
```

1. *Use the fact that the alternating group A_n of degree $n >= 3$ is generated by the set $\{(123), (234), (345), \ldots, (n-2, n-1, n)\}$ of 3-cycles to write a constructor **Alternating** for this class of groups.*

Dimino's Algorithm   Dimino's algorithm is used to compute a complete enumeration of the elements of a finite group, given a generating set for the group. Suppose that we are given a generating set $\{g_1, g_2, \ldots, g_n\}$ for a finite group G. The idea behind Dimino's algorithm is to enumerate, successively, the elements of each of the subgroups

$$G_k = \langle g_1, g_2, \ldots, g_k \rangle$$

of G, which form a chain

$$\langle g_1 \rangle = G_1 \leq G_2 \leq \cdots \leq G_k \leq \cdots \leq G_n = G.$$

These elements can be enumerated by forming products of the generators $g_1, g_2, \ldots, g_n$ in all possible ways, until all the elements of G have been found. Dimino's algorithm does this in a careful way, so as to avoid computing unnecessary products.

We'll use the following utility routine to determine the entries assigned to a table. It can be used when we are certain no entry is a non-NULL expression sequence. Since it is sufficiently simple, it is defined with `option inline;`.

```
> Entries := proc( T )
>        description "return a set of simple table entries";
>        option inline;
>        map( op, { entries( T ) } )
> end proc:
```

Here is the code for Dimino's algorithm.

```
> Dimino := proc( G::Group )
>        description "enumerate the elements of a finite group";
>        local s, g, ord, elements, i, j, prev_ord, rep_pos,
>            elt, addElt, gens;
>
```

```
>       if nargs > 1 then
>           gens := args[ 2 ]
>       else
>           gens := G:-gens
>       end if;
>
>       if not type( gens, '{ set, list }' ) then
>           error "no generating set specified"
>       end if;
>
>       if nops( gens ) = 0 then
>           # trivial group
>           return { G:-id }
>       end if;
>
>       addElt := proc( h )
>           ord := 1 + ord;
>           elements[ ord ] := h
>       end proc;
>
>       elements := table();
>       ord := 0;
>       addElt( G:-id );
>
>       # Handle the first cyclic subgroup
>       s := gens[ 1 ];
>       g := s;
>       while not G:-eq( g, G:-id ) do
>           addElt( g );
>           g := G:-'.'( g, s )
>       end do;
>       userinfo( 1, 'Dimino', "finished first cycle; order is:", ord );
>
>       for i from 2 to nops( gens ) do
>           userinfo( 1, 'Dimino', "Adding generator number:", i );
>           s := gens[ i ];
>           if not G:-member( s, Entries( elements ) ) then
>               prev_ord := ord;
>               addElt( s );
>               for j from 2 to prev_ord do
>                   addElt( G:-'.'( elements[ j ], s ) )
>               end do;
>               rep_pos := 1 + prev_ord;
>               do
>                   for s in gens[ 1 .. i ] do
>                       elt := G:-mul( elements[ rep_pos ], s );
>                       if not G:-member( elt, Entries( elements ) ) then
>                           addElt( elt );
>                           for j from 2 to prev_ord do
>                               addElt( G:-'.'( elements[ j ], elt ) )
>                           end do
>                       end if
>                   end do;
>                   rep_pos := rep_pos + prev_ord;
```

```
>                    if rep_pos > ord then
>                            break
>                    end if
>                end do
>            end if
>        end do;
>        Entries( elements )
> end proc:
```

The coding of this algorithm is generic. The exported members of the group object G are used to effect computations within the procedure. Even comparisons of equality use the export **eq** instead of Maple's builtin comparison operator '='. (The need for this will be seen below.)

Using the Symmetric constructor defined above, we can compute the elements of the symmetric group S_4, using Dimino's algorithm, as follows.

```
> G := Symmetric( 4 );
```

$$G := \mathbf{module}()$$
$$\mathbf{export}$$
$$id, \text{'.'}, mul, inv, eq, member, gens, order, elements;$$
$$\mathbf{option}\ record;$$

$$\mathbf{end\ module}$$

```
> Dimino( G );
```

$$\{[2, 1, 3, 4], [2, 3, 1, 4], [1, 2, 3, 4], [3, 2, 1, 4],$$
$$[2, 3, 4, 1], [3, 2, 4, 1], [1, 3, 4, 2], [3, 1, 4, 2],$$
$$[3, 4, 1, 2], [4, 3, 1, 2], [2, 4, 1, 3], [4, 2, 1, 3],$$
$$[3, 4, 2, 1], [4, 3, 2, 1], [4, 1, 2, 3], [1, 4, 2, 3],$$
$$[3, 1, 2, 4], [1, 3, 2, 4], [4, 1, 3, 2], [1, 4, 3, 2],$$
$$[4, 2, 3, 1], [2, 4, 3, 1], [1, 2, 4, 3], [2, 1, 4, 3]\}$$

Anticipating later developments, we have coded the procedure **Dimino** to accept a second, optional argument that specifies an alternate set of generators to use. Thus, we could compute the same set using the set $\{(12), (23), \ldots, (n-1, n)\}$ of transpositions instead.

```
> Dimino( G, { [2,1,3,4], [1,3,2,4], [1,2,4,3] } );
```

$$\{[2,\ 1,\ 3,\ 4],\ [2,\ 3,\ 1,\ 4],\ [1,\ 2,\ 3,\ 4],\ [3,\ 2,\ 1,\ 4],$$
$$[2,\ 3,\ 4,\ 1],\ [3,\ 2,\ 4,\ 1],\ [1,\ 3,\ 4,\ 2],\ [3,\ 1,\ 4,\ 2],$$
$$[3,\ 4,\ 1,\ 2],\ [4,\ 3,\ 1,\ 2],\ [2,\ 4,\ 1,\ 3],\ [4,\ 2,\ 1,\ 3],$$
$$[3,\ 4,\ 2,\ 1],\ [4,\ 3,\ 2,\ 1],\ [4,\ 1,\ 2,\ 3],\ [1,\ 4,\ 2,\ 3],$$
$$[3,\ 1,\ 2,\ 4],\ [1,\ 3,\ 2,\ 4],\ [4,\ 1,\ 3,\ 2],\ [1,\ 4,\ 3,\ 2],$$
$$[4,\ 2,\ 3,\ 1],\ [2,\ 4,\ 3,\ 1],\ [1,\ 2,\ 4,\ 3],\ [2,\ 1,\ 4,\ 3]\}$$

We still need to pass the group object G for Dimino to access its operations.

Dimino's algorithm is a useful "fallback" algorithm, but many finite groups of interest can be enumerated more efficiently using specific knowledge of their structure. For "small" examples, the implementation presented here suffices, but a well-optimized implementation that takes advantage of fast arithmetic for group elements would be required for serious use.

Representing Subgroups   A subset of a group that forms a group in its own right (using the operations inherited from the group, by restriction) is called a *subgroup*. For example, the 3-member set $\{(123),(132),(1)\}$ is a subgroup of the full symmetric group S_3 of degree 3 (which has 6 members). There are a number of approaches we could take to the representation of subgroups. One way is to represent a subgroup H of a "known" group G by specifying a generating set for H and copying the computational services from the representation of G to the representation of H. Thus, the Maple representations G and H of G and H would both be of type Group.

Instead, we shall adopt a different approach that is better suited to implicit representations of subgroups. This design can be extended to allow implicit representations of subgroups that we need not be able to compute with directly. The idea is to represent a subgroup by a simpler structure that maintains a link to its parent group and an indication of how it is defined in terms of its parent group. Thus, a subgroup will be represented by a module with an export parent that is assigned the group in which the subgroup is contained. A second export has a name depending upon the way in which the subgroup is defined. One way to define a subgroup in terms of its parent is to specify a generating set. Subgroups defined in this way will be represented by a module having the export gens of type set. A second way to define a subgroup is by a "property". For example, the center of a group is defined by the property that all its members commute with every element of the group (or, equivalently, that each among its members commutes with all the generators of the parent group). We can ask that properties be specified by requiring a procedure that tests for membership in the subgroup. Thus, subgroups can be described by either the following interfaces.

parent	the parent group
test	a membership test (a procedure)
gens	a set of generators

Only one of the methods **test** and **gens** need be present. A Maple implementation of this interface is as follows.

```
> 'type/SubGroup' := '{
>       'module'( parent::Group, gens::set ),
>       'module'( parent::Group, test::procedure )
> }':
```

The **SubGroup** constructor must dispatch on the type of its second argument to determine which kind of record to create to model the subgroup.

```
> SubGroup := proc( G::{Group,SubGroup}, how::{set,procedure} )
>       description "subgroup constructor";
>       local S;
>       if type( how, 'procedure' ) then
>           S:= Record( 'parent', 'test' = eval( how, 1 ) )
>       else
>           S := Record( 'parent', 'gens' = how )
>       end if;
>       S:-parent := G;
>       eval( S, 1 )
> end proc:
```

For example, the center of the symmetric group S_3 can be defined as follows.

```
> S3 := Symmetric( 3 ):
> Z := SubGroup( S3, proc( z )
>       local g;
>       use S3 in
>           for g in gens do
>               if not eq( mul( inv( g ), inv( z ), g ), z ) then
>                   return false
>               end if
>           end do;
>       end use;
>       true
> end proc );
```

$$Z := \textbf{module}()$$
$$\textbf{export } parent,\ test;$$
$$\textbf{option } record;$$

$$\textbf{end module}$$

```
> Z:-test( [2,1,3] );
```

false

```
> Z:-test( [2,3,1] );
```

false

```
> Z:-test( [1,2,3] );
```

true

Similarly, we can write a constructor for the centralizer of an element in a group.

```
> Centralizer := proc( G, g )
>     SubGroup( G, proc( s )
>                 use '.' = G:-'.', '=' = G:-eq in
>                 s . g = g . s
>                 end use end proc )
> end proc:
```

Generic Interfaces   Dimino's algorithm is fairly expensive. For many classes of groups, better alternatives to enumerating group elements exist. We will take advantage of the opportunity to use them, relying on Dimino's algorithm only as a "last resort". The advantage of Dimino's algorithm is that it works for *any* finite group. To provide a clean and uniform interface to the enumeration functionality, we develop a frontend procedure that takes care of hiding the details of how we go about choosing the best available algorithm.

```
> GroupElements := proc( G )
>     description "enumerate the elements of a finite group";
>     if type( G, 'Group' ) then
>         if type( G:-elements, 'set' ) then
>             G:-elements
>         elif type( G:-elements, 'procedure' ) then
>             G:-procedure()
>         else
>             G:-elements := Dimino( G )
>         end if
>     else
>         'procname'( args )
>     end if
> end proc:
```

Several elements of the design allow us to take advantage of structural knowledge to improve efficiency. This routine first checks whether the export **elements** of its input group is of type **set**. If it is, then it is taken to be a stored enumeration of the group elements and is simply returned. Otherwise, if the export **elements** is a procedure, then it is taken to be a (perhaps specialized) routine for computing the requested enumeration. Finally, Dimino's algorithm is used as a "last resort" if no better alternative is provided. As a simple optimisation, the result of Dimino's algorithm is stored as a new value for the **elements** export so that it need only be computed once.

Providing the **GroupElements** interface shields the user from having to know what the available alternatives are and how to use them. An additional benefit of the design is that it allows us to *change* the algorithm selection criteria at any time (to correct software faults, or make functional or performance improvements). Code using this interface need not be modified, provided that the routine continues to honor its "contract".

Enumerating Elements in Subgroups Once the elements of the parent group are known, the members of the subgroup can be computed using a call to the builtin Maple command **select**.

```
> select( C:-test, Dimino( G ) );
```

How best to enumerate the elements of a subgroup depends upon how it is defined and what is known about the parent group. The procedure **SubGroupElements** that follows takes a subgroup as argument and attempts to find the "best" way to compute the elements of the subgroup from among the available methods.

```
> SubGroupElements := proc( S )
>       description "enumerate the elements of "
>                   "a subgroup of a group";
>       local P;
>       P := S;
>       while type( P, 'SubGroup' ) do
>           P := P:-parent
>       end do;
>       if type( P, 'Group' ) then
>           if member( :-test, S ) then
>               select( S:-test, GroupElements( P ) )
>           else
>               ASSERT( member( :-gens, S ) );
>               Dimino( P, S:-gens )
>           end if
>       else
>           'procname'( args )
>       end if
```

```
> end proc:
> G := Symmetric( 4 );
```

$$G := \textbf{module}()$$
export
id, '.', *mul*, *inv*, *eq*, *member*, *gens*, *order*, *elements*;
option *record*;

end module

```
> SubGroupElements( Centralizer( G, [ 1, 3, 2, 4 ] ) );
```

$$\{[1, 2, 3, 4], [4, 3, 2, 1], [1, 3, 2, 4], [4, 2, 3, 1]\}$$

With `SubGroupElements` implemented, it is a good idea to extend `GroupElements` to accept subgroups also, thus providing a common interface.

```
> GroupElements := proc( G )
>     description "enumerate the elements of a "
>                 "group or subgroup";
>     if type( G, 'SubGroup' ) then
>         SubGroupElements( G )
>     elif type( G, 'Group' ) then
>         if type( G:-elements, 'set' ) then
>             G:-elements
>         elif type( G:-elements, 'procedure' ) then
>             G:-elements()
>         else
>             G:-elements := Dimino( G )
>         end if
>     else
>         'procname'( args )
>     end if
> end proc:
```

Computing the Order of a Group   Since we have the capability of enumerating all of a group's elements, it is always possible to determine its order. (Note that this is rarely the best way to do this, however.) In many cases, it is possible to provide much better ways to compute the order of a group. For instance, the symmetric group of degree n has order equal to $n!$, so its `order` export could be redefined to compute this number instead.

A generic interface to computing group orders, in the same spirit as `GroupElements` may be written as follows.

```
> GroupOrder := proc( G )
>     description "compute the order of a finite group";
>     if type( G, 'SubGroup' ) then
>         nops( GroupElements( G ) )
>     elif type( G, 'Group' ) then
>         if type( G:-order, 'posint' ) then
>             G:-order
>         elif type( G:-elements, 'set' ) then
>             G:-order := nops( G:-elements )
>         elif type( G:-order, 'procedure' ) then
>             G:-order()
>         else
>             nops( GroupElements( G ) )
>         end if
>     else
>         'procname'( args )
>     end if
> end proc:
```

As with **GroupElements**, this routine checks the possible "shortcuts" that might be available for a group, beginning with those that are likely to involve the least computation and progressing through more and more costly alternatives. Only as a last resort does the procedure call **GroupElements** to compute a full enumeration of the group elements only to return their number.

```
> G := Symmetric( 4 );
```

$$G := \mathbf{module}()$$
export
id, '.', *mul*, *inv*, *eq*, *member*, *gens*, *order*, *elements*;
option *record*;

end module

```
> C := Centralizer( G, [ 1, 3, 2, 4 ] );
```

$$C := \mathbf{module}()$$
export *parent*, *test*;
option *record*;

end module

```
> GroupOrder( G );
```

24

```
> GroupOrder( C );
```

$$4$$

Note that, when the argument G is neither a group nor a subgroup, the procedure `GroupElements` returns unevaluated. This allows us to extend other Maple operations, such as `expand`, `combine` or `simplify` to be effective on algebraic expressions involving unevaluated calls to `GroupOrder`.

Matrix Groups So far, all our groups have been permutation groups returned by one of the constructors presented above. If we are to have any confidence in the genericity of the code we have developed, we must test it on some other kinds of groups. A good source for examples of finite groups are the finite groups of exact matrices.

Equality and Membership Tests for Matrices Because distinct matrices with equal entries compare differently using Maple's equality comparison operator '=', it is necessary to implement a specialized test for membership in a set. For example, consider the matrices

```
> A := Matrix( [[1,0],[0,1]] );
```

$$A := \begin{bmatrix} 1 & 0 \\ 0 & 1 \end{bmatrix}$$

```
> B := Matrix( [[2,3],[3,4]] );
```

$$B := \begin{bmatrix} 2 & 3 \\ 3 & 4 \end{bmatrix}$$

```
> C := Matrix( [[1,0],[0,1]] );
```

$$C := \begin{bmatrix} 1 & 0 \\ 0 & 1 \end{bmatrix}$$

Both A and C have the same entries, and represent *mathematically* identical objects. However, because matrices are mutable data structures (necessary for efficiency in matrix computations), they are distinct as Maple objects. Thus, for instance, we see that:

```
> member( A, { B, C } );
```

$$false$$

To deal with this property of the data structures we are using, we need to implement a *generic* version of the Maple command `member`. This routine, `gmember` accepts arguments after its first that are like those required by `member`, but must be passed an additional, first argument `test` that is an equality test to use. We'll use this utility in our implementation of the matrix group constructor below.

```
> gmember := proc( test, g::anything, S::{set,list}, pos::name )
>     description "a generic membership predicate";
>     local i;
>     if type( test, 'procedure' ) then
>         for i from 1 to nops( S ) do
>             if test( g, S[ i ] ) then
>                 if nargs > 3 then
>                     pos := i
>                 end if;
>                 return true
>             end if
>         end do;
>         false
>     elif test = ''='' then
>         # use the standard membership test
>         :-member( args[ 2 .. -1 ] )
>     else
>         'procname'( args )
>     end if
> end proc:
```

The builtin procedure `Equal` package provides an equality predicate that is suitable for use with matrices.

```
> gmember( LinearAlgebra:-Equal, A, { B, C } );
```

$$true$$

The `MatrixGroup` Constructor Except for the `member` export, most the the exported methods for matrix groups simply delegate to the appropriate routine in the `LinearAlgebra` package. The `MatrixGroup` constructor takes the degree n of the matrix group as its first argument and, if given more than one argument, takes the remaining ones to be matrices that form a set of generators for the group.

```
> MatrixGroup := proc( n::posint )
>     description "matrix group constructor";
>     local matgens, G;
>     use LinearAlgebra in
```

```
>          matgens := { args[ 2 .. -1 ] };
>          G := Record(
>              'id' = Matrix( n, n, ( i, j ) -> 'if'( i = j, 1, 0 ) ),
>              ','.'' = ( ( a, b ) -> MatrixMatrixMultiply( a, b ) ),
>              'mul' = ( () -> foldl( G:-'.', G:-id, args ) ),
>              'inv' = ( m -> MatrixInverse( m ) ),
>              'gens' = matgens,
>              'eq' = ( ( a, b ) -> Equal( a, b ) ),
>              'member' = proc( g, S, pos::name )
>                  local i, s;
>                  if nargs = 1 then
>                      if type( g, 'Matrix( square )' ) then
>                          evalb( Determinant( g ) <> 0 )
>                      else
>                          false
>                      end if
>                  else
>                      gmember( G:-eq, args )
>                  end if
>              end proc,
>              'order', 'elements' );
>
>          if nargs = 1 then
>              G:-order := 1;
>              G:-elements := { G:-id }
>          end if
>      end use;
>      eval( G, 1 )
> end proc:
```

Here, we use the matrix group constructor to generate a dihedral matrix group of order 12.

```
> theta := Pi / 3;
```

$$\theta := \frac{1}{3}\pi$$

```
> a := Matrix( 2, 2, [[ 0, 1 ], [ 1, 0 ]] );
```

$$a := \begin{bmatrix} 0 & 1 \\ 1 & 0 \end{bmatrix}$$

```
> b := Matrix( 2, 2,
>      [[cos(theta),sin(theta)],
>      [-sin(theta),cos(theta)]] );
```

$$b := \begin{bmatrix} \dfrac{1}{2} & \dfrac{1}{2}\sqrt{3} \\[2mm] -\dfrac{1}{2}\sqrt{3} & \dfrac{1}{2} \end{bmatrix}$$

```
> B := MatrixGroup( 2, a, b );
```

$B :=$ **module**()
export
id, '.', *mul*, *inv*, *gens*, *eq*, *member*, *order*, *elements*;
option *record*;

end module

```
> GroupElements( B );
```

$$\left\{ \begin{bmatrix} \dfrac{1}{2} & \dfrac{1}{2}\sqrt{3} \\[2mm] -\dfrac{1}{2}\sqrt{3} & \dfrac{1}{2} \end{bmatrix}, \begin{bmatrix} -\dfrac{1}{2}\sqrt{3} & \dfrac{1}{2} \\[2mm] \dfrac{1}{2} & \dfrac{1}{2}\sqrt{3} \end{bmatrix}, \begin{bmatrix} \dfrac{1}{2}\sqrt{3} & \dfrac{1}{2} \\[2mm] \dfrac{1}{2} & -\dfrac{1}{2}\sqrt{3} \end{bmatrix}, \right.$$

$$\begin{bmatrix} \dfrac{-1}{2} & \dfrac{1}{2}\sqrt{3} \\[2mm] -\dfrac{1}{2}\sqrt{3} & \dfrac{-1}{2} \end{bmatrix}, \begin{bmatrix} \dfrac{1}{2} & -\dfrac{1}{2}\sqrt{3} \\[2mm] \dfrac{1}{2}\sqrt{3} & \dfrac{1}{2} \end{bmatrix}, \begin{bmatrix} -\dfrac{1}{2}\sqrt{3} & \dfrac{-1}{2} \\[2mm] \dfrac{-1}{2} & \dfrac{1}{2}\sqrt{3} \end{bmatrix}, \begin{bmatrix} 0 & 1 \\ 1 & 0 \end{bmatrix},$$

$$\begin{bmatrix} 1 & 0 \\ 0 & 1 \end{bmatrix}, \begin{bmatrix} \dfrac{1}{2}\sqrt{3} & \dfrac{-1}{2} \\[2mm] \dfrac{-1}{2} & -\dfrac{1}{2}\sqrt{3} \end{bmatrix}, \begin{bmatrix} \dfrac{-1}{2} & -\dfrac{1}{2}\sqrt{3} \\[2mm] \dfrac{1}{2}\sqrt{3} & \dfrac{-1}{2} \end{bmatrix}, \begin{bmatrix} -1 & 0 \\ 0 & -1 \end{bmatrix}, \left.\begin{bmatrix} 0 & -1 \\ -1 & 0 \end{bmatrix} \right\}$$

Direct Products To enrich the supply of example groups that we can work with, we'll develop a constructor for the direct product of (two) groups. (Extending the constructor to handle any finite number of groups is straight-forward, but complicates the exposition unnecessarily.) Direct products are very important in the study of finite groups because all finitely generated abelian groups possess an unique "factorisation" as a direct product of cyclic groups. (In the abelian theory, direct products are often referred to as direct *sums*.)

The direct product of two groups A and B is the group G whose elements are all pairs (a, b), with $a \in A$ and $b \in B$. The group product in G is defined by $(a_1, b_1) \cdot (a_2, b_2) = (a_1 \cdot a_2, b_1 \cdot b_2)$. The inverse of an element (a, b) is the pair (a^{-1}, b^{-1}). All the operations are defined component-wise.

We can represent the elements (a, b) of the direct product by two-element lists. Here is the constructor DirectProduct.

```
> DirectProduct := proc( A::Group, B::Group )
>     description "direct product constructor";
>     local G, a, b;
>     if type( A, 'Group' ) and type( B, 'Group' ) then
>         G := Group();
>         G:-id := [ A:-id, B:-id ];
>         G:-'.' := ( u, v ) -> [ A:-'.'( u[1], v[1] ),
>                                 B:-'.'( u[2], v[2] ) ];
>         G:-mul := () -> foldl( G:-'.', G:-id, args );
>         G:-inv := v -> [ A:-inv( v[ 1 ] ),
>                          B:-inv( v[ 2 ] ) ];
>         G:-gens := [ seq( seq( [ a, b ],
>                          a = A:-gens ), b = B:-gens ) ];
>         G:-eq := ( u, v ) -> A:-eq( u[ 1 ], v[ 1 ] )
>                          and B:-eq( u[ 2 ], v[ 2 ] );
>         G:-order := () -> GroupOrder( A ) * GroupOrder( B );
>         G:-member := proc( g, S, pos::name )
>             if nargs = 1 then
>                 A:-member( g[ 1 ] )
>                     and B:-member( g[ 2 ] )
>             else
>                 gmember( G:-eq, args )
>             end if
>         end proc;
>         G:-elements := () -> [ seq( seq( [ a, b ],
>         a = GroupElements( A ) ), b = GroupElements( B ) ) ];
>         eval( G, 1 )
>     else
>         'procname'( args )
>     end if
> end proc:
```

Most of the group methods are quite straightforward, but note that we take the opportunity to use the known group structure to reduce the complexity of some computations such as those for the **order** and **elements** exports.

```
> A := Symmetric( 3 ):
> G := DirectProduct( A, B ):
> GroupOrder( G );
```

$$72$$

```
> nops( GroupElements( G ) );
```

$$72$$

Homomorphisms In all algebraic theories, *homomorphisms* play a key role. A group homomorphism is a mapping from a group to another (possibly the same) group which commutes with the group operations. That is, a map $\varphi : A \longrightarrow B$ of groups A and B is a homomorphism if $\varphi(ab) = \varphi(a)\varphi(b)$, for all a and b in A. A homomorphism is determined uniquely by its effect on a generating set for its domain, so to define a homomorphism, it is enough to specify the images of each among a set of generators for the domain.

We'll use the following interface for homomorphisms.

domain	the domain of the homomorphism
codomain	the codomain of the homomorphism
genmap	the mapping of the generators of the domain into the codomain

This lead directly to a fairly simple constructor for homomorphism objects.

```
> 'type/Homomorphism' := ''module'( domain, codomain, genmap )':
> Homomorphism := proc( A::Group, B::Group, p::procedure )
>     description "homomorphism constructor";
>       Record( 'domain' = A, 'codomain' = B, 'genmap' = p )
> end proc:
```

The *image* of a group homomorphism $\varphi : A \longrightarrow B$ is the subset $\varphi(A)$ of B consisting of all elements of B having the form $\varphi(a)$, for some element a in A. It is a subgroup of B. The various design choices we've made along, the way lead to a very simple formulation for computing or representing images of homomorphisms.

```
> HomImage := proc( hom::Homomorphism )
>     description "compute the image of a homomorphism";
>     SubGroup( hom:-codomain,
>               map( hom:-genmap, hom:-domain:-gens ) )
> end proc:
```

As an example computation, we compute the image of a homomorphism from the symmetric group S_4 onto a two-element matrix group generated by the reflection

```
> Matrix( [ [ 0, 1 ], [ 1, 0 ] ] );
```

$$\begin{bmatrix} 0 & 1 \\ 1 & 0 \end{bmatrix}$$

First, define the groups.

```
> A := Symmetric( 4 ):
> B := MatrixGroup( 2, Matrix( [[0,1],[1,0]] ) ) ):
```

We can define a mapping from the generators of A to the group B by inserting the images of the generators into a procedure's remember table.

```
> h( [2,1,3,4] ) := Matrix( [[0,1],[1,0]] ):
> h( [2,3,4,1] ) := Matrix( [[1,0],[0,1]] ):
```

This defines a Maple procedure h that performs the indicated mapping and returns unevaluated for any other arguments.

```
> eval( h );
```

$$\mathbf{proc}()\,\mathbf{option}\ remember;\ \text{'procname(args)'}\ \mathbf{end\ proc}$$

Now we use A, B and h to construct the homomorphism object.

```
> hom := Homomorphism( A, B, h );
```

$$hom := \mathbf{module}()$$
$$\mathbf{export}\ domain,\ codomain,\ genmap;$$
$$\mathbf{option}\ record;$$
$$\mathbf{end\ module}$$

```
> type( hom, 'Homomorphism' );
```

$$true$$

We can now use the machinery developed earlier in this example to compute the order of the image of this homomorphism.

```
> GroupOrder( HomImage( hom ) );
```

$$2$$

Thus, we see that the homomorphism is surjective (as expected). We can compute the elements explicitly.

```
> GroupElements( B );
```

$$\{\begin{bmatrix} 0 & 1 \\ 1 & 0 \end{bmatrix}, \begin{bmatrix} 1 & 0 \\ 0 & 1 \end{bmatrix}\}$$

```
> GroupElements( HomImage( hom ) );
```

$$\left\{ \begin{bmatrix} 1 & 0 \\ 0 & 1 \end{bmatrix}, \begin{bmatrix} 0 & 1 \\ 1 & 0 \end{bmatrix} \right\}$$

1. *An automorphism α of a group G is called* inner *if there is an element a in G for which $\alpha(g) = a^{-1}ga$, for all g in G. Write a constructor for inner automorphisms of groups.*

Summary The power of generic programming is that we need only implement computation in quotient fields or groups once — in the constructors and generic procedures. The functor `QuotientField` and the various generic group constructors and procedures are parameterized by the computational domains upon which their computed values depend. We view rings, fields, groups and subgroups as collections of computational capabilities, which we use to construct new instances with derived computational capabilities. The ability to override default methods (which may not be efficient, but at least, are always present) with better methods that take advantage of specific structural information allows for efficient computation without sacrificing generality. This leads to a powerful paradigm for software reuse, and is the principal motivation underlying Maple's module system.

6.7   Conclusion

This chapter introduced the concept of Maple modules. It described the structure and flexibility of modules.

Encapsulation and generic programming with modules allow you to write code that can be reused, transported, and easily maintained. By collecting procedures into a module called a package, you can organize your procedures into distinct sets of related functions. You can also use modules to implement objects in Maple.

The descriptions in this chapter are complemented by numerous examples to help you learn the syntax and semantics of modules and provide you with modules that can be customized and used in your own work.

7 Debugging Maple Programs

New programs, whether developed in Maple or any other language, often work incorrectly. Problems that occur in the execution of a program are usually due to syntax errors introduced during implementation, or logic errors in the design of the algorithm. Most errors are subtle and hard to find by visual inspection of the program alone. Maple provides error detection commands and a debugger to help you find these errors.

The Maple debugger lets you stop execution within a Maple procedure, inspect and modify the values of local and global variables, and continue execution, either to completion, or one statement or block at a time. You can stop execution when Maple reaches a particular statement, when it assigns some value to a particular local or global variable, or when a particular error occurs. This facility lets you investigate the inner workings of a program to determine why it is not doing what you expect.

Alternatively, Maple provides a variety of commands to help you find errors in procedures. Among these are commands to trace procedure execution, check assertions, raise exceptions and trap errors, and verify procedure semantics and syntax.

Even when a program is working correctly, you may want to analyze its performance to try to improve its efficiency. Maple commands are available to analyze the time and memory consumption involved in running the program.

7.1   A Tutorial Example

The Maple debugger is a tool that you can use to detect errors in your procedures. Using this facility, you can follow the step-by-step execution of your program to determine why it is not returning the results that you expect.

This section illustrates how to use the Maple debugger as a tool for debugging a Maple procedure. The debugger commands are introduced and described as they are applied. Additional information about the commands is provided in Section 7.2.

The following procedure, sieve, is used as a case study. It implements the *Sieve of Eratosthenes*: given a parameter n, return a count of the prime numbers less than n, inclusive. To debug the sieve procedure, we use breakpoints and watchpoints, which cause Maple to stop the execution of the procedure.

```
> sieve := proc(n::integer)
>         local i, k, flags, count,twicei;
>         count := 0;
>         for i from 2 to n do
>             flags[i] := true
>         end do;
>         for i from 2 to n do
>             if flags[i] then
>                 twicei := 2*i;
>                 for k from twicei by i to n do
>                     flags[k] = false;
>                 end do;
>                 count := count+1
>             end if;
>         end do;
>         count;
> end proc:
```

Numbering the Procedure Statements I

To use the Maple debugger, you must enter a variety of debugger commands. Many of these debugger commands must refer to statements within the procedures that you are debugging. Statement numbers allow such references. The showstat command displays a Maple procedure along with numbers preceeding each line that begins a new statement.

```
> showstat(sieve);

sieve := proc(n::integer)
local i, k, flags, count, twicei;
   1    count := 0;
   2    for i from 2 to n do
   3        flags[i] := true
        end do;
   4    for i from 2 to n do
   5        if flags[i] then
```

```
6         twicei := 2*i;
7         for k from twicei by i to n do
8            flags[k] = false
          end do;
9         count := count+1
       end if
     end do;
10    count
end proc
```

Note that the numbers preceeding each line differ from line numbers that may display in a text editor. For example, keywords that end a statement (such as **end do** and **end if**) are not considered separate commands and are therefore not numbered.

Invoking the Debugger I

To invoke the Maple debugger you must start the execution of a procedure, and the execution must be made to stop within the procedure. To execute a Maple procedure, call it by using a Maple command at the top-level, or call it from another procedure. The simplest way to cause execution to stop within the procedure, is to set a *breakpoint* in the procedure.

Setting a breakpoint   Use the **stopat** command to set a breakpoint in procedure **sieve**.

```
> stopat(sieve);
```

$$[sieve]$$

This command sets a breakpoint before the first statement in procedure **sieve**. When you subsequently execute **sieve**, Maple stops before executing the first statement. When execution does stop, the debugger prompt appears (DBG>).[1]

The following example demonstrates an initial execution of **sieve**.

```
> sieve(10);

sieve:
   1*  count := 0;
```

---

[1]If a procedure has a remember table, you may have to execute a **restart** command before issuing a second or subsequent **stopat** command. For more information about remember tables, see **?remember**.

Preceding the debugger prompt are several pieces of information.

- The previously computed result. (This particular execution stopped at the first statement before making any computations, so no result appears.)

- The name of the procedure in which execution has stopped is `sieve`.

- Execution is stopped before statement number 1. An asterisk (*) follows this statement number to indicate that a breakpoint was set before the statement.

At the debugger prompt, you can evaluate Maple expressions, and invoke debugger commands. Maple evaluates expressions in the context of the stopped procedure. You have access to exactly the same procedure parameters, and local, global, and environment variables, as the stopped procedure. For example, since `sieve` was called with parameter value 10, the formal parameter `n` has the value 10.

```
DBG > n

10
sieve:
    1*   count := 0;
```

Notice that for each expression that Maple evaluates, it displays:

- the result of the expression,

- the name of the stopped procedure,

- the statement number where the procedure stopped followed by the statement, and

- a new debugger prompt.

Note: To remove a breakpoint from a procedure, use the **unstopat** command.

Controlling Execution of a Procedure during Debugging I

Debugger commands control the execution of the procedure once the debugger is active. Some commonly used debugger commands are `next`, `step`, `list`, `into`, `outfrom`, and `cont`.

The `next` command executes the next statement at the current nesting level. After the statement is executed, control is returned to the debugger as though a breakpoint had been set. If the statement is a control structure (an `if` statement or a loop), the debugger executes any statements within the control structure that it would normally execute. It stops execution before the next statement *after* the control structure. Similarly, if the statement contains calls to procedures, the debugger executes these procedure calls in their entirety before execution stops.

```
DBG > next

0
sieve:
    2    for i from 2 to n do
         ...
         end do;
```

The 0 in the first line of the output represents the result of the executed statement—that is, the result of `count := 0`. A "∗" does not appear next to the statement number because there is no breakpoint set immediately before statement 2. The debugger does not show the body of the `for` loop, which itself consists of statements with their own statement numbers, unless execution actually stops within its body. Maple represents the body of compound statements by ellipses (. . .).

Executing the `next` command again results in the following output.

```
DBG > next

true
sieve:
    4    for i from 2 to n do
         ...
         end do;
```

Execution now stops before statement 4. Statement 3 (the body of the previous `for` loop) is at a deeper nesting level. Therefore, the loop is executed **n-1** times. The debugger displays the last result computed in the loop (the assignment of the value **true** to **flags[10]**).

If you want to step into a nested control structure (such as an **if** statement or **for** loop) or a procedure call, use the **step** debugger command.

```
DBG > step

true
sieve:
    5       if flags[i] then
                ...
            end if
```

```
DBG > step

true
sieve:
    6       twicei := 2*i;
```

If you use the **step** debugger command when the next statement to execute is *not* a deeper structured statement, it has the same effect as the **next** debugger command.

```
DBG > step

4
sieve:
    7       for k from twicei by i to n do
                ...
            end do;
```

At any time during the debugging process, you can use the **showstat** debugger command to display the current status of the debugging process.

```
DBG > showstat
```

```
sieve := proc(n::integer)
local i, k, flags, count, twicei;
    1*   count := 0;
    2    for i from 2 to n do
    3       flags[i] := true
         end do;
    4    for i from 2 to n do
    5       if flags[i] then
    6          twicei := 2*i;
    7 !        for k from twicei by i to n do
    8             flags[k] = false
            end do;
    9          count := count+1
         end if
       end do;
   10    count
end proc
```

Notice that the debugger prompt is displayed to indicate that you are still working inside the Maple debugger. The asterisk (*) marks the *unconditional* breakpoint. An exclamation point (!) that follows a statement number (see line 7) indicates the statement at which the procedure is stopped.

To continue the debugging process, issue another debugger command. For example, you can use **into** or **step** to enter the innermost loop. The **into** debugger command is a compromise between the **next** and **step** commands. Execution stops at the next statement within the current procedure regardless of whether it is at the current nesting level or within the body of a control structure (an **if** statement or a loop). In other words, the **into** command steps into nested statements, but not into procedure calls.

```
DBG > into

4
sieve:
    8            flags[k] = false
```

A debugger command that is related to **showstat** is the **list** command. It displays the previous five statements, the current statement, and the next statement, to quickly provide some idea of where the procedure has stopped.

```
DBG > list


sieve := proc(n::integer)
local i, k, flags, count, twicei;
       . . .
   3      flags[i] := true
        end do;
   4   for i from 2 to n do
   5     if flags[i] then
   6        twicei := 2*i;
   7        for k from twicei by i to n do
   8 !        flags[k] = false
           end do;
   9        count := count+1
        end if
      end do;
       . . .
 end proc
```

You can use the **outfrom** debugger command to finish execution at the current nesting level or deeper. Execution of the procedure is stopped once a statement at a shallower nesting level is reached, that is, after a loop terminates, a branch of an **if** statement executes, or the current procedure call returns.

```
DBG > outfrom

true = false
sieve:
   9          count := count+1



DBG > outfrom

1
sieve:
   5      if flags[i] then
            . . .
          end if
```

The `cont` debugger command continues execution, until either the procedure terminates normally or it encounters another breakpoint.

```
DBG > cont
```

$$9\,l$$

You can now see that the procedure does not give the expected output. Although you may find the reason obvious from the previous debugger command examples, in most cases it is not easy to find procedure errors. Therefore, pretend not to recognize the problem, and continue to use the debugger. First, use the `unstopat` command to remove the breakpoint from `sieve`.

```
> unstopat(sieve);
```

$$[]$$

Invoking the Debugger II

The procedure `sieve` keeps track of the changing result in the variable `count`. Therefore, a logical place to look during debugging is wherever Maple modifies `count`. The easiest way to do this is by using a *watchpoint*, which invokes the debugger whenever Maple modifies a watched variable.

Setting a watchpoint Use the `stopwhen` command to set watchpoints. In this case, you want to stop execution whenever Maple modifies the variable `count` in the procedure `sieve`.

```
> stopwhen([sieve,count]);
```

$$[[sieve,\ count]]$$

The `stopwhen` command returns a list of all the variables currently being watched.

Execute the `sieve` procedure again.

```
> sieve(10);
```

```
count := 0
sieve:
  2    for i from 2 to n do
          ...
       end do;
```

Execution stops because Maple has modified **count**, and the debugger displays the assignment statement **count := 0**. As in the case of breakpoints, the debugger then displays the name of the procedure and the next statement to be executed in the procedure. Note that execution stops *after* Maple has assigned a value to **count**.

This first assignment to **count** is correct. Use the **cont** debugger command to continue execution of the procedure.

```
DBG > cont

count := 1
sieve:
  5       if flags[i] then
            ...
          end if
```

If you do not look carefully, this also looks correct. Assume that nothing is wrong and continue execution.

```
DBG > cont

count := 2*l
sieve:
  5       if flags[i] then
            ...
          end if
```

This output is suspicious because Maple should have simplified **2*1**. Notice that it has printed **2*l** (two times the letter l) instead. By studying the source text for the procedure, you can see that the letter "l" was typed instead of the number "1". Since the source of the error has been discovered, there is no reason to continue the execution of the procedure. Use the **quit** debugger command to exit the debugger and then use the **unstopwhen** command to remove the watchpoint from the procedure.

```
DBG > quit
```

```
Warning, computation interrupted
> unstopwhen();
```

                              []

After correcting the source text for **sieve**, issue a **restart** command, read the corrected version of **sieve** back into Maple, and execute the procedure again.

```
> sieve(10);
```

                         9 *l*

This result is still incorrect. There are four primes less than 10, namely 2, 3, 5, and 7. Therefore, invoke the debugger once more, stepping into the innermost parts of the procedure to investigate. Since you do not want to start at the beginning of the procedure, set the breakpoint at statement 6.

```
> stopat(sieve,6);
```

                        [*sieve*]

```
> sieve(10);
```

```
true
sieve:
   6*        twicei := 2*i;
```

```
DBG > step
```

```
4
sieve:
   7          for k from twicei by i to n do
              ...
              end do;
```

```
DBG > step
```

```
4
sieve:
   8              flags[k] = false
```

```
DBG > step
```

```
true = false
sieve:
   8              flags[k] = false
```

The last step reveals the error. The previously computed result should have been **false** (from the assignment of **flags[k]** to the value **false**), but instead **true = false** was returned. An equation was used instead of an assignment. Therefore, Maple did not set **flags[k]** to **false**.

Once again, exit the debugger and correct the source text.

```
DBG > quit
```

```
Warning, computation interrupted
```

The following code represents the corrected procedure.

```
> sieve := proc(n::integer)
>         local i, k, flags, count,twicei;
>         count := 0;
>         for i from 2 to n do
>            flags[i] := true
>         end do;
>         for i from 2 to n do
>            if flags[i] then
>                twicei := 2*i;
>                for k from twicei by i to n do
>                    flags[k] := false;
```

```
>                     end do;
>                   count := count+1
>               end if;
>           end do;
>           count;
> end proc:
```

Execute procedure `sieve` again to test the corrections.

```
> sieve(10);
```

$$4$$

The `sieve` procedure now returns the correct result.

7.2   Maple Debugger Commands

This section provides additional details about the commands used in the tutorial in Section 7.1 and a description of other debugger commands.

Numbering the Procedure Statements II

The `showstat` command is called by using the following syntax. The `procedureName` parameter is optional.

```
showstat( procedureName );
```

If `showstat` is called with no arguments, all procedures that contain breakpoints are displayed.

You can also use the `showstat` command to display a single statement or a range of statements by using the following syntax.

```
showstat( procedureName, number );
showstat( procedureName, range );
```

In these cases, the statements that are not displayed are represented by ellipses (...). The procedure name, its parameters, and its local and global variables are always displayed.

```
> f := proc(x)
>         if x <= 2 then
>           print(x);
>         end if;
```

```
>           print(-x)
>    end proc:


>  showstat(f, 2..3);


f := proc(x)
        ...
    2     print(x)
        end if;
    3    print(-x)
end proc
```

Invoking the Debugger III

This section provides additional information about breakpoints and watchpoints.

Setting breakpoints The stopat command is called by using the following syntax where procedureName is the name of the procedure in which to set the breakpoint, statementNumber is the line number of the statement in the procedure *before* which the breakpoint is set, and condition is a Boolean expression which must be *true* for execution to stop. The statementNumber and condition arguments are optional.

```
stopat( procedureName, statementNumber, condition );
```

This condition argument can refer to any global variable, local variable, or parameter of the procedure. These *conditional* breakpoints are marked by a question mark (?) if showstat is used to display the procedure.

Since the stopat command sets the breakpoint before the specified statement, when Maple encounters a breakpoint, execution stops and Maple engages the debugger *before* the statement. *This means that it is* **not** *possible to set a breakpoint after the last statement in a statement sequence—that is, at the end of a loop body, an if statement body, or a procedure.*

If two identical procedures exist, depending on how you created them, they may share breakpoints. If you entered the procedures individually, with identical procedure bodies, then they do not share breakpoints. If you created a procedure by assigning it to the body of another procedure, then their breakpoints are shared.

```
> f := proc(x) x^2 end proc:
> g := proc(x) x^2 end proc:
> h := op(g):
> stopat(g);
```

$$[g, h]$$

```
> showstat();


g := proc(x)
   1*   x^2
end proc


h := proc(x)
   1*   x^2
end proc
```

Removing breakpoints   The `unstopat` command is called by using the following syntax where `procedureName` is the name of the procedure that contains the breakpoint, and `statementNumber` is the line number of the statement where the breakpoint is set. The `statementNumber` parameter is optional.

```
unstopat( procedureName, statementNumber );
```

If `statementNumber` is omitted in the call to `unstopat`, then *all* breakpoints in procedure `procedureName` are cleared.

Setting explicit breakpoints   You can set an explicit breakpoint by inserting a call to the `DEBUG` command in the source text of a procedure. The `DEBUG` command is called by using the following syntax. The `argument` parameter is optional.

```
DEBUG( argument );
```

If no argument is included in the `DEBUG` command, execution in the procedure stops at the statement *following* the location of the `DEBUG` command and the debugger is invoked.[2]

---

[2]The `showstat` command does not mark explicit breakpoints with a "*" or a "?".

```
> f := proc(x,y) local a;
>          a:=x^2;
>          DEBUG();
>          a:=y^2;
> end proc:


> showstat(f);


f := proc(x, y)
local a;
   1    a := x^2;
   2    DEBUG();
   3    a := y^2
end proc



> f(2,3);

4
f:
   3    a := y^2



DBG > quit


Warning, computation interrupted
```

If the argument of the DEBUG command is a Boolean expression, then execution stops only if the Boolean expression evaluates to **true**. If the Boolean expression evaluates to **false** or **FAIL**, then the DEBUG command is ignored.

```
> f := proc(x,y) local a;
>          a:=x^2;
>          DEBUG(a<1);
>          a:=y^2;
>          DEBUG(a>1);
>          print(a);
> end proc:


> f(2,3);
```

```
9
f:
   5   print(a)
```

```
DBG > quit
```

```
Warning, computation interrupted
```

If the argument of the DEBUG command is anything but a Boolean expression, then the debugger prints the value of the argument instead of the last result when execution stops at the following statement.

```
> f := proc(x)
>          x^2;
>          DEBUG("This is my breakpoint. The current value of x is:", x);
>          x^3
> end proc:
```

```
> f(2);
```

```
"This is my breakpoint. The current value of x is:"
2
f:
   3   x^3
```

Removing explicit breakpoints   The unstopat command cannot remove explicit breakpoints. You must remove breakpoints that were set using DEBUG by editing the source text for the procedure.

```
DBG > unstopat
```

```
[f, g, h]
f:
   3   x^3
```

```
DBG > showstat

f := proc(x)
   1    x^2;
   2    DEBUG("This is my breakpoint. The current value of x is:",x);
   3 !  x^3
end proc
```

```
DBG > quit
```

Warning, computation interrupted

Note: If you display the contents of a procedure by using **print** (or **lprint**) and the procedure contains a breakpoint that was set by using **stopat**, the breakpoint appears as a call to **DEBUG**.

```
> f := proc(x) x^2 end proc:
> stopat(f);
```

$$[f, g, h]$$

```
> print(f);
```

$$\mathbf{proc}(x)\,\mathrm{DEBUG}()\,;\,x^2\,\mathbf{end\ proc}$$

Setting watchpoints   The **stopwhen** command is called by using one of the following.

```
stopwhen( globalVariableName );
stopwhen( [procedureName, variableName] );
```

The first form specifies that the debugger should be invoked whenever the global variable **globalVariableName** is changed. Maple environment variables, such as **Digits**, can also be monitored by using this method.

```
> stopwhen(Digits);
```

[*Digits*]

The second form invokes the debugger whenever the (local or global) variable `variableName` is changed in the procedure `procedureName`.

When `stopwhen` is called in either form or with no arguments, Maple returns a list of the watchpoints that are currently set.

Execution stops *after* Maple has already assigned a value to the watched variable. The debugger displays an assignment statement instead of the last computed result (which would be the right-hand side of the assignment statement).

Clearing watchpoints The syntax to call `unstopwhen` is the same as that for `stopwhen`. Similar to `stopwhen`, `unstopwhen` returns a list of all (remaining) watchpoints.

If no arguments are entered in the call to `unstopwhen`, then *all* watchpoints are cleared.

Setting watchpoints on specified errors You can use an error watchpoint to invoke the debugger whenever Maple returns a specified error message. When a watched error occurs, execution of the procedure stops and the debugger displays the statement in which the error occurred.

Error watchpoints are set by using the `stoperror` command. The `stoperror` command is called by using the following syntax

```
stoperror( "errorMessage" );
```

where `errorMessage` is a *string* or a *symbol* that represents the error message returned from a procedure. A list of the currently set error watchpoints is returned.

If no argument is entered in the call to `stoperror`, the current list of watchpoints is returned.

```
> stoperror();
```

$$[]$$

```
> stoperror( "numeric exception: division by zero" );
```

$$[\text{``numeric exception: division by zero''}]$$

```
> stoperror();
```

$$[\text{``numeric exception: division by zero''}]$$

If the special name `all` is used instead of a specific error message as the parameter to the **stoperror** command, execution of a procedure stops whenever *any* error that would *not* be trapped occurs.

Errors trapped by a traperror construct (**try...catch** statement) do not generate an error message and so **stoperror** cannot be used to catch them. For more information about the **try...catch** structure, see *Trapping errors* on page 390. If the special name `traperror` is used instead of a specific error message as the parameter to the **stoperror** command, execution of a procedure stops whenever *any* error that *is* trapped occurs. If the **errorMessage** parameter is entered in the form **traperror["message"]** to **stoperror**, the debugger is invoked only if the error specified by **"message"** *is* trapped.

When execution of a procedure stops due to an error which causes an exception, continued execution is not possible. Any of the execution control commands, such as **next** or **step** (see *Controlling Execution of a Procedure during Debugging I* and *II* in Section 7.1 and this section, respectively), process the error as if the debugger had not intervened. For example, consider the following two procedures. The first procedure, **f**, calculates **1/x**. The other procedure, **g**, calls **f** but traps the **"division by zero"** error that occurs when **x = 0**.

```
> f := proc(x) 1/x end:
> g := proc(x) local r;
>        try
>          f(x);
>        catch:
>          infinity;
>        end try;
> end proc:
```

If procedure **g** is executed at **x=9**, the reciprocal is returned.

```
> g(9);
```

$$\frac{1}{9}$$

At **x=0**, as expected, infinity is returned.

```
> g(0);
```

$$\infty$$

The **stoperror** command stops execution when you call **f** directly.

```
> stoperror("numeric exception: division by zero");
```

$$["numeric exception: division by zero"]$$

```
> f(0);
Error, numeric exception: division by zero
f:
   1    1/x
```

```
DBG > cont
Error, (in f) numeric exception: division by zero
```

The call to **f** from **g** is inside a traperror (**try...catch** statement), so the **"division by zero"** error does *not* invoke the debugger.

```
> g(0);
```

$$\infty$$

Instead, try to use **stoperror(traperror)**.

```
> unstoperror( "numeric exception: division by zero" );
```

$$[]$$

```
> stoperror( 'traperror' );
```

$$[traperror]$$

This time Maple will not stop at the error in **f**.

```
> f(0);
```

```
Error, (in f) numeric exception: division by zero
```

However, Maple invokes the debugger when the trapped error occurs.

```
> g(0);
```

```
Error, numeric exception: division by zero
f:
   1    1/x
```

```
DBG > step
```

```
Error, numeric exception: division by zero
g:
   3        infinity
```

```
DBG > step
```

∞

In the case that a particular error message is specified in the form `traperror["message"]`, the debugger is invoked only if the error specified by `"message"` *is* trapped.

Clearing watchpoints on specified errors   Error watchpoints are cleared by using the top-level **unstoperror** command. The syntax to call **unstoperror** is the same as for **stoperror**. Like **stoperror**, **unstoperror** returns a list of all (remaining) error watchpoints.

If no argument is entered in the call to **unstoperror**, then *all* error watchpoints are cleared.

```
> unstoperror();
```

```
[ ]
```

Controlling Execution of a Procedure during Debugging II

Once the execution of a procedure is stopped and the debugger is invoked, you can examine the values of variables or perform other experiments (see *Changing the State of a Procedure during Debugging*). After you have examined the state of the procedure, you can cause execution to continue by using a number of different debugger commands.

The most commonly used debugger commands are `cont`, `next`, `step`, `into`, `outfrom`, `return`, and `quit`.

The `return` debugger command causes execution of the currently active procedure call to complete. Execution stops at the first statement after the current procedure.

The other commands were described in the tutorial in Section 7.1. For more information about these and other debugger commands, see `?debugger`.

Changing the State of a Procedure during Debugging

When a breakpoint or watchpoint stops the execution of a procedure, the Maple debugger is invoked. In the debugger mode, you can examine the state of the global variables, local variables, and parameters of the stopped procedure. You can also determine where execution stopped, evaluate expressions, and examine procedures.

While in the debugger mode, you can evaluate any Maple expression and perform assignments to local and global variables. To evaluate an expression, type the expression at the debugger prompt. To perform assignments to variables, use the standard Maple assignment statement.

```
> f := proc(x) x^2 end proc:
> stopat(f);
```

$$[f]$$

```
> f(10);

f:
    1*  x^2
```

```
DBG > sin(3.0)
```

```
.1411200081
f:
    1*   x^2



DBG > cont
```

$$100$$

The debugger evaluates any variable names that you use in the expression in the context of the stopped procedure. Names of parameters or local variables evaluate to their current values within the procedure. Names of global variables evaluate to their current values. Environment variables, such as Digits, evaluate to their values in the stopped procedure's environment.

If an expression corresponds to a debugger command (for example, your procedure has a local variable named step), you can still evaluate it by enclosing it in parentheses.

```
> f := proc(step) local i;
>         for i to 10 by step do
>             i^2
>         end do;
> end proc:


> stopat(f,2);
```

$$[f]$$

```
> f(3);

f:
    2*     i^2




DBG > step

1
f:
    2*     i^2
```

```
DBG > (step)

3
f:
    2*    i^2



DBG > quit
```

Warning, computation interrupted

While execution is stopped, you can modify local and global variables by using the assignment operator (:=). The following example sets a breakpoint in the loop only when the index variable is equal to 5.

```
> sumn := proc(n) local i, sum;
>            sum := 0;
>            for i to n do
>               sum := sum + i
>            end do;
> end proc:


> showstat(sumn);


sumn := proc(n)
local i, sum;
   1    sum := 0;
   2    for i to n do
   3       sum := sum+i
         end do
end proc



> stopat(sumn,3,i=5);
```

$$[sumn]$$

```
> sumn(10);

10
sumn:
    3?    sum := sum+i
```

Reset the index to 3 so that the breakpoint is encountered again.

```
DBG > i := 3

sumn:
    3?      sum := sum+i
```

```
DBG > cont

17
sumn:
    3?      sum := sum+i
```

Maple has added the numbers 1, 2, 3, 4, 3, and 4 and returned 17 as the result. Continuing the execution of the procedure, the numbers 5, 6, 7, 8, 9, and 10 are added and 62 is returned as the result.

```
DBG > cont
```

$$62$$

Examining the State of a Procedure during Debugging

There are two debugger commands available that return information about the state of the procedure execution. The `list` debugger command shows you the location within a procedure where execution stopped, and the `where` debugger command shows you the stack of procedure activations.

The `list` debugger command has the following syntax.

```
list procedureName statementNumber[..statNumber]
```

The `list` debugger command is similar to `showstat`, except in the case where you do not specify any arguments. If no arguments are included in the call to `list`, only the five previous statements, the current statement, and the next statement to be executed are displayed. This provides some context in the stopped procedure. In other words, it indicates the *static* position where execution stopped.

The **where** debugger command shows you the stack of procedure activations. Starting from the top-level, it shows you the statement that is executing and the parameters it passed to the called procedure. The **where** debugger command repeats this for each level of procedure call until it reaches the current statement in the current procedure. In other words, it indicates the *dynamic* position where execution stopped. The **where** command has the following syntax.

```
where numLevels
```

To illustrate these commands, consider the following example. The procedure **check** calls the **sumn** procedure from the previous example.

```
> check := proc(i) local p, a, b;
>            p := ithprime(i);
>            a := sumn(p);
>            b := p*(p+1)/2;
>            evalb( a=b );
> end proc:
```

There is a (conditional) breakpoint in **sumn**.

```
> showstat(sumn);

sumn := proc(n)
local i, sum;
   1    sum := 0;
   2    for i to n do
   3?      sum := sum+i
        end do
end proc
```

When **check** calls **sumn**, the breakpoint invokes the debugger.

```
> check(9);

10
sumn:
   3?      sum := sum+i
```

The **where** debugger command reveals that:

• **check** was invoked from the top-level with argument 9,

- **check** called **sumn** with argument 23, and

- execution stopped at statement number 3 in **sumn**.

```
DBG > where

TopLevel: check(9)
          [9]
check: a := sumn(p)
          [23]
sumn:
    3?      sum := sum+i



DBG > cont
```

$$true$$

The next example illustrates the use of **where** in a recursive function.

```
> fact := proc(x)
>               if x <= 1 then
>                   1
>               else
>                   x * fact(x-1)
>               end if;
> end proc:


> showstat(fact);


fact := proc(x)
   1    if x <= 1 then
   2        1
        else
   3        x*fact(x-1)
        end if
end proc



> stopat(fact,2);
```

$$[fact]$$

```
> fact(5);
```

```
fact:
   2*     1
```

```
DBG > where

TopLevel: fact(5)
        [5]
fact: x*fact(x-1)
        [4]
fact: x*fact(x-1)
        [3]
fact: x*fact(x-1)
        [2]
fact: x*fact(x-1)
        [1]
fact:
   2*     1
```

If you are not interested in the entire history of the nested procedure calls, then use the **numLevels** parameter in the call to **where** to print out only a certain number of levels.

```
DBG > where 3

fact: x*fact(x-1)
        [2]
fact: x*fact(x-1)
        [1]
fact:
   2*     1
```

```
DBG > quit
```

```
Warning, computation interrupted
```

The **showstop** command (and the **showstop** debugger command) displays a report of all currently set breakpoints, watchpoints, and error watchpoints. Outside the debugger at the top-level, the **showstop** command has the following syntax.

```
showstop();
```

The next example illustrates the use of **showstop**.

```
>  f := proc(x) local y;
>           if x < 2 then
>               y := x;
>               print(y^2);
>           end if;
>           print(-x);
>           x^3;
>  end proc:
```

Set some breakpoints.

```
> stopat(f):
> stopat(f,2):
> stopat(int);
```

$$[f,\ int]$$

Set some watchpoints.

```
> stopwhen(f,y):
> stopwhen(Digits);
```

$$[[f,\ y],\ Digits]$$

Set an error watchpoint.

```
> stoperror( "numeric exception: division by zero" );
```

$$[\text{"numeric exception: division by zero"}]$$

The **showstop** command reports all the breakpoints and watchpoints.

```
> showstop();
```

```
Breakpoints in:
    f
    int

Watched variables:
    y in procedure f
    Digits

Watched errors:
```

```
"numeric exception: division by zero"
```

Using Top-Level Commands at the Debugger Prompt

The `showstat`, `stopat`, `unstopat`, `stopwhen`, `unstopwhen`, `stoperror`, and `showstop` commands can be used at the debugger prompt. The following list describes the syntax rules for top-level commands used at the debugger prompt.

- Do *not* enclose the arguments of the command in parentheses.

- Do *not* separate the arguments of the command with commas. The arguments must be separated by a space character.

- Do *not* use colons or semicolons to end statements.

- The procedure name is *not* required by any command. Commands that use a procedure name assume the currently stopped procedure if one is not specified.

- For the `stoperror` command, the quotation marks (`""`) are *not* required.

Except for these rules, the debugger prompt call for each command is of the same form and takes the same arguments as the corresponding top-level command call.

Restrictions

At the debugger prompt, the only permissible Maple statements are debugger commands, expressions, and assignments. The debugger does not permit statements such as `if`, `while`, `for`, `read`, and `save`. However, you can use `'if'` to simulate an `if` statement, and `seq` to simulate a loop.

The debugger cannot set breakpoints in, or step into, built-in kernel routines, such as `diff` and `has`. These routines are implemented in C and compiled into the Maple kernel. Debugging information about these routines is not accessible to Maple since the routines deal with objects at a level lower than the debugger can access.

Finally, if a procedure contains two identical statements that are expressions, the debugger cannot determine with certainty the statement at which execution stopped. If this situation occurs, you can still use the debugger and execution can continue. The debugger merely issues a warning that the displayed statement number may be incorrect.[3]

7.3   Detecting Errors

This section describes some simple commands that you can use for detecting errors in procedures that are written in Maple. If you are not successful in finding the error by using these commands, you can use the Maple debugger, which is discussed in Sections 7.1 and 7.2, to display the stepwise execution of a procedure.

Tracing a Procedure

The simplest tools available for error detection in Maple are the `printlevel` global variable, and the `trace` and `tracelast` commands. These facilities enable you to trace the execution of both user-defined and Maple library procedures. However, they differ in the type of information that is returned about a procedure.

The `printlevel` variable is used to control how much information is displayed when a program is executed. By assigning a large integer value to `printlevel`, you can monitor the execution of statements to selected levels of nesting within procedures. The default value of `printlevel` is 1. Larger, positive integer values cause the display of more intermediate steps in a computation. Negative integer values suppress the display of information.

The `printlevel` global variable is set by using the following syntax, where n is the level to which Maple commands are evaluated.

```
printlevel := n;
```

To determine what value of n to use, remember that statements within a particular procedure are recognized in levels that are determined by the nesting of conditional or repetition statements, and by the nesting of procedures. Each loop or `if` condition increases the evaluation level by 1, and each procedure call increases the evaluation level by 5. Alternatively, you can use a sufficiently large value of n to ensure that all levels are traced.

---

[3]This problem occurs because Maple stores all identical expressions as a single occurrence of the expression, and the debugger has no way to determine at which invocation execution stopped.

For example, `printlevel := 1000` displays information in procedures up to 200 levels deep.

```
> f := proc(x) local y; y := x^2; g(y) / 4; end proc;
```

$$f := \mathbf{proc}(x)\,\mathbf{local}\,y;\; y := x^2;\; 1/4 * \mathrm{g}(y)\,\mathbf{end\ proc}$$

```
> g := proc(x) local z; z := x^2; z * 2; end proc;
```

$$g := \mathbf{proc}(x)\,\mathbf{local}\,z;\; z := x^2;\; 2 * z\,\mathbf{end\ proc}$$

```
> f(3);
```

$$\frac{81}{2}$$

```
> printlevel := 5;
```

$$printlevel := 5$$

```
> f(3);
```

```
{--> enter f, args = 3
```

$$y := 9$$

$$\frac{81}{2}$$

```
<-- exit f (now at top level) = 81/2}
> printlevel := 10;
```

$$printlevel := 10$$

```
> f(3);
```

```
{--> enter f, args = 3
```

$$y := 9$$

```
{--> enter g, args = 9
```

$$z := 81$$

$$162$$

```
<-- exit g (now in f) = 162}
```

$$\frac{81}{2}$$

```
<-- exit f (now at top level) = 81/2}
```

$$\frac{81}{2}$$

The amount of information that is displayed depends on whether the call to the procedure was terminated with a colon or a semicolon. If a colon is used, only entry and exit points of the procedure are printed. If a semicolon is used, the results of the statements are also printed.

To reset the value of the **printlevel** variable, reassign its value to **1**.

```
> printlevel := 1;
```

$$printlevel := 1$$

By assigning a large value to **printlevel**, the trace of *all* subsequent Maple procedure calls is displayed. To display the trace of *specific* procedures, you can use the **trace** command. The **trace** command has the following syntax, where **arguments** is one or more procedure names.

```
trace(arguments);
```

The **trace** command returns an expression sequence containing the names of the traced procedures. To begin tracing, you must call the procedure.

```
> trace(f,g);
```

$$f, g$$

```
> f(3):
```

```
{--> enter f, args = 3
{--> enter g, args = 9
<-- exit g (now in f) = 162}
<-- exit f (now at top level) = 81/2}
```

```
> f(3);
```

```
{--> enter f, args = 3
```

$$y := 9$$

```
{--> enter g, args = 9
```

$$z := 81$$

$$162$$

```
<-- exit g (now in f) = 162}
```

$$\frac{81}{2}$$

```
<-- exit f (now at top level) = 81/2}
```

$$\frac{81}{2}$$

Like `printlevel`, the amount of information that is displayed during tracing when `trace` is used depends on whether the call to the procedure was terminated with a colon or a semicolon. If a colon is used, only entry and exit points of the procedure are printed. If a semicolon is used, the results of the statements are also printed.

To turn off the tracing of specific procedures, use the **untrace** command.[4]

```
> untrace(f,g);
```

$$f, g$$

```
> f(3);
```

$$\frac{81}{2}$$

If a procedure returns an error message, you can use the `tracelast` command to determine the last statement executed and the values of variables at the time of the error. The `tracelast` command has the following syntax.

```
tracelast;
```

When a procedure returns an error message, the following information is returned from a call to `tracelast`.

- The first line displays which procedure was called and what parameter was used.

- The second line displays the **#** symbol, the procedure name with the line number of the statement that was executed, and the statement that was executed.

- Finally, if there are any local variables in the procedure, they are displayed with their corresponding values.

---

[4]You can use **debug** and **undebug** as alternate names for **trace** and **untrace**.

```
> f := proc(x) local i,j,k;
>           i := x;
>           j = x^2;
>           seq(k, k=i..j);
> end proc;
```

$$f := \mathbf{proc}(x)$$
$$\mathbf{local}\, i,\, j,\, k;$$
$$i := x\,;\, j = x^2\,;\, \mathrm{seq}(k,\, k = i..j)$$
$$\mathbf{end\ proc}$$

```
> f(2,3);
```

Error, (in f) unable to execute seq

```
> tracelast;
```

```
f called with arguments: 2, 3
#(f2,3): seq(k,k = i .. j)
```

Error, (in f) unable to execute seq

```
locals defined as: i = 2, j = j, k = k
```

You can find the error in this procedure by studying the results of the tracelast command—the assignment to the local variable j incorrectly used an equal sign (=) instead of an assignment operator (:=).

The information provided by tracelast can become unavailable whenever Maple does a garbage collection. Therefore, it is advisable to use tracelast immediately after an error occurs. [5]

Using Assertions

An *assertion* is a statement about a procedure that you "assert" to be true. You can include assertions in your procedure to guarantee pre- and post-conditions, and loop invariants during execution by using the ASSERT command. You can also use assertions to guarantee the value returned by a procedure or the value of local variables inside a procedure. The ASSERT command has the following syntax.

---

[5] For more information about garbage collection in Maple, see ?gc.

```
ASSERT(condition, message);
```

If `condition` evaluates to `false`, an error is generated and `message` is printed. If the first argument evaluates to `true`, ASSERT returns NULL.

To check assertions, you must turn assertion checking on prior to executing a procedure that contains an **ASSERT** command. To query the current state of assertion checking, and to turn assertion checking on and off, you must use the `kernelopts` command.[6]

The default state for assertion checking is `false`.

```
> kernelopts(ASSERT);  #query the current state
```

$$false$$

If you enter a `kernelopts` command to turn assertion checking on, `kernelopts` returns its *previous* value.

```
> kernelopts(ASSERT=true);
```

$$false$$

At any time during the Maple session, you can confirm whether assertion checking is on by entering the following command.

```
> kernelopts(ASSERT);
```

$$true$$

If assertion checking is on and a procedure that contains an **ASSERT** statement is executed , the condition represented by the **ASSERT** statement is checked.

```
> f := proc(x,y) local i,j;
>       i:=0;
>       j:=0;
>       while (i <> x) do
>          ASSERT(i > 0,'invalid index');
>          j := j + y;
>          i := i + 1;
>       end do;
>       j;
> end proc;
```

---

[6]For more information about `kernelopts`, see ?kernelopts.

$$f := \mathbf{proc}(x, y)$$
$$\mathbf{local}\, i,\, j;$$
$$\quad i := 0\,;$$
$$\quad j := 0\,;$$
$$\quad \mathbf{while}\, i \neq x\, \mathbf{do}$$
$$\qquad \text{ASSERT}(0 < i,\ `invalid\ index`)\,;\ j := j + y\,;\ i := i + 1$$
$$\quad \mathbf{end\ do};$$
$$\quad j$$
$$\mathbf{end\ proc}$$

```
> f(2,3);
```

```
Error, (in f) assertion failed, invalid index
```

Use the `kernelopts` command again to turn assertion checking off. (Again, `kernelopts` returns its *previous* value.) When assertion checking is off, the overhead of processing an `ASSERT` statement within a procedure is negligible.

```
> kernelopts(ASSERT=false);
```

$$true$$

Related to assertions are Maple warning messages. The `WARNING` command causes a specified warning, preceded by the string `"Warning,"`, to display. The `WARNING` command has the following syntax.

```
WARNING( msgString, msgParam1, msgParam2, ...);
```

The `msgString` parameter is the text of the warning message and `msgParam`*i* are optional parameters to substitute into `msgString`, if any.

```
> f := proc(x)
>       if x < 0 then
>           WARNING("the result is complex")
>       end if;
>       sqrt(x)
>   end proc;
```

$$f := \mathbf{proc}(x)$$

  $\mathbf{if}\, x < 0 \,\mathbf{then}\, \mathrm{WARNING}(\text{``the result is complex''})\,\mathbf{end\ if};$

  $\mathrm{sqrt}(x)$

end proc

```
> f(-2);
```

```
Warning, the result is complex
```

$$I\sqrt{2}$$

You can turn the `WARNING` command off by using `interface(warnlevel=0)`. In this case, the warning is not displayed and the call to `WARNING` has no effect.

```
> interface(warnlevel=0);
> f(-2);
```

$$I\sqrt{2}$$

Handling Exceptions

An *exception* is an event that occurs during the execution of a procedure that disrupts the normal flow of instructions. Many kinds of errors can cause exceptions—for example, attempting to read from a file that doesn't exist. Maple has two mechanisms available when such situations arise:

- the `error` statement to raise an exception, and

- the `try...catch...finally` block to handle exceptions.

Raising exceptions The `error` statement raises an exception. Execution of the current statement sequence is interrupted, and the block and procedure call stack is popped until either an exception handler is encountered, or execution returns to the top-level (in which case the exception becomes an error). The `error` statement has the following syntax.

```
error msgString, msgParam1, msgParam2, ...
```

The `msgString` parameter is a string that gives the text of the error message. It can contain numbered parameters of the form %n or %-n, where n is an integer. These numbered parameters are used as placeholders for actual values. In the event that the exception is ever printed as an error message, the actual values are specified by the `msgParams`.

For example, the error message `"f has a 2nd argument, x, which is missing"` is specified by the following `error` statement.

```
error "%1 has a %-2 argument, %3, which is missing", f, 2, x
```

A numbered parameter of the form %n displays the nth `msgParam` in line-printed notation (i.e., as `lprint` would display it). A numbered parameter of the form %-n displays the nth `msgParam`, assumed to be an integer, in ordinal form. For example, the %-2 in the error statement above is displayed as "2nd". The special parameter %0 displays all the `msgParams`, separated by a comma and a space.

The `error` statement evaluates its arguments, and then creates an exception object which is an expression sequence with the following elements.

- The name of the procedure in which the exception was raised, or the constant 0 if the exception was raised at the top-level.

- The `msgString`.

- The `msgParams`, if any.

The created exception object is assigned to the global variable `lastexception` as an expression sequence.[7]

The `error` statement normally causes an immediate exit from the current procedure to the Maple session. Maple prints an error message of the following form.

```
Error, (in procName) msgText
```

In this case, `msgText` is the text of the error message (which is constructed from the `msgString` and optional `msgParams` of the `error` statement), and `procName` is the procedure in which the error occurred. If

---

[7]The actual arguments to the `error` statement are also assigned to `lasterror` for compatibility with older versions of Maple. For more information, see `?traperror`.

the procedure does not have a name, procName is displayed as **unknown**. If the error occurs at the top-level, outside of any procedure, the (in procName) part of the message is omitted.

The **error** statement is commonly used when parameter declarations are not sufficient to check that the actual parameters to a procedure are of the correct type. The following **pairup** procedure takes a list L of the form $[x_1, y_1, x_2, y_2, \ldots, x_n, y_n]$ as input, and creates from it a list of the form $[[x_1, y_1], [x_2, y_2], \ldots, [x_n, y_n]]$. A simple type check cannot determine if list L has an even number of elements, so you need to check this explicitly by using an **error** statement.

```
> pairup := proc(L::list)
>               local i, n;
>               n := nops(L);
>               if irem(n,2) = 1 then
>                   error "list must have an even number of "
>                       "entries, but had %1", n
>               end if;
>               [seq( [L[2*i-1],L[2*i]], i=1..n/2 )]
> end proc:


> pairup([1, 2, 3, 4, 5]);

Error, (in pairup) list must have an even number of
entries, but had 5


> pairup([1, 2, 3, 4, 5, 6]);
```

$$[[1, 2], [3, 4], [5, 6]]$$

Trapping errors The **try** statement is a mechanism for executing procedure statements in a controlled environment so that if an error occurs, it does not immediately terminate the procedure. The **try** statement has the following syntax (the **finally** clause is optional).

```
try tryStatSeq
    catch catchStrings : catchStatSeq
    finally finalStatSeq
end try
```

If procedure execution enters a **try...catch** block, the tryStatSeq is executed. If no exceptions occur during the execution of tryStatSeq, procedure execution continues with the statement after **end try**.

If procedure execution enters a `try...catch...finally` block, the `tryStatSeq` is executed. If no exceptions occur during the execution of `tryStatSeq`, the `finalStatSeq` in the `finally` clause is executed. Execution then continues with the statement after `end try`.

If an exception does occur during the execution of `tryStatSeq`, execution of `tryStatSeq` terminates immediately. The exception object corresponding to the exception is compared against each `catchString`. Any number of catch clauses can be provided, and each can have any number of `catchStrings`, separated by commas. Alternatively, a catch clause need not have a catch string. Any given `catchString` (or a catch clause without one) can appear only once in a `try...end try` construct.

If a matching catch clause is found, or the catch clause contains no `catchStrings`, the `catchStatSeq` of that catch clause is executed, and the exception is considered to have been caught. If no matching catch clause is found, the exception is considered *not caught*, and is re-raised outside the `try` block.

When Maple is looking for a matching catch clause, the following definition of "matching" is used.

- Neither the exception object nor the `catchStrings` are evaluated (the exception object has already been evaluated by the error statement that produced it).

- The `catchStrings` are considered to be prefixes of the exception object's `msgString`. If a `catchString` has `n` characters, only the first `n` characters of the `msgString` need match the `catchString`. This permits the definition of classes of exceptions.

- A missing `catchString` will match any exception.

- The "result" of a `try` statement (the value that `%` returns if it is evaluated immediately after execution of the `try` statement) is the result of the last statement executed within the `try` statement.

A `catchStatSeq` can contain an `error` statement with no arguments, which also re-raises the exception. When an exception is re-raised, a new exception object is created that records the current procedure name, and the message and parameters from the original exception.

Under normal circumstances, the `finalStatSeq` of the `finally` clause, if there is one, is always executed before control leaves the `try` statement. This is true in the case that an exception occurs, independent of whether it is caught or whether another exception occurs in the `catch` clause.

This is true even if a `catchStatSeq` re-raises the exception, raises a new one, or executes a `return`, `break`, or `next` statement.

Under certain abnormal circumstances, the `finalStatSeq` is not executed:

- If an exception is raised in a catch clause and this exception is caught by the debugger and the user exits the debugger, the user's command to stop execution overrides everything.

- If one of the following untrappable exceptions occurs, the exception is not caught, and `finalStatSeq` is not executed:

  1. Computation timed out. (This can only be caught by `timelimit`, which raises a "time expired" exception that can be caught.)

  2. Computation interrupted. (In other words, the user pressed CTRL+C, BREAK, or equivalent.)

  3. Internal system error. (This indicates a bug in Maple itself.)

  4. `ASSERT` or local variable type assertion failure. (Assertion failures are not trappable because they indicate a coding error, not an algorithmic failure.)

  5. Stack overflow. (If a stack overflow occurs, there is generally not enough stack space to do anything such as running cleanup code.)

If an exception occurs during the execution of a `catchStatSeq` or the `finalStatSeq`, it is treated in the same way as if it occurred outside the `try...end try` statement.

A useful application of the `try` and `error` statements is to abort an expensive computation as quickly and cleanly as possible. For example, suppose that you are trying to compute an integral by using one of several methods, and in the middle of the first method, you determine that it will not succeed. You would like to abort that method and go on to try another method. The following code implements this example.

```
> try
>    result := MethodA(f,x)
> catch "FAIL":
>    result := MethodB(f,x)
> end try:
```

`MethodA` can abort its computation at any time by executing the statement `error "FAIL"`. The catch clause will catch that exception, and proceed to try `MethodB`. If any other error occurs during the execution of

`MethodA`, or if an error occurs during the execution of `MethodB`, it is not caught.

Another useful application of the **try** statement is to ensure that certain resources are freed when you are done with them, regardless of whether or not anything went wrong while you were using them. For example, you can use the following code to access Maple's I/O facilities to read the lines of a file and process them in some way.

```
> f := fopen("myfile",TEXT,READ):
> try
>    line := readline(f);
>    while line < 0 do
>        ProcessContentsOfLine(line);
>        line := readline(f)
>    end do
> finally
>    fclose(f)
> end try:
```

In this example, if any exception occurs while reading or processing the lines of the file, it is not caught because there is no catch clause. However, `fclose(f)` is executed before execution leaves the **try** statement, regardless of whether or not there was an exception.

The next example uses both **catch** and **finally** clauses to write to a file instead of reading from one.

```
> f := fopen("myfile",TEXT,WRITE):
> try
>    for i to 100 do
>        fprintf(f,"Result %d is %q\n",i,ComputeSomething(i))
>    end do
> catch:
>    fprintf(f,"Something went wrong: %q\n",lastexception);
>    error
> finally
>    fclose(f)
> end try:
```

If any exception occurs, it is caught with the catch clause that has no `catchString`, and the exception object is written into the file. The exception is re-raised by executing the **error** statement with no `msgString`. In all cases, the file is closed by executing `fclose(f)` in the **finally** clause.

Checking Syntax

Maple's `maplemint` command generates a list of semantic errors for a specified procedure, if any. The semantic errors for which `maplemint` checks include parameter name conflicts, local and global variable name conflicts, unused variable declarations, and unreachable code. The `maplemint` command has the following syntax.

```
maplemint( procedureName );
```

In the case where the specified procedure is free of semantic errors, `maplemint` returns NULL.

```
> f := proc() local a,i; global c;
>         for i from 1 to 10 do
>            print(i);
>            for i from 1 to 5 do
>              if (a=5) then
>                 a:=6;
>                 return true;
>                 print('test');
>              end if;
>            end do;
>         end do;
> end proc;
```

```
> maplemint(f);

    This code is unreachable:
      print(test)
    These global variables were declared, but never used:
      c
    These local variables were used before they were assigned
    a value:
      a
    These variables were used as the same loop variable for
    nested loops:
      i
```

Similar to `maplemint`, Maple also has an *external* program utility called `mint`. The `mint` program is called from outside Maple and it is used to check both semantic and syntax errors in an external Maple source file. For more information about `mint`, see `?mint`.

7.4   Conclusion

This chapter surveyed a variety of Maple commands that are available to help you find errors in procedures. In particular, the Maple debugger was presented as a tool that you can use to find and correct errors.

8 Numerical Programming in Maple

Representation and manipulation of expressions in symbolic mode, that is, in terms of variables, functions, and exact constants, is a powerful feature of the Maple system. However, practical scientific computation also demands *floating-point* calculations which represent quantities by approximate *numerical* values. Typically, numerical computations are used for one of three reasons.

First, not all problems have analytical or symbolic solutions. For example, of the many partial differential equations known, only a small subset have known closed-form solutions. But, you can usually find numerical solutions.

Second, the analytic answer that Maple returns to your problem may be very large or complex. You are not likely to do calculations by hand which involve rational numbers containing many digits or equations with hundreds of terms, but Maple does not mind such expressions. To understand big expressions, sometimes it helps to compute a floating-point approximation.

Third, you may not always need an exact answer. Computing an analytic answer of infinite precision is not necessary when your only interest is in an approximation. This situation typically arises in plotting. Calculating the points in the graph too accurately is wasteful because normal plotting devices are not capable of displaying ten digits of resolution.

While the rest of this book primarily shows Maple's powerful symbolic methods, the focus of this chapter is on how to perform floating-point calculations in Maple. You will quickly discover that Maple has some extraordinary capabilities in this regard. You have your choice of software floating-point calculations of arbitrary precision or hardware floating-point arithmetic. The former is unaffected, save for speed, by the machine you are using. The latter is determined by the architecture of your computer, but offers the advantage of exceptional speed.

8.1   The Basics of evalf

The `evalf` command is the primary tool in Maple for performing floating-point calculations. It causes Maple to evaluate in software floating-point mode. Maple's software floating-point arithmetic (see section 8.3) has an n-digit machine floating-point model as its basis, but allows computations at arbitrary precision. The environment variable `Digits`, which has an initial setting of 10, determines the default number of digits for calculations.

```
> evalf(Pi);
```

$$3.141592654$$

You may alter the number of digits either by changing the value of `Digits`, or by specifying the number as an index to `evalf`. Note that when you specify the number of digits as an index to `evalf`, the default, `Digits`, remains unchanged.

```
> Digits := 20:
> evalf(Pi);
```

$$3.1415926535897932385$$

```
> evalf[200](Pi);
```

$$3.14159265358979323846264338327950288419\\716939937510582097494459230781640628620\\899862803482534211706798214808651328230\\664709384460955058223172535940812848111\\745028410270193852110555964462294895493\\03820$$

```
> evalf(sqrt(2));
```

$$1.4142135623730950488$$

```
> Digits := 10:
```

The number of digits you specify is the number of *decimal* digits that Maple uses during calculations. Specifying a larger number of digits is likely to give you a more accurate answer, and the maximum value of `Digits` is sufficiently large enough to be considered infinite for practical purposes. Unlike most hardware implementations of floating-point arithmetic, Maple stores and performs software operations on floating-point numbers in base 10.

Because all floating-point computations are carried out in *finite precision*, with intermediate results generally being rounded to `Digits` precision, it is possible for such round-off errors to accumulate in long computations. Maple ensures that the results of any *single* floating-point arithmetic operation ($+$, $-$, $*$, or $/$) are fully accurate. Further, many of the basic functions in Maple, such as the trigonometric functions and their inverses, the exponential and logarithm functions, and some of the other standards special functions for mathematics, are accurate to within .6 *units of last place* (ulps), meaning that if the `Digits` + 1st digit of the true result is a 4, Maple may round it up, or if it is a 6, Maple may round it down. Most mathematical functions in Maple, including numerical integration, achieve this accuracy on nearly all inputs.

Sometimes a definite integral has no closed form solution in terms of standard mathematical functions. You can use `evalf` to obtain an answer via numerical integration.

```
> r := Int(exp(x^3), x=0..1);
```

$$r := \int_0^1 e^{(x^3)} \, dx$$

```
> value(r);
```

$$\int_0^1 e^{(x^3)} \, dx$$

```
> evalf(r);
```

$$1.341904418$$

In other cases, Maple can find an exact solution, but the form of the exact solution is almost incomprehensible. The function **Beta** below is one of the special functions that appear in mathematical literature.

```
> q := Int( x^99 * (1-x)^199 / Beta(100, 200), x=0..1/5 );
```

$$q := \int_0^{1/5} \frac{x^{99}\,(1-x)^{199}}{B(100,\ 200)}\,dx$$

```
> value(q);
```

$$2785229054578052117925524865043430599840384980090969034217041762205271552389776190682816696442051841690247452471818797202945961766386779717574634134906442572750186110143575015735201811298949\\ 972548449 \Big/ 2177412809103715164688738497155211593438496176725167103101324312241148610308262514475552524051323083132387178403327502493606037826303413768253736738334608318334616522866113357176260162148352832620593365691185012466147181896006639730419830500271656525956842642699484713375568389892578125000}\ 0 \frac{1}{B(100,\ 200)}$$

```
> evalf(q);
```

$$.3546007367\,10^{-7}$$

Note that the two examples above use the **Int** command rather than **int** for the integration. If you use **int**, Maple first tries to integrate your expression symbolically. Thus, when evaluating the commands below, Maple spends time finding a symbolic answer and then converts it to a floating-point approximation, rather than performing straight numerical integration.

```
> evalf( int(x^99 * (1-x)^199 / Beta(100, 200), x=0..1/5) );
```

$$.3546007367 \, 10^{-7}$$

When you want Maple to perform numerical calculations, you should not use commands like `int`, `limit`, and `sum` that evaluate their arguments symbolically.

In general, results from `evalf(Int(...))` , `evalf(Sum(...))` , and `evalf(Limit(...))`, will be more accurate than results obtained from the corresponding `evalf(int(...))`, `evalf(sum(...))`, and `evalf(limit(...))` operations. More generally, symbolic evaluation can be suppressed by using unevaluation quotes. For example, `evalf(sin(Pi/3)) = evalf(1/2 * 3^(1/2))` while `evalf('sin'(Pi/3))` computes a floating-point approximation to `sin(evalf(Pi/3))`.

8.2   Hardware Floating-Point Numbers

Maple offers an alternative to software floating-point numbers: your computer's hardware floating-point arithmetic. Hardware floating-point calculations are typically much faster than software floating-point calculations. However, hardware floating-point arithmetic depends on your particular type of computer, and you cannot increase the precision.

The `evalhf` command evaluates an expression using hardware floating-point arithmetic.

```
> evalhf( 1/3 );
```

$$.333333333333333314$$

```
> evalhf( Pi );
```

$$3.14159265358979312$$

Your computer most likely does hardware floating-point arithmetic using a certain number of binary digits. The special construct, `evalhf(Digits)`, approximates the corresponding number of decimal digits.

```
> d := evalhf(Digits);
```

$$d := 15.$$

Therefore, `evalhf` and `evalf` return similar results if `evalf` uses a setting of `Digits` that is close to `evalhf(Digits)`. Maple usually shows you two or three digits more than the value of `evalhf(Digits)` specifies. When you perform hardware floating-point calculations, Maple must convert all the base-10 software floating-point numbers to base-2 hardware floating-point numbers, and then convert the result back to base 10. The extra decimal digits allow Maple to reproduce the binary number precisely if you use it again in a subsequent hardware floating-point calculation.

```
> expr := ln( 2 / Pi * ( exp(2)-1 ) );
```

$$expr := \ln(2\,\frac{e^2 - 1}{\pi})$$

```
> evalhf( expr );
```

$$1.40300383684168617$$

```
> evalf[round(d)]( expr );
```

$$1.40300383684169$$

The results that `evalhf` returns, even including for `evalhf(Digits)`, are not affected by the value of `Digits`.

```
> Digits := 4658;
```

$$Digits := 4658$$

```
> evalhf( expr );
```

$$1.40300383684168617$$

```
> evalhf(Digits);
```

$$15.$$

```
> Digits := 10;
```

$$Digits := 10$$

You can use the `evalhf(Digits)` construct to tell whether hardware floating-point arithmetic provides sufficient precision in a particular application. If `Digits` is less than `evalhf(Digits)`, then you may be able to take advantage of the faster hardware floating-point calculations; otherwise, you should use software floating-point arithmetic to perform the calculation, with sufficient digits. The `evaluate` procedure below takes an *unevaluated* parameter, `expr`. Without the `uneval` declaration, Maple would evaluate `expr` symbolically before invoking `evaluate`.

```
> evaluate := proc(expr::uneval)
>    if Digits < evalhf(Digits) then
>        evalf(evalhf(expr));
>    else
>        evalf(expr);
>    end if;
> end proc:
```

The `evalhf` command knows how to evaluate many of Maple's functions, but not all. For example, you cannot evaluate an integral using hardware floating-point arithmetic.

```
> evaluate( Int(exp(x^3), x=0..1) );
```

```
Error, (in evaluate) unable to evaluate function 'Int'
in evalhf
```

You can improve the `evaluate` procedure so that it traps such errors and tries to evaluate the expression using software floating-point numbers instead.

```
> evaluate := proc(expr::uneval)
>    local result;
>    if Digits < evalhf(Digits) then
>        try
>            evalf(evalhf(expr));
>        catch:
>            evalf(expr);
>        end try;
>    else
>        evalf(expr);
>    end if;
> end proc:
```

```
> evaluate( Int(exp(x^3), x=0..1) );
```

$$1.341904418$$

The `evaluate` procedure provides a model of how to write procedures that take advantage of hardware floating-point arithmetic whenever possible.

Newton Iterations

You can use Newton's method to find numerical solutions to equations. As section 3.1 describes, if x_n is an approximate solution to the equation $f(x) = 0$, then x_{n+1}, given by the following formula, is typically a better approximation.

$$x_{n+1} = x_n - \frac{f(x_n)}{f'(x_n)}$$

This section illustrates how to take advantage of hardware floating-point arithmetic to calculate Newton iterations.

The `iterate` procedure below takes a function, `f`, its derivative, `df`, and an initial approximate solution, `x0`, as input to the equation $f(x) = 0$. `iteration` calculates at most N successive Newton iterations until the difference between the new approximation and the previous one is small. The `iterate` procedure prints out the sequence of approximations so you can follow the workings of the procedure.

```
> iterate := proc( f::procedure, df::procedure,
>                  x0::numeric, N::posint )
>    local xold, xnew;
>    xold := x0;
>    xnew := evalf( xold - f(xold)/df(xold) );
>    to  N-1 while abs(xnew-xold) > 10^(1-Digits) do
>        xold := xnew;
>        print(xold);
>        xnew := evalf( xold - f(xold)/df(xold) );
>    end do;
>    xnew;
> end proc:
```

The procedure below calculates the derivative of f and passes all the necessary information to `iterate`.

```
> Newton := proc( f::procedure, x0::numeric, N::posint )
>    local df;
>    df := D(f);
>    print(x0);
>    iterate(f, df, x0, N);
> end proc:
```

Now you can use `Newton` to solve the equation $x^2 - 2 = 0$.

```
> f := x -> x^2 - 2;
```

$$f := x \rightarrow x^2 - 2$$

```
> Newton(f, 1.5, 15);
```

$$1.5$$

$$1.416666667$$

$$1.414215686$$

$$1.414213562$$

$$1.414213562$$

The version of **Newton** below uses hardware floating-point arithmetic if possible. Since **iterate** only tries to find a solution to an accuracy of 10^(1-Digits), **Newton** uses **evalf** to round the result of the hardware floating-point computation to an appropriate number of digits.

```
> Newton := proc( f::procedure, x0::numeric, N::posint )
>     local df, result;
>     df := D(f);
>     print(x0);
>     if Digits < evalhf(Digits) then
>         try
>             evalf(evalhf(iterate(f, df, x0, N)));
>         catch:
>             iterate(f, df, x0, N);
>         end try;
>     else
>         iterate(f, df, x0, N);
>     end if;
> end proc:
```

Below, **Newton** uses hardware floating-point arithmetic for the iterations and rounds the result to software precision. You can tell which numbers are hardware floating-point numbers because they have more digits than the software floating-point numbers, given the present setting of **Digits**.

```
> Newton(f, 1.5, 15);
```

$$1.5$$

$$1.41666666666666674$$

$$1.41421568627450988$$

$$1.41421356237468987$$

$$1.41421356237309514$$

$$1.414213562$$

You may find it surprising that `Newton` must use software floating-point arithmetic to find a root of the Bessel function below.

```
> F := z -> BesselJ(1, z);
```

$$F := z \to \text{BesselJ}(1,\, z)$$

```
> Newton(F, 4, 15);
```

$$4$$

$$3.826493523$$

$$3.831702467$$

$$3.831705970$$

$$3.831705970$$

The reason is that `evalhf` does not know about `BesselJ` and the symbolic code for `BesselJ` uses the `type` command and remember tables, which `evalhf` does not allow.

```
> evalhf( BesselJ(1, 4) );
```

```
Error, remember tables are not supported in evalhf
```

Using a `try-catch` block as in the `Newton` procedure above, allows your procedure to work even when `evalhf` fails.

You may wonder why the `Newton` procedure above prints out so many digits when it is trying to find a ten-digit approximation. The reason is that the `print` command is located inside the `iterate` procedure which is inside a call to `evalhf`, where all numbers are hardware floating-point numbers, and print as such.

Computing with Arrays of Numbers

Use the `evalhf` command for calculations with numbers. The only structured Maple objects allowed in a call to `evalhf` are arrays of numbers, either table-based arrays or rtable-based Arrays. If an array has undefined entries, `evalhf` initializes them to zero. The procedure below calculates the polynomial $2 + 5x + 4x^2$.

```
> p := proc(x)
>    local a, i;
>    a := array(0..2);
>    a[0] := 2;
>    a[1] := 5;
>    a[2] := 4;
>    sum( a[i]*x^i, i=0..2 );
> end proc:
```

```
> p(x);
```

$$2 + 5x + 4x^2$$

If you intend to enclose p in a call to `evalhf`, you cannot define the local array a using `array(1..3, [2,5,4])`, since lists are not allowed inside `evalhf`. You can, however, enclose p in a call to `evalhf` if the parameter x is a number.

```
> evalhf(p(5.6));
```

$$155.439999999999997$$

You can also pass an array of numbers as a parameter inside a call to `evalhf`. The procedure below calculates the determinant of a 2×2 matrix. The (2,2) entry in the array a below is undefined.

```
> det := proc(a::array(2))
>    a[1,1] * a[2,2] - a[1,2] * a[2,1];
> end proc:
```

```
> a := array( [[2/3, 3/4], [4/9]] );
```

$$a := \begin{bmatrix} \dfrac{2}{3} & \dfrac{3}{4} \\ \dfrac{4}{9} & a_{2,2} \end{bmatrix}$$

```
> det(a);
```

$$\frac{2}{3}\,a_{2,2} - \frac{1}{3}$$

If you call **det** from inside a call to **evalhf**, Maple uses the value 0 for the undefined entry, `a[2,2]`.

```
> evalhf( det(a) );
```

$$-.333333333333333314$$

evalhf passes arrays by value, so the `(2,2)` entry of **a** is still undefined.

```
> a[2,2];
```

$$a_{2,2}$$

If you want **evalhf** to modify an array that you pass as a parameter to a procedure, you must enclose the name of the array in a **var** construct. The **var** construct is special to **evalhf** and is necessary only if you want **evalhf** to modify an array of numbers that is accessible at the session level.

```
> evalhf( det( var(a) ) );
```

$$-.333333333333333314$$

Now **a** is an array of floating-point numbers.

```
> eval(a);
```

$$[.666666666666666629\,, .75000000000000000]$$
$$[.444444444444444420\,, 0.]$$

The **evalhf** command always returns a single floating-point number, but the **var** construct allows you to calculate a whole array of numbers with one call to **evalhf**. Section 9.7 illustrates the use of **var** to calculate a grid of function values that you can use for plotting.

You can also create arrays of hardware floating-point values directly with the **Array** command. Proper use of this command can save significant amounts of time, especially in plotting routines, which rely heavily on arrays of floating-point values. See the help pages for `Array`, `Matrix`, and `Vector` for more details and examples.

8.3 Floating-Point Models in Maple

In addition to being able to represent symbolic constants, such as π and γ, and exact integers and rational numbers, such as 37 and 3/4, Maple has the ability to represent *approximations* to numeric values, using its *floating-point* system. Numbers in this system are represented by pairs of integers, (`m`,`e`). The first integer is called the `significand` or `mantissa`. The second integer is called the `exponent`. The number represented is

$$m \times 10^e.$$

Examples of floating-point numbers in Maple are 3.1415, 1.0, −0.0007, 1.0e0, and 2e1234567. The last two are examples of floating-point numbers entered in *scientific notation*: the "e" separates the mantissa and exponent parts of the number. Such numbers can also be used to represent complex numbers (as can exact integers and rationals): $1.0 + 2.7 * I$, etc.

In some contexts, Maple distinguishes between *software floats* and *hardware floats*. The `evalhf` evaluator (discussed in section 8.2), for example, works with hardware floats, and Maple can construct certain kinds of matrices and vectors with hardware float entries. Generally, however, Maple works with software floats to carry out approximate (but usually very accurate) numerical calculations.

Floating-point number systems are *approximations* to the mathematical set of real (and complex) numbers, and hence necessarily have some limitations. Most importantly, such systems have limited range (there are largest and smallest representable numbers) and limited precision (the entire set of representable floating-point numbers is finite). One very important feature of Maple's software floating-point system is that you have control over at least the latter of these: you can specify the precision at which Maple is to work when doing floating-point computation.

Some of the specific details of these computation systems are provided in the next few sections.

Software Floats

Maple's software floating-point computations are carried out in base 10. The precision of a computation is determined by the setting of `Digits`. The maximum exponent, minimum exponent, and maximum value for `Digits` are machine wordsize dependent. You can obtain the values for these limits from the `Maple_floats` command.

This software floating-point system is designed as a natural extension of the industry standard for hardware floating-point computation, known as IEEE 754. Thus, there are representations for `infinity` and `undefined` (what IEEE 754 calls a `"NaN"`, meaning `"Not a Number"`). Complex numbers are represented by using the standard `x + I*y` format.

One important feature of this system is that the floating-point representation of zero, `0.`, retains its arithmetic sign in computations. That is, Maple distinguishes between `+0.` and `-0.` when necessary. In most situations, this difference is irrelevant, but when dealing with functions such as `ln(x)`, which have a discontinuity across the negative real axis, preserving the sign of the imaginary part of a number on the negative real axis is important.

For more intricate applications, Maple implements extensions of the IEEE 754 notion of a `numeric event`, and provides facilities for monitoring events and their associated status flags. The `"Maple Numerics Overview"` help page is a good starting place to learn more about this system. See `?numerics`.

Roundoff Error

When you perform floating-point arithmetic, whether using software or hardware floats, you are using *approximate* numbers rather than precise real numbers or expressions. Maple can work with exact (symbolic) expressions. The difference between an exact real number and its floating-point approximation is called the *roundoff error*. For example, suppose you request a floating-point representation of π.

```
> pi := evalf(Pi);
```

$$\pi := 3.141592654$$

Maple rounds the precise value π to ten significant digits because `Digits` is set to its default value of 10. You can approximate the roundoff error above by temporarily increasing the value of `Digits` to 15.

```
> evalf[15](Pi - pi);
```

$$-.41021\,10^{-9}$$

Roundoff errors arise not only from the representation of input data, but also as a result of performing arithmetic operations. Each time you perform an arithmetic operation on two floating-point numbers, the infinitely-precise result usually will not be representable in the floating-point number system and therefore the computed result will also have an associated roundoff error.

For example, suppose you multiply two ten-digit numbers with `Digits` = 10. The result can easily have nineteen or twenty digits, but Maple will only store the first ten digits.

```
> 1234567890 * 1937128552;
```

$$2391516709101395280$$

```
> evalf(1234567890) * evalf(1937128552);
```

$$.2391516709\,10^{19}$$

Whenever you apply one of the four basic arithmetic operations (addition, subtraction, multiplication, or division) to two floating-point numbers, the result is the correctly rounded representation of the infinitely precise result, unless overflow or underflow occurs. Of course, Maple may need to compute an extra digit or two behind the scenes to ensure that the answer is correct.

Even so, sometimes a surprising amount of error can accumulate, particularly when subtracting two numbers which are of similar magnitude. In the calculation below, the accurate sum of x, y, and z is $y = 3.141592654$.

```
> x := evalf(987654321);
```

$$x := .987654321\,10^{9}$$

```
> y := evalf(Pi);
```

$$y := 3.141592654$$

```
> z := -x;
```

$$z := -.987654321\,10^{9}$$

```
> x + y + z;
```

$$3.1$$

Catastrophic cancellation is the name of this phenomenon. During the subtraction the eight leading digits cancel out, leaving only two significant digits in the result.

One advantage of Maple's software floats, in contrast to fixed-precision floating-point numbers systems, is that the user can increase the precision to alleviate some of the consequences of roundoff errors. For example, increasing `Digits` to 20 dramatically improves the result.

```
> Digits := 20;
```

$$Digits := 20$$

```
> x + y + z;
```

$$3.141592654$$

You should employ standard numerical analysis techniques to avoid large errors accumulating in your calculations. Often, reordering the operations leads to a more accurate final result. For example, when computing a sum, add the numbers with the smallest magnitude first.

8.4   Extending the `evalf` Command

The `evalf` command knows how to evaluate many functions and constants, such as `sin` and `Pi`. You can also define your own functions or constants, and extend `evalf` by adding information about how to compute such functions or constants.

Defining Your Own Constants

You may define a new constant and write procedures that manipulate this constant symbolically. You could then write a procedure that can calculate a floating-point approximation of your constant to any number of digits. If you assign the procedure a name of the form `‘evalf/constant/name‘`, then Maple invokes the procedure when you use `evalf` to evaluate an expression containing your constant, *name*.

Suppose you want the name MyConst to represent the following infinite series:

$$MyConst = \sum_{i=1}^{\infty} \frac{(-1)^i \pi^i}{2^i i!}.$$

You can calculate approximations to the above series in many ways; the procedure below is one implementation. Note that if a_i is the ith term in the sum, then $a_{i+1} = -a_i(\pi/2)/i$ gives the next term. You can calculate an approximation to the series by adding terms until Maple's model for software floating-point numbers cannot distinguish the new partial sum from the previous one. Using numerical analysis, you can prove that this algorithm calculates Digits accurate digits of MyConst if you use two extra digits inside the algorithm. Therefore, the procedure below increments Digits by two and uses evalf to round the result to the proper number of digits before returning. The procedure does not have to reset the value of Digits because Digits is an environment variable.

```
> 'evalf/constant/MyConst' := proc()
>    local i, term, halfpi, s, old_s;
>    Digits := Digits + 2;
>    halfpi := evalf(Pi/2);
>    old_s := 1;
>    term := 1.0;
>    s := 0;
>    for i from 1 while s <> old_s do
>       term := -term * halfpi / i;
>       old_s := s;
>       s := s + term;
>    end do;
>    evalf[Digits-2](s);
> end proc:
```

When you invoke evalf on an expression containing MyConst, Maple invokes 'evalf/constants/MyConst' to calculate an approximate value.

```
> evalf(MyConst);
```

$$-.7921204237$$

```
> evalf[40](MyConst);
```

$$-.7921204236492380914530443801650212299661$$

You can express the particular constant, MyConst, in closed form and, in this case, you can use the closed-form formula to calculate approximations to MyConst more efficiently.

```
> Sum( (-1)^i * Pi^i / 2^i / i!, i=1..infinity );
```

$$\sum_{i=1}^{\infty} \frac{(-1)^i \, \pi^i}{2^i \, i!}$$

```
> value(%);
```

$$e^{(-1/2\,\pi)} \left(1 - e^{(1/2\,\pi)}\right)$$

```
> expand(%);
```

$$\frac{1}{\sqrt{e^\pi}} - 1$$

```
> evalf(%);
```

$$-.7921204237$$

Defining Your Own Functions

If you define your own functions, you may want to write your own procedure for calculating numerical approximations to the function values. When you invoke `evalf` on an expression containing an unevaluated call to a function F, then Maple calls the procedure `'evalf/F'` if such a procedure exists.

Suppose you want to study the function $x \mapsto (x - \sin(x))/x^3$.

```
> MyFcn := x -> (x - sin(x)) / x^3;
```

$$MyFcn := x \to \frac{x - \sin(x)}{x^3}$$

This function is not defined at $x = 0$, but you can extend it as a continuous function by placing the limiting value in **MyFcn**'s remember table.

```
> MyFcn(0) := limit( MyFcn(x), x=0 );
```

$$MyFcn(0) := \frac{1}{6}$$

For small values of x, $\sin(x)$ is almost equal to x, so the subtraction $x - \sin(x)$ in the definition of MyFcn can lead to inaccuracies due to catastrophic cancellation. When you evaluate v below to ten digits, only the first two are correct.

```
> v := 'MyFcn'( 0.000195 );
```

$$v := \mathrm{MyFcn}(.000195)$$

```
> evalf(v);
```

$$.1618368482$$

```
> evalf(v, 2*Digits);
```

$$.16666666634973617222$$

If you depend on accurate numerical approximations of MyFcn, you must write your own procedure to provide them. You could write such a procedure by exploiting the series expansion of MyFcn.

```
> series( MyFcn(x), x=0, 11 );
```

$$\frac{1}{6} - \frac{1}{120}x^2 + \frac{1}{5040}x^4 - \frac{1}{362880}x^6 + \mathrm{O}(x^8)$$

The general term in the series is

$$a_i = (-1)^i \frac{x^{2i}}{(2i+3)!}, \qquad i \geq 0.$$

Note that $a_i = -a_{i-1}x^2/((2i+2)(2i+3))$. For small values of x, you can then calculate an approximation to MyFcn(x) by adding terms until Maple's model for software floating-point numbers cannot distinguish the new partial sum from the previous one. For larger values of x, catastrophic cancellation is not a problem, so you can use evalf to evaluate the expression. Using numerical analysis, you can prove that this algorithm calculates Digits accurate digits of the function value if you use three extra digits inside the algorithm. Therefore, the procedure below increments Digits by three and uses evalf to round the result to the proper number of digits before returning.

```
> 'evalf/MyFcn' := proc(xx::algebraic)
>    local x, term, s, old_s, xsqr, i;
>    x := evalf(xx);
>    Digits := Digits+3;
>    if type(x, numeric) and abs(x)<0.1 then
>        xsqr := x^2;
>        term := evalf(1/6);
>        s := term;
>        old_s := 0;
>        for i from 1 while s <> old_s do
>            term := -term * xsqr / ((2*i+2)*(2*i+3));
>            old_s := s;
>            s := s + term;
>        end do;
>    else
>        s := evalf( (x-sin(x))/x^3 );
>    end if;
>    eval[Digits-3](s);
> end proc:
```

When you invoke `evalf` on an expression containing an unevaluated call to `MyFcn`, Maple invokes `'evalf/MyFcn'`.

```
> evalf( 'MyFcn'(0.000195) );
```

$$.1666666663498$$

You should now recode the symbolic version of `MyFcn` so that it takes advantage of `'evalf/MyFcn'` if the argument is a floating-point number.

```
> MyFcn := proc(x::algebraic)
>    if type(x, float) then
>        evalf('MyFcn'(x));
>    else
>        (x - sin(x)) / x^3;
>    end if;
> end proc:
```

The `evalf` command automatically looks for `'evalf/MyFcn'` when used in the `evalf('MyFcn')` syntax.

```
> MyFcn(0) := limit( MyFcn(x), x=0 );
```

$$\mathrm{MyFcn}(0) := \frac{1}{6}$$

Now you can properly evaluate `MyFcn` with numeric as well as symbolic arguments.

```
> MyFcn(x);
```

$$\frac{x - \sin(x)}{x^3}$$

```
> MyFcn(0.099999999);
```

$$.1665833531735$$

```
> MyFcn(0.1);
```

$$.1665833531700$$

Section 3.4 describes how to extend many other Maple commands.

8.5   Using the Matlab Package

Another way to accomplish numerical computations in Maple is to use the Matlab package, which provides a way to access several of the MATLAB built-in functions (assuming you have a copy of MATLAB properly installed on your computer). The mathematical functions provided are:

- chol: Cholesky factorization

- defined: test whether varaible exists

- det: determinant

- dimensions: compute dimensions of matrix

- eig: eigenvalues and eigenvectors

- evalM: evaluate expression

- fft: discrete Fourier transforms

- getvar: get numeric array or matrix

- inv: matrix inverse

- lu: LU decomposition

- ode45: solve ordinary differential equation

- `qr`: QR orthogonal-triangular decomposition

- `size`: compute size of matrix

- `square`: determine whether matrix is square

- `transpose`: matrix transposition

There are also a handful of support and utility commands provided.

Matlab converts all Maple structures to `hfarrays` — arrays of hardware floating-point values — before it performs any computations. The results you get will usually be in terms of hfarrays, not standard Maple matrices. The `convert( ,array)` command has been extended to handle any conversions between the two.

For more information on all these commands and the `Matlab` package in general, please refer to the online help for `Matlab`. To learn how to start the MATLAB application from your Maple session, see the online help for `Matlab[openlink]`.

8.6   Conclusion

The various techniques described in this chapter afford an important extension to Maple's programming language and its ability to perform symbolic manipulations. With numerical techniques at your disposal, you can solve equations which are otherwise unsolvable, investigate the properties of complicated solutions, and quickly obtain numerical estimates.

Symbolic calculations give precise representations, but in some cases can be expensive to compute even with such a powerful tool as Maple. At the other extreme, hardware floating-point arithmetic allows you fast computation directly from Maple. This involves, however, limited accuracy. Software floating-point offers a balance. As well as sometimes being much faster than symbolic calculations, you also have the option to control the precision of your calculations, thus exerting control over errors.

Software floating-point calculations and representations mimic the IEEE 754 standard representation closely, except for the great advantage of arbitrary precision. Because of the similarity with this popular standard, you can readily apply the knowledge of accumulation of error and numerical analysis principles that numerous texts and papers contain. When you need to know that your calculations are precise, this wealth of information at your disposal should provide you with confidence in your results.

9   Programming with Maple Graphics

Maple has a wide range of commands for generating both two- and three-dimensional plots. For mathematical expressions, you can use library procedures, such as `plot` and `plot3d`, or one of the many specialized graphics routines found in the `plots` and `plottools` packages, the `DEtools` package (for working with differential equations), and the `stats` package (for statistical data). The input to these commands is typically one or more Maple formulæ, operators, or functions, along with information about domains and possibly ranges. In all cases, the graphic commands allow for the setting of options, specifying such attributes as coloring, shading, or axes style.

The purpose of this chapter is to reveal the structure of the procedures that Maple uses to generate graphical output, and allow you to generate your own graphics procedures. This chapter includes basic information about argument conventions, setting defaults, and processing of plotting options. A major part of the material describes the data structures that Maple uses for plotting, along with various techniques to build such data structures in order to produce graphics in Maple. In addition, you will see how some of the existing functions in the `plots` and `plottools` packages produce specific plotting data structures.

9.1   Basic Plot Functions

This section illustrates some of the basic workings of the graphics procedures in Maple, as well as some of the properties that are common to all Maple plotting commands. Also, it discusses plotting Maple operators or functions versus formula expressions and the setting of optional information.

Several of Maple's graphics procedures take mathematical expressions as their input. Examples of such commands include **plot**, **plot3d**, **animate**, **animate3d**, and **complexplot**. All these commands allow the input to be in one of two forms: formulæ or functions. The former consists of expressions such as $x^2y - y^3 + 1$ or $3\sin(x)\sin(y) + x$, both formulæ in the variables x and y. If p and q are functions with two arguments, then $p + q$ is an example of a function expression. The graphics procedures use the way you specify the domain information to determine if the input is a function expression or a formula in a specified set of variables. For example, the command below generates a three-dimensional plot of the surface which $\sin(x)\sin(y)$ defines. This formula is in terms of x and y.

```
> plot3d( sin(x) * sin(y), x=0..4*Pi, y=-2*Pi..2*Pi );
```

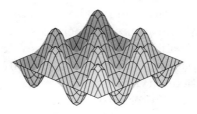

If instead, you define two functions, each with two arguments,

```
> p := (x, y) -> sin(x):   q := (x, y) -> sin(y):
```

then you can plot the surface that $p * q$ determines in the following manner.

```
> plot3d( p * q, 0..4*Pi, -2*Pi..2*Pi );
```

Both cases produce the same three-dimensional plot. In the first example, you supply the information that the input is an expression in x and y by giving the second and third arguments in the form x = *range* and y = *range*, while in the second example, there are no variable names.

Working with formula expressions is simple, but in many cases, functions provide a better mechanism for constructing mathematical functions. The following constructs a mathematical function which, for a given input, computes the required number of iterations (to a maximum of 10) for the sequence $z_{n+1} = z_n^2 + c$ to exit the disk of radius 2 for various complex starting points $c = x + iy$.

```
> mandelbrotSet := proc(x, y)
>    local z, m;
>    z := evalf( x + y*I );
>    m := 0;
>    to 10 while abs(z) < 2 do
>       z := z^2 + (x+y*I);
>       m := m + 1;
>    end do:
>    m;
> end proc:
```

You now have a convenient method for computing a three-dimensional Mandelbrot set on a 50×50 grid.

```
> plot3d( mandelbrotSet, -3/2..3/2, -3/2..3/2, grid=[50,50] );
```

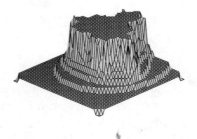

Creating a Maple graphic at the command level displays it on the plotting device (that is, your terminal). In many cases, you can then interactively alter the graph using the tools available with these plotting devices. Examples of such alterations include changing the drawing style, the axes style, and the view point. You can include this information by using optional arguments to plot3d.

```
> plot3d( sin(x)*sin(y), x=-2*Pi..2*Pi, y=-2*Pi..2*Pi,
>         style=patchnogrid, axes=frame );
```

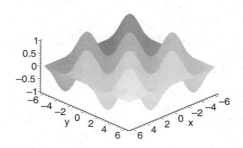

```
> plot3d( mandelbrotSet, -1.5..1.5, -1.5..1.5, grid=[50,50],
>          style=wireframe, orientation=[143,31] );
```

Every plotting procedure allows for optional arguments. You give the optional information in the form *name=option*. Some of these options affect the amount of information concerning the function that you give to the plotting procedures. The **grid** option that the Mandelbrot set example uses is an instance of using an optional argument. You can use other options for specifying visual information once you have determined the graphical points. The type of axes, shading, surface style, line styles, and coloring are but a few of the options available in this category. Obtain information about all the allowable options for the two-dimensional and three-dimensional cases using the help pages **?plot,options** and **?plot3d,options**.

Any graphics routine you create should allow users a similar set of options. When writing programs that call existing Maple graphics routines, simply pass the potential optional arguments directly to these routines.

9.2   Programming with Plotting Library Functions

This section gives examples of programming with the graphics procedures in Maple.

Plotting a Loop

Consider the first problem of plotting a loop from a list of data.

```
> L1 := [ [5,29], [11,23], [11,36], [9,35] ];
```

$$L1 := [[5, 29], [11, 23], [11, 36], [9, 35]]$$

The `plot` command draws lines between the listed points.

```
> plot( L1 );
```

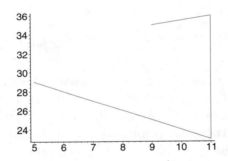

You may want to write a procedure that also draws a line from the last to the first point. All you need to do is append the first point in L1 to the end of L1.

```
> L2 := [ op(L1), L1[1] ];
```

$$L2 := [[5, 29], [11, 23], [11, 36], [9, 35], [5, 29]]$$

```
> plot( L2 );
```

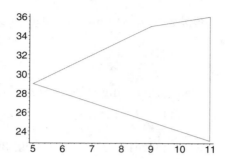

The procedure `loopplot` automates this technique.

```
> loopplot := proc( L )
>    plot( [ op(L), L[1] ] );
> end proc;
```

$$loopplot := \mathbf{proc}(L)\,\mathrm{plot}([\mathrm{op}(L),\,L_1])\,\mathbf{end}\ \mathbf{proc}$$

This procedure has a number of shortcomings. You should always verify the input, L, to `loopplot` to be a list of points, where a point is a list of two constants. That is, L should be of type `list([constant, constant])`. The `loopplot` command should also allow a number of plotting options. All `loopplot` has to do is pass on the options to `plot`. Inside a procedure, `args` is the sequence of arguments in the call to the procedure, and `nargs` is the number of arguments. Thus `args[2..nargs]` is the sequence of options passed to `loopplot`. The `loopplot` procedure should pass all but its first argument, L, directly to `plots`.

```
> loopplot := proc( L::list( [constant, constant] ) )
>    plot( [ op(L), L[1] ], args[2..nargs] );
> end proc:
```

The above version of `loopplot` gives an informative error message if you try to use it with improper arguments, and it also allows plotting options.

```
> loopplot( [[1, 2], [a, b]] );
```

```
Error, invalid input: loopplot expects its 1st
argument, L, to be of type list([constant, constant]),
but received [[1, 2], [a, b]]
```

```
> loopplot( L1, linestyle=3 );
```

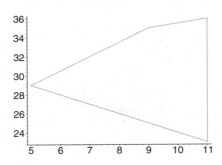

Exercise

1. Improve `loopplot` so that it can handle the empty list as input.

A Ribbon Plot Procedure

This section ends with the creation of a `ribbonplot` procedure, a three-dimensional plot of a list of two-dimensional formulæ or functions.

The `ribbonplot` procedure uses the the `display` procedure from the `plots` package to display the plots. This procedure is called explicitly using its full name so that `ribbonplot` will work even when the short names for the functions in the `plots` package have not been loaded.

The `hasoption` command helps you handle options. In the `ribbonplot` procedure, `hasoption` returns `false` if `numpoints` is not among the options listed in `opts`. If `opts` contains a `numpoints` option, then `hasoption` assigns the value of the `numpoints` option to `n`, and returns the remaining options in the fourth argument (in this case, modifying the value of the list `opts`).

```
> ribbonplot := proc( Flist, r1::name=range )
>     local i, m, p, y, n, opts;
>     opts := [ args[3..nargs] ];
>     if not hasoption( opts, 'numpoints', 'n', 'opts' )
>     then n := 25 # default numpoints
>     end if;
>
>     m := nops( Flist );
>     # op(opts) is any additional options
>     p := seq( plot3d( Flist[i], r1, y=(i-1)..i,
>                       grid=[n, 2], op(opts) ),
>               i=1..m );
>     plots[display]( p );
> end proc:
```

Now `ribbonplot` uses the number of grid points you ask it to.

```
> ribbonplot( [cos(x), cos(2*x), sin(x), sin(2*x)],
>             x=-Pi..Pi, numpoints=16 );
```

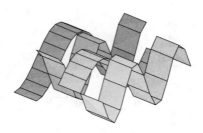

The input to `ribbonplot` above must be a list of expressions. You should extend `ribbonplot` so that it also accepts a list of functions. One difficulty with this extension is that you need to create two-dimensional functions from one-dimensional functions, something that was not a problem in the initial examples of `ribbonplot`. For this you can create an auxiliary procedure, `extend`, which makes use of the `unapply` command.

```
> extend := proc(f)
>   local x,y;
>   unapply(f(x), x, y);
> end proc:
```

For example, the `extend` procedure converts the $R \to R$ function $x \mapsto \cos(2x)$ to a $R^2 \to R$ function.

```
> p := x -> cos(2*x):
> q := extend(p);
```

$$q := (x, y) \to \cos(2\,x)$$

The following gives the new `ribbonplot` code.

```
> ribbonplot := proc( Flist, r1::{range, name=range} )
>     local i, m, p, n, opts, newFlist;
>     opts := [ args[3..nargs] ];
>     if type(r1, range) then
>       #  Functional input.
>         if not hasoption( opts, 'numpoints', 'n', 'opts' )
>         then n := 25 # default numpoints
>         end if;
>         m := nops( Flist );
>       #   change plot3d for functional input
>         p := seq( plot3d( extend( Flist[i] ), r1, (i-1)..i,
```

```
>                          grid=[n,2], op(opts) ),
>                  i=1..m );
>        plots[display]( p );
>     else
>        # Expressions. Convert each to a function of lhs(r1).
>        newFlist := map( unapply, Flist, lhs(r1) );
>        # Use lhs(r1) as the default x-axis label.
>        opts := [ 'labels'=[lhs(r1), "", "" ],
>                  args[3..nargs] ];
>        ribbonplot( newFlist, rhs(r1), op(opts) )
>     end if
> end proc:
```

Here is a ribbon plot of three functions.

```
> ribbonplot( [cos, sin, cos + sin], -Pi..Pi );
```

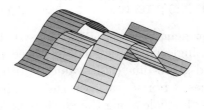

9.3   Maple's Plotting Data Structures

Maple generates plots by sending the user interface an unevaluated PLOT or PLOT3D function call. The information included inside these functions determines the objects they will graph. Every command in the plots package creates such a function. View this flow of information in the following manner. A Maple command produces a PLOT structure and passes it to the user interface. In the user interface, Maple constructs primitive graphic objects based on the PLOT structure. It then passes these objects to the chosen device driver for display. This process is shown schematically in figure 9.1.

You can assign the plotting data structures to variables, transform them into other structures, save them, or even print them out.

You can see examples of a plot structure in either two- or three-dimensions by line printing such a structure.

Figure 9.1 How plots are displayed

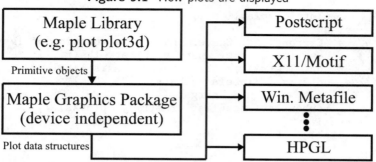

```
> lprint( plot(2*x+3, x=0..5, numpoints=3, adaptive=false) );

PLOT(CURVES([[0., 3.], [2.61565849999999989, 8.2313170\
0000000066], [5., 13.]],COLOUR(RGB,1.0,0.,0.)),
AXESLABELS("x",""),VIEW(0. .. 5.,DEFAULT))
```

Here, **plot** generates a **PLOT** data structure that includes the information for a single curve defined by three points, with the curve colored with the red-green-blue (**RGB**) values $(1.0, 0, 0)$, which corresponds to red. The plot has a horizontal axis running from 0 to 5. Maple, by default, determines the scale along the vertical axes using the information that you provide in the vertical components of the curve. The **numpoints = 3** and **adaptive = false** settings ensure that the curve consists of only three points.

The second example is the graph of $z = xy$ over a 3×4 grid. The **PLOT3D** structure contains a grid of z values over the rectangular region $[0, 1] \times [0, 2]$.

```
> lprint( plot3d(x*y, x=0..1, y=0..2, grid=[3,4]) );

PLOT3D(GRID(0. .. 1.,0. .. 2.,Array(1 .. 3,1 .. 4,{(2,
2) = .333333333333333314, (2, 3) = .666666666666666629
, (2, 4) = 1., (3, 2) = .666666666666666629, (3, 3) =
1.33333333333333326, (3, 4) = 2.},datatype = float[8],
storage = rectangular,order = C_order)),AXESLABELS(x,y
,""))
```

The structure includes labels x and y for the plane but no label for the z-axis.

The third example is again the graph of $z = xy$ but this time in cylindrical coordinates. The **PLOT3D** structure now contains a mesh of points that make up the surface, along with the information that the plotting device should display the surface in a point style.

```
> lprint( plot3d( x*y, x=0..1, y=0..2, grid=[3,2],
>                  coords=cylindrical, style=point ) );
```

```
PLOT3D(MESH(Array(1 .. 3,1 .. 2,1 .. 3,{(1, 2, 3) = 2.
, (2, 2, 1) = .877582561890372758, (2, 2, 2) = .479425\
538604203006, (2, 2, 3) = 2., (3, 2, 1) = 1.0806046117\
3627952, (3, 2, 2) = 1.68294196961579300, (3, 2, 3) =
2.},datatype = float[8],storage = rectangular,order =
C_order)),STYLE(POINT))
```

Since the plot is not in cartesian coordinates there are no default labels, it follows that the PLOT3D structure does not contain any AXESLABELS.

The PLOT Data Structure

You can construct and manipulate a plotting data structure directly to create two- and three-dimensional plots. All you need is a correct arrangement of the geometric information inside a PLOT or PLOT3D function. The information inside this function determines the objects that the plotting device displays. Here Maple evaluates the expression

```
> PLOT( CURVES( [ [0,0], [2,1] ] ) );
```

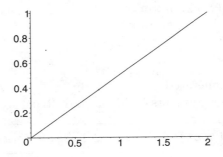

and passes it to the Maple interface which determines that this is a plot data structure. The Maple interface then dismantles the contents and passes the information to a plot driver which then determines the graphical information that it will render onto the plotting device. In the latest example, the result is a single line from the origin to the point $(2, 1)$. The CURVES data structure consists of one or more lists of points each generating a curve, along with some optional arguments (for example, line style or line thickness information). Thus, the expression

```
> n := 200:
> points := [ seq( [2*cos(i*Pi/n), sin(i*Pi/n) ], i=0..n) ]:
> PLOT( CURVES( evalf(points) ) );
```

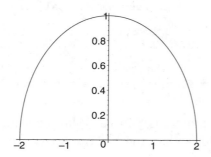

generates the plot of a sequence of $n + 1$ points in the plane. The points found inside the PLOT data structure must be numeric. If you omit the evalf statement, then non-numeric objects within the PLOT structure, such as $\sin(\pi/200)$, cause an error.

> PLOT(CURVES(points));

```
Plotting error, non-numeric vertex definition
```

> type(sin(Pi/n), numeric);

$$false$$

Hence, no plot is generated.

In general, the arguments inside a PLOT structure are all of the form

---
ObjectName(ObjectInformation, LocalInformation)
---

where *ObjectName* is a function name; for example, one of CURVES, POLYGONS, POINTS, or TEXT; *ObjectInformation* contains the basic geometric point information that describes the particular object; and the optional *LocalInformation* contains information about options that apply only to this particular object. *ObjectInformation* depends on the *ObjectName*. In the case where the *ObjectName* is CURVES or POINTS, the *ObjectInformation* consists of one or more lists of two-dimensional points. Each list supplies the set of points making up a single curve in the plane. Similarly, when *ObjectName* is POLYGONS, then the object information consists of one or more lists of points where each list describes the vertices of a single polygon in the plane. When *ObjectName* is TEXT, the object information consists of a point location along with a text string. The optional information is also in the form of an unevaluated function call. In the two-dimensional case, the options include AXESSTYLE, STYLE, LINESTYLE, THICKNESS, SYMBOL, FONT, AXESTICKS, AXESLABELS, VIEW, and SCALING.

You can also place some of these as *LocalInformation* inside a POINTS, CURVES, TEXT, or POLYGONS object; *LocalInformation* overrides the global option for the rendering of that object. The COLOR option allows for a further format when you place it on an object. In the case of an object having multiple subobjects (for example multiple points, lines, or polygons), you can supply one color value for each object.

Here is a simple way to generate a filled histogram of sixty-three values of the function $y = \sin(x)$ from 0 to 6.3. Maple colors each trapezoid individually by the HUE value corresponding to $y = |\cos(x)|$.

```
> p := i -> [ [(i-1)/10, 0], [(i-1)/10, sin((i-1)/10)],
>             [i/10, sin(i/10)], [i/10, 0] ]:
```

Now p(i) is the list of corners of the ith trapezoid. For example, p(2) contains the corners of the second trapezoid.

```
> p(2);
```

$$[[\frac{1}{10}, 0], [\frac{1}{10}, \sin(\frac{1}{10})], [\frac{1}{5}, \sin(\frac{1}{5})], [\frac{1}{5}, 0]]$$

Define the function h to give the color of each trapezoid.

```
> h := i -> abs( cos(i/10) ):
> PLOT( seq( POLYGONS( evalf( p(i) ),
>              COLOR(HUE, evalf( h(i) )) ),
>           i = 1..63) );
```

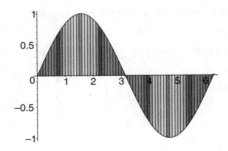

A Sum Plot

You can create procedures that directly build PLOT data structures. For example, given an unevaluated sum you can compute the partial sums, and place the values in a CURVES structure.

```
> s := Sum( 1/k^2, k=1..10 );
```

$$s := \sum_{k=1}^{10} \frac{1}{k^2}$$

You can use the **typematch** command to pick the unevaluated sum apart into its components.

```
> typematch( s, 'Sum'( term::algebraic,
>              n::name=a::integer..b::integer ) );
```

$$true$$

The **typematch** command assigns the parts of the sum to the given names.

```
> term, n, a, b;
```

$$\frac{1}{k^2}, \; k, \; 1, \; 10$$

You can now calculate the partial sums.

```
> sum( term, n=a..a+2 );
```

$$\frac{49}{36}$$

The following defines a procedure, **psum**, which calculates a floating-point value of the mth partial sum.

```
> psum := evalf @ unapply( Sum(term, n=a..(a+m)), m );
```

$$psum := evalf@ \left(m \to \sum_{k=1}^{1+m} \frac{1}{k^2} \right)$$

You can now create the necessary list of points.

```
> points := [ seq( [[i,psum(i)], [i+1,psum(i)]],
>     i=1..(b-a+1) ) ];
```

$points := [[[1,\ 1.250000000],\ [2,\ 1.250000000]],$
$\qquad [[2,\ 1.361111111],\ [3,\ 1.361111111]],$
$\qquad [[3,\ 1.423611111],\ [4,\ 1.423611111]],$
$\qquad [[4,\ 1.463611111],\ [5,\ 1.463611111]],$
$\qquad [[5,\ 1.491388889],\ [6,\ 1.491388889]],$
$\qquad [[6,\ 1.511797052],\ [7,\ 1.511797052]],$
$\qquad [[7,\ 1.527422052],\ [8,\ 1.527422052]],$
$\qquad [[8,\ 1.539767731],\ [9,\ 1.539767731]],$
$\qquad [[9,\ 1.549767731],\ [10,\ 1.549767731]],$
$\qquad [[10,\ 1.558032194],\ [11,\ 1.558032194]]]$

```
> points := map( op, points );
```

$points := [[1,\ 1.250000000],\ [2,\ 1.250000000],$
$\qquad [2,\ 1.361111111],\ [3,\ 1.361111111],\ [3,\ 1.423611111],$
$\qquad [4,\ 1.423611111],\ [4,\ 1.463611111],\ [5,\ 1.463611111],$
$\qquad [5,\ 1.491388889],\ [6,\ 1.491388889],\ [6,\ 1.511797052],$
$\qquad [7,\ 1.511797052],\ [7,\ 1.527422052],\ [8,\ 1.527422052],$
$\qquad [8,\ 1.539767731],\ [9,\ 1.539767731],\ [9,\ 1.549767731],$
$\qquad [10,\ 1.549767731],\ [10,\ 1.558032194],\ [11,\ 1.558032194]]$

This list has the right form.

```
> PLOT( CURVES( points ) );
```

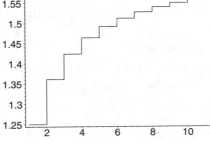

The `sumplot` procedure automates this technique.

```
> sumplot := proc( s )
>    local term, n, a, b, psum, m, points, i;
>    if typematch( s, 'Sum'( term::algebraic,
>        n::name=a::integer..b::integer ) ) then
>        psum := evalf @ unapply( Sum(term, n=a..(a+m)), m );
```

```
>          points := [ seq( [[i,psum(i)], [i+1,psum(i)]],
>             i=1..(b-a+1) ) ];
>          points := map(op, points);
>          PLOT( CURVES( points ) );
>       else
>          error "expecting a Sum structure as input"
>       end if
> end proc:
```

Here is a **sumplot** of an alternating series.

```
> sumplot( Sum((-1)^k/k, k=1..25 ));
```

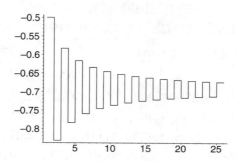

The limit of this sum is $-\ln 2$.

```
> Sum((-1)^k/k, k=1..infinity):    % = value(%);
```

$$\sum_{k=1}^{\infty} \frac{(-1)^k}{k} = -\ln(2)$$

See ?plot,structure for more details on the PLOT data structure.

The PLOT3D Data Structure

The three-dimensional plotting data structure has a form similar to the PLOT data structure. Thus, for example, the Maple expression below generates a three-dimensional plot of three lines and axes of type **frame**.

```
> PLOT3D( CURVES( [ [3, 3, 0], [0, 3, 1],
>                   [3, 0, 1], [3, 3, 0] ] ),
>         AXESSTYLE(FRAME) );
```

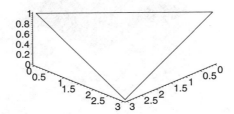

The following procedure creates the sides of a box and colors them yellow.

```
> yellowsides := proc(x, y, z, u)
>    # (x,y,0) = coordinates of a corner.
>    # z = height of box
>    # u = side length of box
>     POLYGONS(
>       [ [x,y,0], [x+u,y,0], [x+u,y,z], [x,y,z] ],
>       [ [x,y,0], [x,y+u,0], [x,y+u,z], [x,y,z] ],
>       [ [x+u, y,0], [x+u,y+u,0], [x+u,y+u,z], [x+u,y,z] ],
>       [ [x+u, y+u,0], [x,y+u,0], [x,y+u,z], [x+u,y+u,z] ],
>            COLOR(RGB,1,1,0) );
> end proc:
```

The **redtop** procedure generates a red lid for the box.

```
> redtop := proc(x, y, z, u)
>    # (x,y,z) = coordinates of a corner.
>    # u = side length of square
>     POLYGONS( [ [x,y,z], [x+u,y,z], [x+u,y+u,z], [x,y+u,z] ],
>            COLOR(RGB, 1, 0, 0) );
>    end proc:
```

You can now put the sides and the top inside a **PLOT3D** structure to display them.

```
> PLOT3D( yellowsides(1, 2, 3, 0.5),
>         redtop(1, 2, 3, 0.5),
>         STYLE(PATCH) );
```

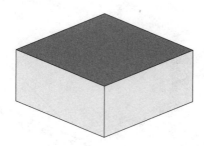

Using **yellowsides** and **redtop** you can create a three-dimensional histogram plot. Here is the histogram corresponding to $z = 1/(x+y+4)$, for $0 \leq x \leq 4$ and $0 \leq y \leq 4$.

```
> sides := seq( seq( yellowsides(i, j, 1/(i+j+4), 0.75),
>     j=0..4), i=0..4):
> tops := seq( seq( redtop( i, j, 1/(i+j+4), 0.75),
>     j=0..4 ), i=0..4 ):
```

Histograms look nice when you enclose them in a box of axes. Axes are generated using **AXESSTYLE**.

```
> PLOT3D( sides, tops, STYLE(PATCH), AXESSTYLE(BOXED) );
```

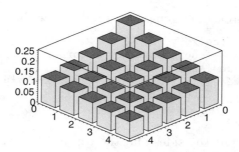

You can modify the above construction to create a **listbarchart3d** procedure which, for a given list of lists of heights, gives a three-dimensional bar chart as above for its output.

The names of the objects that can appear inside a **PLOT3D** data structure include all those that you can use in the **PLOT** data structure. Thus **POINTS**, **CURVES**, **POLYGONS**, and **TEXT** are also available for use inside an unevaluated **PLOT3D** call. As in the two-dimensional case, when the object name is **CURVES** or **POINTS**, the point information consists of one or more lists of three-dimensional points, each list supplying the set of points making up a single curve in three-dimensional space. In the case of a POLYGONS structure, the point information consists of one or more lists of points. In this case, each list describes the vertices of a single polygon in three-dimensional space. There are two extra objects for PLOT3D structures. GRID is a structure that describes a functional grid. It consists of two ranges defining a grid in the x–y plane and a list of lists of z values over this grid. In the following example LL contains 4 lists each of length 3. Therefore the grid is 4×3, and x runs from 1 to 3 in increments of $2/3$, whereas y runs from 1 to 2 in increments of $1/2$.

```
> LL := [ [0,1,0], [1,1,1], [2,1,2], [3,0,1] ]:
```

```
> PLOT3D( GRID( 1..3, 1..2, LL ), AXESLABELS(x,y,z),
>          ORIENTATION(135, 45), AXES(BOXED) );
```

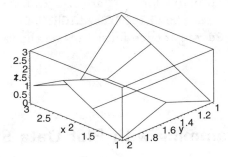

The MESH structure contains a list of lists of three-dimensional points describing a surface in three dimensions.[1]

```
> LL := [ [ [0,0,0], [1,0,0], [2,0,0], [3,0,0] ],
>          [ [0,1,0], [1,1,0], [2.1, 0.9, 0],
>                     [3.2, 0.7, 0] ],
>          [ [0,1,1], [1,1,1], [2.2, 0.6, 1],
>                     [3.5, 0.5, 1.1] ] ];
```

$$LL := [[[0, 0, 0], [1, 0, 0], [2, 0, 0], [3, 0, 0]],$$
$$[[0, 1, 0], [1, 1, 0], [2.1, .9, 0], [3.2, .7, 0]],$$
$$[[0, 1, 1], [1, 1, 1], [2.2, .6, 1], [3.5, .5, 1.1]]]$$

The MESH structure represents the quadrilaterals spanned by

$$LL_{i,j}, LL_{i,j+1}, LL_{i+1,j}, LL_{i+1,j+1}$$

---

[1] An $n \times m \times 3$ hfarray is also allowed as input to MESH.

for all meaningful values of i and j.

```
> PLOT3D( MESH( LL ), AXESLABELS(x,y,z), AXES(BOXED),
>          ORIENTATION(-140, 45) );
```

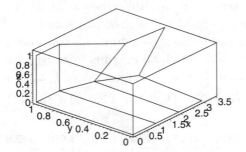

All the options available for PLOT are also available for PLOT3D. In addition, you can also use the GRIDSTYLE, LIGHTMODEL, and AMBIENTLIGHT options. See ?plot3d,structure for details on the various options to the PLOT3D structure.

9.4   Programming with Plot Data Structures

This section describes some of the tools that are available for programming at the PLOT and PLOT3D data structure level. Plotting data structures have the advantage of allowing *direct* access to all the functionality that Maple's plotting facilities provide. The examples in section 9.3 show the extent of the facilities' power. You could easily thicken the lines in the sum plot by adding local information to the objects in that example. This section provides a simple set of examples that describe how to program at this lower level.

Writing Graphic Primitives

You can write procedures that allow you to work with plot objects at a more conceptual level. For example, the line and disk commands in the plottools package provide a model for programming primitives such as points, lines, curves, circles, rectangles, and arbitrary polygons in both two and three dimensions. In all cases, you can specify options, such as line or patch style and color, in the same format as in other plotting procedures in Maple.

```
> line := proc(x::list, y::list)
>     # x and y represent points in either 2-D or 3-D
>     local opts;
>     opts := [ args[3..nargs] ];
>     opts := convert( opts, PLOToptions );
>     CURVES( evalf( [x, y] ), op(opts) );
> end proc:
```

Inside a procedure, **nargs** is the number of arguments and **args** is the actual argument sequence. Thus, in **line**, **args[3..nargs]** is the sequence of arguments that follow x and y. The **convert(..., PLOToptions)** command converts user-level options to the format that **PLOT** requires.

```
> convert( [axes=boxed, color=red], PLOToptions );
```

$$[\text{AXESSTYLE}(BOX), \text{COLOUR}(RGB, 1.00000000, 0., 0.)]$$

The **disk** procedure below is similar to **line** except that you can specify the number of points that **disk** should use to generate the disk. Therefore **disk** must handle that option, **numpoints**, separately. The **hasoption** command determines whether a certain option is present.

```
> disk := proc(x::list, r::algebraic)
>     # draw a disk of radius r centered at x in 2-D.
>     local i, n, opts, vertices;
>     opts := [ args[3..nargs] ] ;
>     if not hasoption( opts, numpoints, n, 'opts' )
>     then n := 50;
>     end if;
>     opts := convert(opts, PLOToptions);
>     vertices := seq( evalf( [ x[1] + r*cos(2*Pi*i/n),
>                               x[2] + r*sin(2*Pi*i/n) ] ),
>                      i = 0..n );
>     POLYGONS( [vertices], op(opts) );
> end proc:
```

You can now display two disks connected by a line as follows.

```
> with(plots):
```

```
Warning, the name changecoords has been redefined
```

```
> display( disk([-1, 0], 1/2, color=plum),
>          line([-1, 1/2], [1, 1/2]),
>          disk([1, 0], 1/2, thickness=3),
>          scaling=constrained );
```

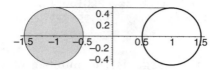

Note how the options to the individual objects apply only to those objects.

Plotting Gears

This example shows how you can manipulate plotting data structures to embed two-dimensional plots into a three-dimensional setting. The procedure below creates a little piece of the boundary of a two-dimensional graph of a gear-like structure.

```
> outside := proc(a, r, n)
>    local p1, p2;
>    p1 := evalf( [ cos(a*Pi/n), sin(a*Pi/n) ] );
>    p2 := evalf( [ cos((a+1)*Pi/n), sin((a+1)*Pi/n) ] );
>    if r = 1 then p1, p2;
>    else p1, r*p1, r*p2, p2;
>    end if
> end proc:
```

For example

```
> outside( Pi/4, 1.1, 16 );
```

$$[.9881327882, .1536020604], [1.086946067, .1689622664],$$
$$[1.033097800, .3777683623],$$
$$[.9391798182, .3434257839]$$

```
> PLOT( CURVES( [%] ), SCALING(CONSTRAINED) );
```

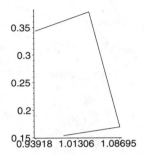

When you put the pieces together, you get a gear. SCALING(CONSTRAINED), which corresponds to the option scaling=constrained, is used to ensure that the gear appears round.

```
> points := [ seq( outside(2*a, 1.1, 16), a=0..16 ) ]:
> PLOT( CURVES(points), AXESSTYLE(NONE), SCALING(CONSTRAINED) );
```

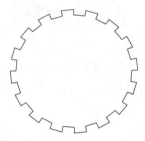

You can fill this object using the POLYGONS object. However, you must be careful, as Maple assumes that the polygons are convex. Hence, you should draw each wedge-shaped section of the gear as a triangular polygon.

```
> a := seq( [ [0, 0], outside(2*j, 1.1, 16) ], j=0..15 ):
> b := seq( [ [0, 0], outside(2*j+1, 1, 16) ], j=0..15 ):
> PLOT( POLYGONS(a,b), AXESSTYLE(NONE), SCALING(CONSTRAINED) );
```

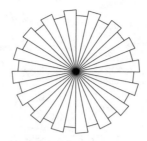

Adding **STYLE(PATCHNOGRID)** to the above structure and combining it with the curve from the first picture gives you a filled gear-like structure. To embed this in three dimensions, say at a thickness of t units, you can use the utility procedures

```
> double := proc( L, t )
>    local u;
>    [ seq( [u[1], u[2], 0], u=L ) ],
>    [ seq( [u[1], u[2], t], u=L ) ];
> end proc:
```

which take a list of vertices and create two copies in three-dimensional space, one at height 0 and the second at height t, and

```
> border := proc( L1, L2 )
>    local i, n;
>    n := nops(L1);
>    seq( [ L1[i], L2[i], L2[i+1], L1[i+1] ], i = 1..n-1 ),
>       [ L1[n], L2[n], L2[1], L1[1] ];
> end proc:
```

which input two lists of vertices and join the corresponding vertices from each list into vertices that make up quadrilaterals. You can create the top and bottom vertices of the gear embedded into three-dimensional space as follows.

```
> faces :=
> seq( double(p,1/2),
>       p=[ seq( [ outside(2*a+1, 1.1, 16), [0,0] ],
>                a=0..16 ),
>           seq( [ outside(2*a, 1,16), [0,0] ], a=0..16 )
>          ] ):
```

Now **faces** is a sequence of doubled outside values.

```
> PLOT3D( POLYGONS( faces ) );
```

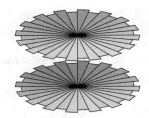

As above, the following are the points on the outline of a gear.

```
> points := [ seq( outside(2*a, 1.1, 16), a=0..16 ) ]:
> PLOT( CURVES(points), AXESSTYLE(NONE), SCALING(CONSTRAINED) );
```

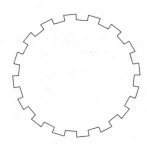

If you double these points, you get vertices of the polygons making up the border of the three-dimensional gear.

```
> bord := border( double( [ seq( outside(2*a+1, 1.1, 16),
>                                 a=0..15 ) ], 1/2) ):
> PLOT3D( seq( POLYGONS(b), b=bord ) );
```

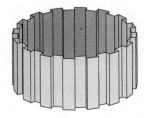

To display the gear you need to put these together in a single PLOT3D structure. Use STYLE(PATCHNOGRID) as a local option to the top and bottom of the gear so that they do not appear as several triangles.

```
> PLOT3D( POLYGONS(faces, STYLE(PATCHNOGRID) ),
>         seq( POLYGONS(b), b=bord ),
>       STYLE(PATCH), SCALING(CONSTRAINED) );
```

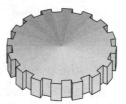

Note that the global STYLE(PATCH) and SCALING(CONSTRAINED) options apply to the whole PLOT3D structure, except where the local STYLE(PATCHNOGRID) option to the top and bottom of the gear overrides the global STYLE(PATCH) option.

Polygon Meshes

Section 9.3 describes the MESH data structure which you generate when you use plot3d to draw a parametrized surface. This simple matter involves converting a mesh of points into a set of vertices for corresponding polygons. Using polygons rather than a MESH structure allows you to modify the individual polygons. The procedure polygongrid creates the vertices of a quadrangle at the (i, j)th grid value.

```
> polygongrid := proc(gridlist, i, j)
>    gridlist[j][i], gridlist[j][i+1],
>    gridlist[j+1][i+1], gridlist[j+1][i];
> end proc:
```

You can then use makePolygongrid to construct the appropriate polygons.

```
> makePolygongrid := proc(gridlist)
>    local m,n,i,j;
>    n := nops(gridlist);
>    m := nops(gridlist[1]);
>    POLYGONS( seq( seq( [ polygongrid(gridlist, i, j) ],
>              i=1..m-1), j=1..n-1) );
> end proc:
```

The following is a mesh of points in two-dimensional space.

```
> L := [ seq( [ seq( [i-1, j-1], i=1..3 ) ], j=1..4 ) ];
```

$$L := [[[0, 0], [1, 0], [2, 0]], [[0, 1], [1, 1], [2, 1]],$$
$$[[0, 2], [1, 2], [2, 2]], [[0, 3], [1, 3], [2, 3]]]$$

The makePolygongrid procedure creates the POLYGONS structure corresponding to L.

```
> grid1 := makePolygongrid( L );
```

$$grid1 := \text{POLYGONS}([[0, 0], [1, 0], [1, 1], [0, 1]],$$
$$[[1, 0], [2, 0], [2, 1], [1, 1]], [[0, 1], [1, 1], [1, 2], [0, 2]],$$
$$[[1, 1], [2, 1], [2, 2], [1, 2]], [[0, 2], [1, 2], [1, 3], [0, 3]],$$
$$[[1, 2], [2, 2], [2, 3], [1, 3]])$$

Put the polygons inside a PLOT structure to display them.

```
> PLOT( grid1 );
```

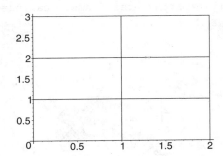

You can also use the convert(..., POLYGONS) command to convert GRID or MESH structures to polygons; see ?convert,POLYGONS. convert(..., POLYGONS) calls the procedure 'convert/POLYGONS' which, in the case of a MESH structure, works as the makePolygongrid procedure above.

9.5 Programming with the `plottools` Package

While the plotting data structure has the advantage of allowing direct access to all the functionality that Maple's plotting facilities provide, it does not allow you to specify colors (such as red or blue) in an intuitive way, nor does it allow you to use all the representations of numeric data, such as π or $\sqrt{2}$, that you find in Maple.

This section shows you how to work with basic graphic objects at a level higher than that of the plotting data structures. The `plottools` package provides commands for creating lines, disks, and other two-dimensional objects, along with commands to generate shapes such as spheres, tori, and polyhedra. For example, one can draw a sphere of unit radius and a torus at specified center using a patch style of rendering and a frame style of axis

```
> with(plots): with(plottools):

Warning, the name changecoords has been redefined
Warning, the name arrow has been redefined


> display( sphere( [0, 0, 2] ), torus( [0, 0, 0] ),
>          style=patch, axes=frame, scaling=constrained );
```

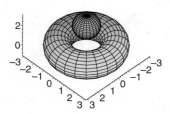

and rotate it at various angles via the functions in the `plottools` package.

```
> rotate( %, Pi/4, -Pi/4, Pi/4 );
```

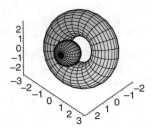

A Pie Chart

You can write a plotting procedure to build a pie chart of a list of integer data. The **piechart** procedure below uses the following **partialsum** procedure which calculates the partial sums of a list of numbers up to a given term.

```
> partialsum := proc(d, i)
>    local j;
>    evalf( Sum( d[j], j=1..i ) )
> end proc:
```

For example

```
> partialsum( [1, 2, 3, -6], 3 );
```

$$6.$$

The **piechart** procedure first computes the relative weights of the data along with the centers of each pie slice. **piechart** uses a **TEXT** structure to place the data information at the center of each pie slice and the **pieslice** command from the **plottools** package to generate the pie slices. Finally, **piechart** also varies the colors of each slice by defining a color function based on hue coloring.

```
> piechart := proc( data::list(integer) )
>    local b, c, i, n, x, y, total;
>
>    n  := nops(data);
>    total := partialsum(data, n);
>    b := 0, seq( evalf( 2*Pi*partialsum(data, i)/total ),
>                 i =1..n );
>    x := seq( ( cos(b[i])+cos(b[i+1]) ) / 3, i=1..n ):
>    y := seq( ( sin(b[i])+sin(b[i+1]) ) / 3, i=1..n ):
>    c := (i, n) -> COLOR(HUE, i/(n + 1)):
>    PLOT( seq( plottools[pieslice]( [0, 0], 1,
```

```
>                           b[i]..b[i+1], color=c(i, n) ),
>                   i=1..n),
>             seq( TEXT( [x[i], y[i]],
>                           convert(data[i], name) ),
>                   i = 1..n ),
>             AXESSTYLE(NONE), SCALING(CONSTRAINED) );
> end proc:
```

Here is a piechart with six slices.

```
> piechart( [ 8, 10, 15, 10, 12, 16 ] );
```

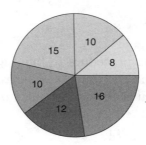

The **AXESSTYLE(NONE)** option ensures that Maple does not draw any axes with the pie chart.

A Dropshadow Procedure

You can use the existing procedures to create other types of plots that are not part of the available Maple graphics library. For example, the following procedure computes the three-dimensional plot of a surface, $z = f(x, y)$, that has a dropshadow projection onto a plane located below the surface. The procedure makes use of the commands **contourplot**, **contourplot3d**, **display** from the **plots** package, and **transform** from the **plottools** package.

```
> dropshadowplot := proc(F::algebraic, r1::name=range,
>       r2::name=range, r3::name=range)
>    local minz, p2, p3, coption, opts, f, g, x, y;
>
>    # set the number of contours (default 8)
>    opts := [args[5..nargs]];
>    if not hasoption( opts, 'contours', coption, 'opts' )
>    then coption := 8;
>    end if;
>
>    # determine the base of the plot axes
>    # from the third argument
>    minz := lhs(`if`(r3::range, r3, rhs(r3)));
>    minz := evalf(minz);
```

```
>
>
>     # create 2d and 3d contour plots for F.
>     p3 := plots[contourplot3d]( F, r1, r2,
>              'contours'=coption, op(opts) );
>     p2 := plots[contourplot]( F, r1, r2,
>              'contours'=coption, op(opts) );
>
>     # embed contour plot into R^3 via plottools[transform]
>     g := unapply( [x,y,minz], x, y );
>     f := plottools[transform]( g );
>     plots[display]([ f(p2), p3 ]);
> end proc:
```

The `filled=true` option to `contourplot` and `contourplot3d` causes these two commands to fill the regions between the level curves with a color that indicates the level.

```
> expr := -5 * x / (x^2+y^2+1);
```

$$expr := -5\,\frac{x}{x^2 + y^2 + 1}$$

```
> dropshadowplot( expr, x=-3..3, y=-3..3, z=-4..3,
>     filled=true, contours=3, axes=frame );
```

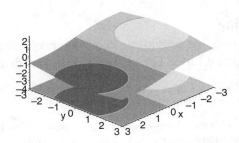

The first section of the dropshadow procedure determines if you have specified a `contours` option in the optional arguments (those after the fourth argument), making use of the `hasoption` procedure. The next section of `dropshadowplot` determines the z value of the base. Note that you must take care since you specify ranges differently for formula that for function input. The remaining sections create the correct plotting objects which represent the two types of contour plots. `dropshadowplot` embeds the two-dimensional contour plot into three-dimensional space using the transformation

$$(x, y) \mapsto [x, y, minz]$$

going from $R^2 \to R^3$. Finally, it displays the two plots together in one three-dimensional plotting object.

Note that you can either provide an alternate number of levels or even specify the precise contour locations via the `contours` option. Thus,

```
> dropshadowplot( expr, x=-3..3, y=-3..3, z=-4..3,
>                 filled=true, contours=[-2,-1,0,1,2] );
```

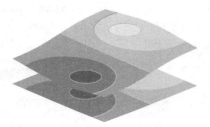

produces a plot similar to that shown above, except now it produces 5 contours at levels $-2, -1, 0, 1$, and 2.

Creating a Tiling

The `plottools` package provides a convenient environment for programming graphical procedures. For example, you can draw circular arcs in a unit square.

```
> with(plots): with(plottools):
```

```
Warning, the name changecoords has been redefined
Warning, the name arrow has been redefined
```

```
> a := rectangle( [0,0], [1,1] ),
>      arc( [0,0], 0.5, 0..Pi/2 ),
>      arc( [1,1], 0.5, Pi..3*Pi/2 ):
> b := rectangle( [1.5,0], [2.5,1] ),
>      arc( [1.5,1], 0.5, -Pi/2..0 ),
>      arc( [2.5,0], 0.5, Pi/2..Pi ):
```

You must use `display` from `plots` to show the objects that `rectangle` and `arc` create.

```
> display( a, b, axes=none, scaling=constrained );
```

You can tile the plane with a and b type rectangles. The following procedure creates such a $m \times n$ tiling using a function, g, to determine when to use an a-tile and when to use a b-tile. The function g should return either 0, to use an a-tile, or 1, to use a b-tile.

```
> tiling := proc(g, m, n)
>    local i, j, r, h, boundary, tiles;
>
>    # define an a-tile
>    r[0] := plottools[arc]( [0,0], 0.5, 0..Pi/2 ),
>           plottools[arc]( [1,1], 0.5, Pi..3*Pi/2 );
>    # define a b-tile
>    r[1] := plottools[arc]( [0,1], 0.5, -Pi/2..0 ),
>           plottools[arc]( [1,0], 0.5, Pi/2..Pi );
>    boundary := plottools[curve]( [ [0,0], [0,n],
>                   [m,n], [m,0], [0,0]] ).;
>    tiles := seq( seq( seq( plottools[translate](h, i, j),
>              h=r[g(i, j)] ), i=0..m-1 ), j=0..n-1 );
>    plots[display]( tiles, boundary, args[4..nargs] );
> end proc:
```

As an example, define the following procedure which randomly returns either 0 or 1.

```
> oddeven := proc() rand() mod 2 end proc:
```

Create a 20×10 tiling (called a Truchet tiling) with no axes and constrained scaling.

```
> tiling( oddeven, 20, 10, scaling=constrained, axes=none);
```

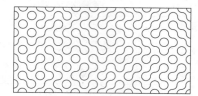

When you use the same procedure again, the random tiling is different.

```
> tiling( oddeven, 20, 10, scaling=constrained, axes=none);
```

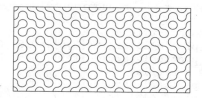

A Smith Chart

The commands in the `plottools` package allow for easy creation of such useful graphs as a Smith Chart, used in microwave circuit analysis.

```
> smithChart := proc(r)
>    local i, a, b, c ;
>    a := PLOT( seq( plottools[arc]( [-i*r/4,0],
>                                    i*r/4, 0..Pi ),
>                 i = 1..4 ),
>       plottools[arc]( [0,r/2], r/2,
>                       Pi-arcsin(3/5)..3*Pi/2 ),
>       plottools[arc]( [0,r], r, Pi..Pi+arcsin(15/17) ),
>       plottools[arc]( [0,2*r], 2*r,
>                       Pi+arcsin(3/5)..Pi+arcsin(63/65) ),
>       plottools[arc]( [0,4*r], 4*r,
>                       Pi+arcsin(15/17)..Pi+arcsin(63/65) )
>             );
>    b := plottools[transform]( (x, y) -> [x,-y] )(a);
>    c := plottools[line]( [ 0, 0], [ -2*r, 0] ):
>    plots[display]( a, b, c, axes = none,
>                    scaling = constrained,
```

```
>                              args[2..nargs] );
> end proc:
```

Here is a Smith Chart of radius 1.

```
> smithChart( 1 );
```

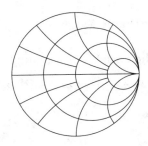

Exercise

1. Make a Smith Chart by building appropriate circular arcs above the axes, creating a copy reflected on the axis (using the **transform** procedure), and then adding a final horizontal line. The parameter r denotes the radius of the largest circle. Modifying the **smithChart** procedure to add text to mark appropriate grid markers is a simple operation.

Modifying Polygon Meshes

You can easily construct a new plot tool that works like those in the **plottools** package. For example, you can cut out or modify polygon structures by first working with individual faces and then mapping the results onto entire polygons. Thus, you can have a procedure that cuts out the inside of a single face of a polygon.

```
> cutoutPolygon := proc( vlist_in::{list, hfarray},
>                        scale::numeric )
>    local vlist, i, center, outside, inside, n, edges, polys;
>
>    vlist := 'if'(vlist_in::hfarray, op(3, eval(vlist_in)),
>              vlist_in);
>    n := nops(vlist);
>    center := add( i, i=vlist ) / n;
>    inside := seq( scale*(vlist[i]-center) + center,
>              i=1..n);
>    outside := seq( [ inside[i],  vlist[i],
>                vlist[i+1], inside[i+1] ],
>              i=1..n-1 ):
>    polys := POLYGONS( outside,
```

```
>                              [ inside[n], vlist[n],
>                                vlist[1], inside[1] ],
>                              STYLE(PATCHNOGRID) );
>     edges := CURVES( [ op(vlist), vlist[1] ],
>                              [ inside, inside[1] ] );
>     polys, edges;
> end proc:
```

Note that `cutoutPolygon` was written to handle input in either list form or `hfarray` form.

The following are the corners of a triangle.

```
> triangle := [ [0,2], [2,2], [1,0] ];
```

$$triangle := [[0, 2], [2, 2], [1, 0]]$$

The `cutoutPolygon` procedure converts `triangle` to three polygons (one for each side) and two curves.

```
> cutoutPolygon( triangle, 1/2 );
```

$$\text{POLYGONS}([[\tfrac{1}{2}, \tfrac{5}{3}], [0, 2], [2, 2], [\tfrac{3}{2}, \tfrac{5}{3}]],$$

$$[[\tfrac{3}{2}, \tfrac{5}{3}], [2, 2], [1, 0], [1, \tfrac{2}{3}]], [[1, \tfrac{2}{3}], [1, 0], [0, 2], [\tfrac{1}{2}, \tfrac{5}{3}]],$$

$$\text{STYLE}(PATCHNOGRID)), \text{CURVES}($$

$$[[0, 2], [2, 2], [1, 0], [0, 2]], [[\tfrac{1}{2}, \tfrac{5}{3}], [\tfrac{3}{2}, \tfrac{5}{3}], [1, \tfrac{2}{3}], [\tfrac{1}{2}, \tfrac{5}{3}]])$$

Use the `display` command from the `plots` package to show the triangle.

```
> plots[display]( %, color=red );
```

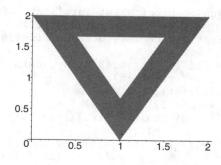

The `cutout` procedure below applies `cutoutPolygon` to every face of a polyhedron.

```
> cutout := proc(polyhedron, scale)
>    local v;
>    seq( cutoutPolygon( v, evalf(scale) ), v=polyhedron);
> end proc:
```

You can now cut out 3/4 of each face of a dodecahedron.

```
> display( cutout( dodecahedron([1, 2, 3]), 3/4 ),
>          scaling=constrained);
```

As a second example, you can take a polygon and raise or lower its barycenter.

```
> stellateFace := proc( vlist::list, aspectRatio::numeric )
>    local apex, i, n;
>
>    n := nops(vlist);
>    apex := add( i, i = vlist ) * aspectRatio / n;
>    POLYGONS( seq( [ apex, vlist[i],
>                     vlist[modp(i, n) + 1] ],
>                i=1..n) );
> end proc:
```

The following are the corners of a triangle in three-dimensional space.

```
> triangle := [ [1,0,0], [0,1,0], [0,0,1] ];
```

$$triangle := [[1, 0, 0], [0, 1, 0], [0, 0, 1]]$$

The `stellateFace` procedure creates three polygons, one for each side of the triangle.

```
> stellateFace( triangle, 1 );
```

$$\text{POLYGONS}([[\tfrac{1}{3}, \tfrac{1}{3}, \tfrac{1}{3}], [1, 0, 0], [0, 1, 0]],$$

$$[[\tfrac{1}{3}, \tfrac{1}{3}, \tfrac{1}{3}], [0, 1, 0], [0, 0, 1]], [[\tfrac{1}{3}, \tfrac{1}{3}, \tfrac{1}{3}], [0, 0, 1], [1, 0, 0]])$$

Since these **POLYGONS** belong in three-dimensional space, you must put them inside a **PLOT3D** structure to display them.

```
> PLOT3D( % );
```

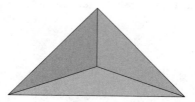

Again, you can extend **stellateFace** to work for arbitrary polyhedra having more than one face.

```
> stellate := proc( polyhedron, aspectRatio)
>    local v;
>    seq( stellateFace( v, evalf(aspectRatio) ),
>         v=polyhedron );
> end proc:
```

This allows for the construction of stellated polyhedra.

```
> stellated := display( stellate( dodecahedron(), 3),
>          scaling= constrained ):
> display( array( [dodecahedron(), stellated] ) );
```

You can use convert(..., POLYGONS) to convert a GRID or MESH structure to the equivalent set of POLYGONS. Here is a POLYGONS version of the Klein bottle.

```
> kleinpoints := proc()
>    local bottom, middle, handle, top, p, q;
>
>    top := [ (2.5 + 1.5*cos(v)) * cos(u),
>             (2.5 + 1.5*cos(v)) * sin(u), -2.5 * sin(v) ]:
>    middle := [ (2.5 + 1.5*cos(v)) * cos(u),
>                (2.5 + 1.5*cos(v)) * sin(u), 3*v - 6*Pi ]:
>    handle := [ 2 - 2*cos(v) + sin(u), cos(u),
>                3*v - 6*Pi ]:
>    bottom := [ 2 + (2+cos(u))*cos(v), sin(u),
>                -3*Pi + (2+cos(u)) * sin(v) ]:
>    p := plot3d( {bottom, middle, handle, top},
>                 u=0..2*Pi, v=Pi..2*Pi, grid=[9,9] ):
>    p := select( x -> op(0,x)=MESH, [op(p)] );
>    seq( convert(q , POLYGONS), q=p );
> end proc:
> display( kleinpoints(), style=patch,
>          scaling=constrained, orientation=[-110,71] );
```

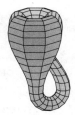

You can then use the commands for manipulation of polygons to alter the view of the Klein bottle.

```
> display( seq( cutout(k, 3/4), k=kleinpoints() ),
>          scaling=constrained );
```

9.6   Example: Vector Field Plots

This section describes the problem of plotting a vector field of two dimensional vectors in the plane. The example herein serves to pinpoint some of the tools available for plot objects on grids in two- and three-dimensional space.

The command to plot a vector field should have the following syntax.

```
vectorfieldplot(  F, r1, r2 , options )
```

The input, F, is a list of size two, giving the functions that make up the horizontal and vertical components of the vector field. The arguments $r1$ and $r2$ describe the domain grid of the vectors. The three arguments F, $r1$, and $r2$ are similar in form to the input you need to use for `plot3d`. Similarly, the optional information includes any sensible specification that `plot` or `plot3d` allows. Thus, options of the form `grid = [m,n]`, `style = patch`, and `color = colorfunction` are valid options.

The first problem is to draw a vector. Let $[x, y]$ represent a point, the starting point of the arrow, and $[a, b]$, the components of the vector. You can determine the shape of an arrow by three independent parameters, $t1$, $t2$, and $t3$. Here $t1$ denotes the thickness of the arrow, $t2$ the thickness of the arrow head, and $t3$ the ratio of the length of the arrow head in comparison to the length of the arrow itself.

The procedure `arrow` below from the `plottools` package constructs seven vertices of an arrow. It then builds the arrow by constructing two polygons: a triangle (spanned by v_5, v_6, and v_7) for the head of the arrow and a rectangle (spanned by v_1, v_2, v_3, and v_4) for the tail; it then removes boundary lines by setting the **style** option inside the polygon structure. It also constructs the boundary of the entire arrow via a closed curve through the vertices.

```
> myarrow := proc( point::list, vect::list, t1, t2, t3)
>    local a, b, i, x, y, L, Cos, Sin, v, locopts;
>
>    a := vect[1]; b := vect[2];
>    if has( vect, 'undefined') or (a=0 and b=0) then
>       RETURN( POLYGONS( [ ] ) );
>    end if;
>    x := point[1]; y := point[2];
>    # L = length of arrow
>    L := evalf( sqrt(a^2 + b^2) );
>    Cos := evalf( a / L );
>    Sin := evalf( b / L);
>    v[1] := [x + t1*Sin/2, y - t1*Cos/2];
>    v[2] := [x - t1*Sin/2, y + t1*Cos/2];
>    v[3] := [x - t1*Sin/2 - t3*Cos*L + a,
>             y + t1*Cos/2 - t3*Sin*L + b];
>    v[4] := [x + t1*Sin/2 - t3*Cos*L + a,
>             y - t1*Cos/2 - t3*Sin*L + b];
>    v[5] := [x - t2*Sin/2 - t3*Cos*L + a,
>             y + t2*Cos/2 - t3*Sin*L + b];
>    v[6] := [x + a, y + b];
>    v[7] := [x + t2*Sin/2 - t3*Cos*L + a,
>             y - t2*Cos/2 - t3*Sin*L + b];
>    v := seq( evalf(v[i]), i= 1..7  );
>
>    # convert optional arguments to PLOT data structure form
>    locopts := convert( [style=patchnogrid,
>                          args[ 6..nargs ] ],
>                         PLOToptions );
>    POLYGONS( [v[1], v[2], v[3], v[4]],
>              [v[5], v[6], v[7]], op(locopts) ),
>    CURVES( [v[1], v[2], v[3], v[5], v[6],
>             v[7], v[4], v[1]] );
> end proc:
```

Note that you must build the polygon structure for the arrow in two parts, because each polygon must be convex. In the special case where the vector has both components equal to zero or an **undefined** component, such as a value resulting from a non-numeric value (for example, a complex value or a singularity point), the **myarrow** procedure returns a trivial polygon. Here are four arrows.

```
> arrow1 := PLOT(myarrow( [0,0], [1,1], 0.2, 0.4, 1/3,
>                color=red) ):
> arrow2 := PLOT(myarrow( [0,0], [1,1], 0.1, 0.2, 1/3,
>                color=yellow) ):
> arrow3 := PLOT(myarrow( [0,0], [1,1], 0.2, 0.3, 1/2,
>                color=blue) ):
```

```
> arrow4 := PLOT(myarrow( [0,0], [1,1], 0.1, 0.5, 1/4,
>                  color=green) ):
```

The `display` command from the `plots` package can show an array of plots.

```
> with(plots):
```

```
Warning, the name changecoords has been redefined
```

```
> display( array( [[arrow1, arrow2], [arrow3, arrow4 ]] ),
>     scaling=constrained );
```

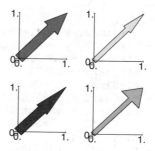

The remainder of this section presents a number of solutions to the programming problem of generating a vector field plot, each a bit more powerful than its predecessors. The first and simplest solution requires the input to be in functional (rather than expression) form. You first need three utility procedures that process the domain information, generate a grid of function values, and place the information in a `PLOT3D` structure.

The procedure `domaininfo` determines the endpoints and increments for the grid. `domaininfo` takes as input the two ranges `r1` and `r2` and the two grid sizes m and n, and returns the grid information as an expression sequence of four elements.

```
> domaininfo := proc(r1, r2, m, n)
>     lhs(r1), lhs(r2),
>     evalf( (rhs(r1) - lhs(r1))/(m-1) ),
>     evalf( (rhs(r2) - lhs(r2))/(n-1) );
> end proc:
```

Here is an example using multiple assignments to assign the four values returned to separate variables.

```
> a, b, dx, dy := domaininfo( 0..12, 20..100, 7, 9);
```

$$a, b, dx, dy := 0, 20, 2., 10.$$

Now a, b, dx, and dy have the following values.

```
> a, b, dx, dy;
```

$$0, 20, 2., 10.$$

For the conversion to a grid of numerical points, you can take advantage of the extendibility of Maple's **convert** command. The procedure `'convert/grid'` below takes a function f as input and evaluates it over the grid which r1, r2, m, and n specify.

```
> 'convert/grid' := proc(f, r1, r2, m, n)
>    local a, b, i, j, dx, dy;
>    # obtain  information about domain
>    a,b,dx,dy := domaininfo( r1, r2, m, n );
>    # output grid of function values
>    [ seq( [ seq( evalf( f( a + i*dx, b + j*dy ) ),
>       i=0..(m-1) ) ], j=0..(n-1) ) ];
> end proc:
```

Now you can evaluate the undefined function, f, on a grid as follows.

```
> convert( f, grid, 1..2, 4..6, 3, 2 );
```

$$[[f(1., 4.), f(1.500000000, 4.), f(2.000000000, 4.)],$$
$$[f(1., 6.), f(1.500000000, 6.), f(2.000000000, 6.)]]$$

The final utility procedure determines the scalings which ensure that the arrows do not overlap. Then **generateplot** calls upon the **myarrow** procedure to draw the vectors. Note that **generateplot** moves the origin of each arrow to center it over its grid-point.

```
> generateplot := proc(vect1, vect2, m, n, a, b, dx, dy)
>    local i, j, L, xscale, yscale, mscale;
>
>    # Determine scaling factors.
>    L := max( seq( seq( vect1[j][i]^2 + vect2[j][i]^2,
>             i=1..m ), j=1..n ) );
>    xscale := evalf( dx/2/L^(1/2) );
>    yscale := evalf( dy/2/L^(1/2) );
>    mscale := max(xscale, yscale);
>
>    # Generate plot data structure.
>    # Each arrow is centered over its point.
>    PLOT( seq( seq( myarrow(
>       [ a + (i-1)*dx - vect1[j][i]*xscale/2,
>          b + (j-1)*dy - vect2[j][i]*yscale/2 ],
```

```
>               [ vect1[j][i]*xscale, vect2[j][i]*yscale ],
>            mscale/4, mscale/2, 1/3 ), i=1..m), j=1..n) );
>        # Thickness of tail = mscale/4
>        # Thickness of head = mscale/2
> end proc:
```

With these utility functions in place, you are ready to make the first vectorfieldplot command by putting them all together.

```
> vectorfieldplot := proc(F, r1, r2, m, n)
>     local vect1, vect2, a, b, dx, dy;
>
>       # Generate each component over the grid of points.
>       vect1 := convert( F[1], grid, r1, r2 ,m, n );
>       vect2 := convert( F[2], grid, r1, r2 ,m, n );
>
>       # Obtain the domain grid information from r1 and r2.
>       a,b,dx,dy := domaininfo(r1, r2, m, n);
>
>       # Generate the final plot structure.
>       generateplot(vect1, vect2, m, n, a, b, dx, dy)
> end proc:
```

Try the procedure on the vector field $(\cos(xy), \sin(xy))$.

```
> p := (x,y) -> cos(x*y): q := (x,y) -> sin(x*y):
> vectorfieldplot( [p, q], 0..Pi, 0..Pi, 15, 20 );
```

The vectorfieldplot code shows how to write a procedure that generates vector field plots based on alternative descriptions of the input. For example, you could create a procedure listvectorfieldplot, with the input consisting of a list of m lists, each of which consists of n pairs of points. Each pair of points represents the components of a vector. The domain grid would be $1, \ldots, m$ in the horizontal direction and $1, \ldots, n$ in the vertical direction (as for listplot3d from the plots package).

```
> listvectorfieldplot := proc(F)
>     local m, n, vect1, vect2;
```

```
>
>     n := nops( F );  m := nops( F[1] );
>     # Generate the 1st and 2nd components  of F.
>     vect1 := map( u -> map( v -> evalf(v[1]) , u) , F);
>     vect2 := map( u -> map( v -> evalf(v[2]) , u) , F);
>
>     # Generate the final plot structure.
>     generateplot(vect1, vect2, m, n, 1, 1, m-1, n-1)
> end proc:
```

For example, the list

```
> l := [ [ [1,1], [2,2], [3,3] ],
>        [ [1,6], [2,0], [5,1] ] ]:
```

plots

```
> listvectorfieldplot( l );
```

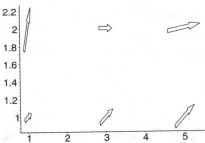

At this stage, the vectorfieldplot procedure still has problems. The first is that the procedure only works with function input, rather than with both function and formula input. You can solve this by converting formula expressions to procedures, and then having vectorfieldplot call itself recursively with the new output as in the ribbonplot procedure in section 9.2.

A second problem is that vectorfieldplot only works with lists as input, not hfarrays.

To overcome such problems, ensure that you first convert all input functions to functions that only output a numeric real value or the value undefined, the only type of data the Maple plotting data structure accepts. You may also want to use the more efficient hardware floating-point calculations rather than software floating-point operations, whenever possible. Section 9.7 describes how to do this. Instead of writing your own procedure for computing the grid, you can use the library function convert(..., gridpoints) which, in the case of a single input, generates a structure of the following form.

```
[ a.. b, c.. d, [ [z11, ... , z1n], ... ,
     [ zm1 , ... , zmn ] ] ]
```

The third argument may also be an hfarray.

It uses either expressions or procedures as input. The output gives the domain information $a..b$ and $c..d$ along with the z values of the input that it evaluates over the grid.

```
> convert( sin(x*y), 'gridpoints',
>    x=0..Pi, y=0..Pi, grid=[2, 3] );
```

$$[0...3.14159265358979, 0...3.14159265358979, [$$
$$[0., 0., 0.],$$
$$[0., -.975367972083633571, -.430301217000074065]]]$$

When $xy > 0$ and $\ln(-xy)$ is complex, the grid contains the value **undefined**.

```
> convert( (x,y) -> log(-x*y), 'gridpoints',
>    1..2, -2..1, grid=[2,3] );
```

$$[1...2., -2...1., [[.693147180559945286,$$
$$-.693147180559945286, undefined],$$
$$[1.386294361, 0., undefined]]]$$

The version of `vectorfieldplot` below makes use of the `convert(...,gridpoints)` procedure. The `vectorfieldplot` command should allow a number of options. In particular, it should allow a `grid = [m,n]` option. You can accomplish this by passing the options to `convert(...,gridpoints)`. The utility procedure `makevectors` handles the interface to `convert(..., gridpoints)`.

```
> makevectors := proc( F, r1, r2  )
>    local v1, v2;
>
>    # Generate the numerical grid
>    # of components of the vectors.
>    v1 := convert( F[1], 'gridpoints', r1, r2,
>                   args[4 .. nargs] );
>    v2 := convert( F[2], 'gridpoints', r1, r2,
>                   args[4 .. nargs] );
>
>    # The domain information is contained in first
>    # two operands of v1. The function values in
>    # the 3rd components of v1 and v2.
>    [ v1[1], v1[2], v1[3], v2[3] ]
```

```
> end proc:
```

Here is the new version of `vectorfieldplot`.

```
> vectorfieldplot := proc(F, r1, r2)
>    local R1, R2, m, n, a, b, v1, v2, dx, dy, v;
>
>    v := makevectors( F, r1, r2, args[4..nargs] );
>    R1 := v[1];  R2 := v[2];  v1 := v[3];  v2 := v[4];
>
>    n := nops(v1); m := nops(v1[1]);
>    a,b,dx,dy := domaininfo(R1, R2, m, n);
>
>    generateplot(v1, v2, m, n, a, b, dx, dy);
> end proc:
```

Test this procedure.

```
> p := (x,y) -> cos(x*y):
> q := (x,y) -> sin(x*y):
> vectorfieldplot( [p, q], 0..Pi, 0..Pi,
>    grid=[3, 4] );
```

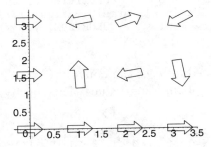

All the versions of `vectorfieldplot` so far have scaled each arrow so that each vector fits into a single grid box. No overlapping of arrows occurs. However, the arrows still vary in length. Often this results in graphs that have a large number of very small, almost invisible vectors. For example, a plot of the gradient field of $F = \cos(xy)$ exhibits this behavior.

```
> vectorfieldplot( [y*cos(x*y), x*sin(x*y)],
>    x=0..Pi, y=0..Pi, grid=[15,20]);
```

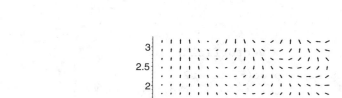

The final version of `vectorfieldplot` differs in that all the arrows have the same length—the color of each vector provides the information about the magnitudes of the arrows. You must add a utility procedure that generates a grid of colors from the function values.

```
> 'convert/colorgrid' := proc( colorFunction )
>    local colorinfo, i, j, m, n;
>
>    colorinfo := op( 3, convert(colorFunction,
>        'gridpoints', args[2..nargs] ) );
>    map( x -> map( y -> COLOR(HUE, y), x) , colorinfo );
> end proc:
```

The above procedure uses the `convert( ... , gridpoints)` to generate a list of lists of function values that specify the colors (using hue coloring).

```
> convert( sin(x*y), 'colorgrid',
>           x=0..1, y=0..1, grid=[2,3] );
```

$$[[\text{COLOR}(HUE, 0.), \text{COLOR}(HUE, 0.), \text{COLOR}(HUE, 0.)$$
$$], [\text{COLOR}(HUE, 0.),$$
$$\text{COLOR}(HUE, .479425538604203006),$$
$$\text{COLOR}(HUE, .841470984807896505)]]$$

Here is the final version of `vectorfieldplot`.

```
> vectorfieldplot := proc( F, r1, r2 )
>    local v, m, n, a, b, dx, dy, opts, p, v1, v2,
>          L, i, j, norms, colorinfo,
>          xscale, yscale, mscale;
>
>    v := makevectors( F, r1, r2, args[4..nargs] );
>    v1 := v[3];   v2 := v[4];
>    n := nops(v1); m := nops( v1[1] );
```

```
>
>      a,b,dx,dy := domaininfo(v[1], v[2], m, n);
>
>      # Determine the function used for coloring the arrows.
>      opts := [ args[ 4..nargs] ];
>      if not hasoption( opts, color, colorinfo, 'opts' ) then
>          # Default coloring will be via
>          # the scaled magnitude of the vectors.
>          L := max( seq( seq( v1[j][i]^2 + v2[j][i]^2,
>                     i=1..m ), j=1..n ) );
>          colorinfo := ( F[1]^2 + F[2]^2 )/L;
>      end if;
>
>      # Generate the information needed to color the arrows.
>      colorinfo := convert( colorinfo, 'colorgrid',
>            r1, r2, op(opts) );
>
>      # Get all the norms of the vectors using zip.
>      norms := zip( (x,y) -> zip( (u,v)->
>          if u=0 and v=0 then 1 else sqrt(u^2 + v^2) end if,
>              x, y), v1, v2);
>      #  Normalize v1 and v2 (again using zip ).
>      v1 := zip( (x,y) -> zip( (u,v)-> u/v, x, y),
>            v1, norms );
>
>      v2 := zip( (x,y) -> zip( (u,v)-> u/v, x, y),
>            v2, norms );
>
>      # Generate scaling information and plot data structure.
>      xscale := dx/2.0;  yscale := dy/2.0;
>      mscale := max(xscale, yscale);
>
>      PLOT( seq( seq( myarrow(
>          [ a + (i-1)*dx - v1[j][i]*xscale/2,
>            b + (j-1)*dy - v2[j][i]*yscale/2 ],
>          [ v1[j][i]*xscale, v2[j][i]*yscale ],
>          mscale/4, mscale/2, 1/3,
>          'color'=colorinfo[j][i]
>                  ), i=1..m ), j=1..n ) );
> end proc:
```

With this new version you can obtain the following plots.

```
> vectorfieldplot( [y*cos(x*y), x*sin(x*y)],
>    x=0..Pi, y=0..Pi,grid=[15,20] );
```

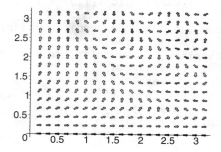

You can color the vectors via a function, such as $\sin(xy)$.

```
> vectorfieldplot( [y*cos(x*y), x*sin(x*y)],
>    x=0..Pi, y=0..Pi, grid=[15,20], color=sin(x*y) );
```

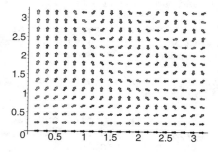

Other vector field routines can be derived from the routines above. For example, you can also write a complex vector field plot that takes complex number locations and complex number descriptions of vectors as input. You simply need to generate the grid of points in an alternate manner.

In the **plottools** package, there is the **arrow** function, which generates arrows and vectors. This function is more versatile than the procedures described in this section.

9.7   Generating Grids of Points

Section 9.6 points out that the simple operation of obtaining an array of grid values for a given procedure, that is, the problem of computing the values of a function you wish to plot over a grid of points, is not an obvious task. You must deal with efficiency, error conditions, and non-numeric output. You can handle the case where the input is a formula in two variables in the same way as in the **ribbonplot** procedure from section 9.2. Thus, for simplicity of presentation, this section avoids this particular case.

The goal is to compute an array of values for f at each point on a $m \times n$ rectangular grid. That is, at the locations

$$x_i = a + (i - 1)\delta_x \quad \text{and} \quad y_j = c + (j - 1)\delta_y$$

where $\delta_x = (b - a)/(m - 1)$ and $\delta_y = (d - c)/(n - 1)$. Here i and j vary from 1 to m and 1 to n, respectively.

Consider the function $f : (x, y) \mapsto 1/\sin(xy)$. You need to evaluate f over the $m \times n$ grid with the ranges $a, \ldots, b$ and $c, \ldots, d$.

```
> f := (x,y) -> 1 / sin(x*y);
```

$$f := (x, y) \to \frac{1}{\sin(x\,y)}$$

The first step is to convert the function f to a numeric procedure. Since Maple requires numeric values (rather than symbolic) for plots, ask Maple to convert f to a form which returns numerical answers or the special value **undefined**.

```
> fnum := convert( f , numericproc );
```

$fnum := \mathbf{proc}(\_X, \_Y)$
   local err;
      $err := \mathrm{traperror}(\mathrm{evalhf}(\mathrm{f}(\_X, \_Y)))$;
      if type($[err]$, $[numeric]$) **then** err
      else
         $err := \mathrm{traperror}(\mathrm{evalf}(\mathrm{f}(\_X, \_Y)))$;
         if type($[err]$, $[numeric]$) **then** err **else** $undefined$ **end if**
      end if
   end proc

The above procedure, which is the result of this conversion, attempts to calculate the numerical values as efficiently as possible. Hardware floating-point arithmetic, although of limited precision, is more efficient than software floating-point and is frequently sufficient for plotting. Thus, **fnum** tries **evalhf** first. If **evalhf** is successful, it returns a numeric result;

otherwise, it generates an error message. If this happens, `fnum` attempts the calculation again by using software floating-point arithmetic by calling `evalf`. Even this calculation is not always possible. In the case of f, the function is undefined whenever $x = 0$ or $y = 0$. In such cases, the procedure `fnum` returns the name `undefined`. Maple's plot display routines recognize this special name.

At the point $(1, 1)$, the function f has the value $1/\sin(1)$ and so `fnum` returns a numerical estimate.

```
> fnum(1,1);
```

$$1.18839510577812123$$

However, if you instead try to evaluate this same function at $(0, 0)$, Maple informs you that the function is undefined at these coordinates.

```
> fnum(0,0);
```

undefined

Creating such a procedure is the first step in creating the grid of values.

For reasons of efficiency, you should, whenever you can, compute not only the function values but also the grid points by using hardware floating-point arithmetic. In addition, you should do as much computation as possible in a single call to `evalhf`. Whenever you use hardware floating-point arithmetic, Maple must first convert the expression to a series of commands of hardware floating-point numbers, and then convert the result of these back to Maple's format for numbers.

Write a procedure that generates the coordinates of the grid in the form of an array. Since the procedure is to plot surfaces, the array is two-dimensional. The following procedure returns an array `z` of function values.

```
> evalgrid := proc( F, z, a, b, c, d, m, n )
>    local i, j, dx, dy;
>
>    dx := (b-a)/m; dy := (d-c)/n;
>    for i to m do
>       for j to n do
>          z[i, j] := F( a + (i-1)*dx, c + (j-1)*dy );
>       end do;
>    end do;
> end proc:
```

This `evalgrid` procedure is purely symbolic and does not handle error conditions.

```
> A := array(1..2, 1..2):
> evalgrid( f, 'A', 1, 2, 1, 2, 2, 2 ):
> eval(A);
```

$$
\begin{bmatrix}
\dfrac{1}{\sin(1)} & \dfrac{1}{\sin(\frac{3}{2})} \\[2em]
\dfrac{1}{\sin(\frac{3}{2})} & \dfrac{1}{\sin(\frac{9}{4})}
\end{bmatrix}
$$

```
> evalgrid( f, 'A', 0, Pi, 0, Pi, 15, 15 ):
```

`Error, (in f) numeric exception: division by zero`

Write a second procedure, `gridpoints`, which makes use of `evalgrid`. The procedure should accept a function, two ranges, and the number of grid points to generate in each dimension. Like the procedure `fnum` which Maple generated from your function f above, this routine should attempt to create the grid using hardware floating-point arithmetic. Only if this fails, should `gridpoints` resort to software floating-point arithmetic.

```
> gridpoints := proc( f, r1, r2, m, n )
>     local u, x, y, z, a, b, c, d;
>
>     # Domain information:
>     a := lhs(r1); b := rhs(r1);
>     c := lhs(r2); d := rhs(r2);
>
>     z := hfarray(1..m, 1..n);
>     if Digits <= evalhf(Digits) then
>         # Try to use hardware floats
>         # - notice the need for var in this case.
>         u := traperror( evalhf( evalgrid(f, var(z),
>             a, b, c, d, m, n) ) );
>         if lasterror = u then
>             # Use software floats, first converting f to
>             # a software float function.
>             z := array( 1..m, 1..n );
>             evalgrid( convert( f, numericproc ),
>                       z, a, b, c, d, m, n );
>         end if;
>     else
>         # Use software floats, first converting f to
>         # a software float function.
>         z := array( 1..m, 1..n );
>         evalgrid( convert(f, numericproc), z,
```

```
>               a, b, c, d, m, n );
>     end if;
>     eval(z);
> end proc:
```

The second argument to **evalgrid** must be the array (or hfarray) which receives the results; Maple must not convert it to a number before it calls **evalhf**. Indicate this special status to Maple using the special function **var** whenever you call **evalgrid** from within **evalhf**. Chapter 8 discusses numerical calculations in detail.

Test the procedures. Here **gridpoints** can use hardware floating-point arithmetic to calculate two of the numbers, but it must resort to software calculations in four cases where the function turns out to be undefined.

```
> gridpoints( (x,y) -> 1/sin(x*y) , 0..3, 0..3, 2, 3 );
```

$$[undefined, undefined, undefined]$$
$$[undefined, 1.00251130424672485,$$
$$7.08616739573718667]$$

In the following example, **gridpoints** can use hardware floating-point for all the calculations. Therefore, this calculation is faster, although the difference will not be apparent unless you try a much larger example.

```
> gridpoints( (x,y) -> sin(x*y) ,  0..3, 0..3, 2, 3  );
```

$$[0., 0., 0.]$$
$$[0., .997494986604054445, .141120008059867213]$$

If you ask for more digits than hardware floating-point arithmetic can provide, then **gridpoints** must always use software floating-point operations.

```
> Digits := 22:
> gridpoints( (x,y) -> sin(x*y) ,  0..3,   0..3, 2, 3  );
```

$$[0., 0., 0.]$$
$$[0., .9974949866040544309417,$$
$$.1411200080598672221007]$$

```
> Digits := 10:
```

The `gridpoints` procedure is remarkably similar to the `convert(...,`
`gridpoints)` procedure which is part of the standard Maple library. The
library command includes more checking of the arguments and, therefore,
will likely suffice for many of your needs.

9.8 Animation

Maple has the ability to generate animations in either two or three dimensions. As with all of Maple's plotting facilities, such animations produce
user-accessible data structures. Data structures of the following type represent animations.

```
PLOT( ANIMATE( ... ) )
```

or

```
PLOT3D( ANIMATE( ... ) )
```

Inside the `ANIMATE` function is a sequence of frames; each frame is
a list of the same plotting objects that can appear in a single plotting
structure. Every procedure that creates an animation builds such a sequence of frames. You can see an example by printing the output of such
a procedure.

```
> lprint( plots[animate]( x*t, x=-1..1, t = 1..3,
>         numpoints=3, frames = 3 ) );

PLOT(ANIMATE([CURVES([[-1., -1.], [0., 0.], [1.0000000\
00, 1.]],COLOUR(RGB,1.00000000,0.,0.))],[CURVES([[-1.,
-2.], [0., 0.], [1.000000000, 2.]],COLOUR(RGB,1.000000\
00,0.,0.))],[CURVES([[-1., -3.], [0., 0.], [1.00000000\
0, 3.]],COLOUR(RGB,1.00000000,0.,0.))]),AXESLABELS(x,
``),VIEW(-1. .. 1.,DEFAULT))
```

The function `points` below is a parametrization of the curve $(x, y) = (1 + \cos(t\pi/180)^2, 1 + \cos(t\pi/180)\sin(t\pi/180))$.

```
> points := t -> evalf(
>         [ (1 + cos(t/180*Pi)) * cos(t/180*Pi ),
>           (1 + cos(t/180*Pi)) * sin(t/180*Pi ) ] ):
```

For example,

```
> points(2);
```

$$[1.998172852, .06977773357]$$

You can plot a sequence of points.

```
> PLOT( POINTS( seq( points(t), t=0..90 ) ) );
```

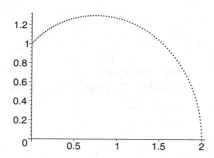

You can now make an animation. Make each frame consist of the polygon spanned by the origin, $(0, 0)$, and the sequence of points on the curve.

```
> frame := n -> [ POLYGONS([ [ 0, 0 ],
>                   seq( points(t), t = 0..60*n) ],
>                   COLOR(RGB, 1.0/n, 1.0/n, 1.0/n) ) ]:
```

The animation consists of six frames.

```
> PLOT( ANIMATE( seq( frame(n), n = 1..6 ) ) );
```

The **display** command from the **plots** package can show an animation in static form.

```
> with(plots):
```

```
Warning, the name changecoords has been redefined
```

```
> display( PLOT(ANIMATE(seq(frame(n), n = 1..6))) );
```

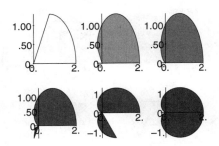

The **varyAspect** procedure below illustrates how a stellated surface varies with the aspect ratio. The procedure takes a graphical object as input and creates an animation in which each frame is a stellated version of the object with a different aspect ratio.

```
> with(plottools):

Warning, the name arrow has been redefined


> varyAspect := proc( p )
>    local n, opts;
>    opts := convert( [ args[2..nargs] ], PLOT3Doptions );
>    PLOT3D( ANIMATE( seq( [ stellate( p, n/sqrt(2)) ],
>                          n=1..4 ) ),
>            op( opts ));
> end proc:
```

Try the procedure on a dodecahedron.

```
> varyAspect( dodecahedron(), scaling=constrained );
```

Here is the static version.

```
> display( varyAspect( dodecahedron(),
>                      scaling=constrained ) );
```

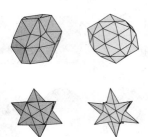

The Maple library provides three methods for creating animations: the `animate` and `animate3d` commands in the `plots` package, or the `display` command with the `insequence = true` option set. For example, you can show how a Fourier series approximates a function, f, on an interval $[a, b]$ by visualizing the function and successive approximations as the number of terms increase with each frame. You can derive the nth partial sum of the Fourier series by using $f_n(x) = c_0/2 + \sum_{k=1}^{n} c_k \cos(\frac{2\pi}{b-a}kx) + s_k \sin(\frac{2\pi}{b-a}kx)$, where

$$c_k = \frac{2}{b-a} \int_a^b f(x) \cos\left(\frac{2\pi}{b-a}kx\right) \, dx$$

and

$$s_k = \frac{2}{b-a} \int_a^b f(x) \sin\left(\frac{2\pi}{b-a}kx\right) \, dx.$$

The `fourierPicture` procedure below first calculates and plots the kth Fourier approximation for k up to n. Then `fourierPicture` generates an animation of these plots, and finally it adds a plot of the function itself as a backdrop.

```
> fourierPicture :=
> proc( func, xrange::name=range, n::posint)
>    local x, a, b, l, k, j, p, q, partsum;
>
>    a := lhs( rhs(xrange) );
>    b := rhs( rhs(xrange) );
>    l := b - a;
>    x := 2 * Pi * lhs(xrange) / l;
>
>    partsum := 1/l * evalf( Int( func, xrange) );
>    for k from 1 to n do
>       # Generate the terms of the Fourier series of func.
>       partsum := partsum
>          + 2/l * evalf( Int(func*sin(k*x), xrange) )
```

```
>                    * sin(k*x)
>            + 2/1 * evalf( Int(func*cos(k*x), xrange) )
>                    * cos(k*x);
>        # Plot k-th Fourier approximation.
>        q[k] := plot( partsum, xrange, color=blue,
>                      args[4..nargs] );
>     end do;
>     # Generate sequence of frames.
>     q := plots[display]( [ seq( q[k], k=1..n ) ],
>                          insequence=true );
>     # Add the function plot, p, to each frame.
>     p := plot( func, xrange, color = red, args[4..nargs] );
>     plots[display]( [ q, p ] );
> end proc:
```

You can now use `fourierPicture` to see, for example, the first six Fourier approximations of e^x.

```
> fourierPicture( exp(x), x=0..10, 6 ):
```

This is the static version.

```
> display( fourierPicture( exp(x), x=0..10, 6 ) );
```

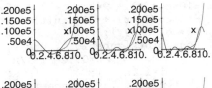

Below are the first six Fourier approximations of `x -> signum(x-1)`. The `signum` function is discontinuous, so the `discont=true` option is called for.

```
> fourierPicture( 2*signum(x-1), x=-2..3, 6,
>                 discont=true );
```

Again, these pages require a static version.

```
> display( fourierPicture( 2*signum(x-1), x=-2..3, 6,
>                 discont=true ) );
```

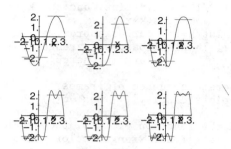

You can also create similar animations with other series approximations, such as Taylor, Padé, and Chebyshev–Padé, with the generalized series structures that Maple uses.

Animation sequences exist in both two and three dimensions. The procedure below ties a trefoil knot by using the **tubeplot** function in the **plots** package.

```
> TieKnot := proc( n:: posint )
>     local i, t, curve, picts;
>     curve := [ -10*cos(t) - 2*cos(5*t) + 15*sin(2*t),
>                -15*cos(2*t) + 10*sin(t) - 2*sin(5*t),
>                10*cos(3*t) ]:
>     picts := [ seq( plots[tubeplot]( curve,
>                           t=0..2*Pi*i/n, radius=3),
>                i=1..n ) ];
>     plots[display]( picts, insequence=true, style=patch);
> end proc:
```

You can tie the knot in, say, six stages.

```
> TieKnot(6);
```

Here is the static version.

```
> display( TieKnot(6) );
```

You can combine the graphical objects from the `plottools` package with the display in-sequence option to animate physical objects in motion. The `springPlot` procedure below creates a spring from a three-dimensional plot of a helix. `springPlot` also creates a box and a copy of this box and moves one of the boxes to various locations depending on a value of u. For every u, you can locate these boxes above and below the spring. Finally `springPlot` makes a sphere and translates it to locations above the top of the top box with the height again varying with a parameter. Finally, it produces the entire animation by organizing a sequence of positions and showing them in sequence by using `display`.

```
> springPlot := proc( n )
>    local u, curve, springs, box, tops, bottoms,
>          helix, ball, balls;
>    curve := (u,v) -> spacecurve(
>       [cos(t), sin(t), 8*sin(u/v*Pi)*t/200],
>       t=0..20*Pi,
>       color=black, numpoints=200, thickness=3 ):
>    springs := display( [ seq(curve(u,n), u=1..n) ],
>                        insequence=true ):
>    box := cuboid( [-1,-1,0], [1,1,1], color=red ):
>    ball := sphere( [0,0,2], grid=[15, 15], color=blue ):
>    tops :=  display( [ seq(
>       translate( box, 0, 0, sin(u/n*Pi)*4*Pi/5 ),
>       u=1..n ) ], insequence=true ):
>    bottoms := display( [ seq( translate(box, 0, 0, -1),
>       u=1..n ) ], insequence=true ):
>    balls := display( [ seq( translate( ball, 0, 0,
>       4*sin( (u-1)/(n-1)*Pi ) + 8*sin(u/n*Pi)*Pi/10 ),
>       u=1..n ) ],  insequence=true ):
>    display( springs, tops, bottoms, balls,
>       style=patch, orientation=[45,76],
>       scaling=constrained );
> end proc:
```

The code above uses the short names of the commands from the `plots` and `plottools` packages in order to improve readability. You must either use long names or remember to load these two packages before using `springPlot`.

```
> with(plots): with(plottools):
> springPlot(6);
> display( springPlot(6) );
```

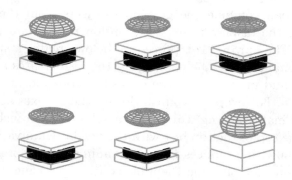

Section 9.5 describes how the commands in the **plottools** package can help you with graphics procedures.

9.9   Programming with Color

As well as coloring each type of object in the plot data structures, you can also add colors to plotting routines. The **color** option allows you to specify colors in the form of a solid color, by name, by **RGB** or **HUE** values, or via a color function in the form of a Maple formula or function. Try each of the following commands for yourself.

```
> plot3d( sin(x*y), x=-3..3, y=-3..3, color=red );
> plot3d( sin(x*y), x=-3..3, y=-3..3,
>    color=COLOUR(RGB, 0.3, 0.42, 0.1) );

> p := (x,y) -> sin(x*y):
> q := (x,y) -> if x < y then 1 else x - y end if:

> plot3d( p, -3..3, -3..3, color=q );
```

Although usually less convenient, you may also specify the color attributes at the lower level of graphics primitives. At the lowest level, you can accomplish a coloring of a graphical object by including a COLOUR function as one of the options inside the object.

```
> PLOT( POLYGONS( [ [0,0], [1,0], [1,1] ],
>                 [ [1,0], [1,1], [2,1], [2,0] ],
>                 COLOUR(RGB, 1/2, 1/3, 1/4 ) ) );
```

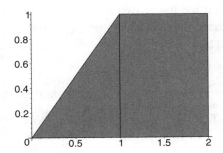

You can use different colors for each polygon via either

```
PLOT( POLYGONS( P1, ... , Pn ,
      COLOUR(RGB, p1, ..., pn)) )
```

or

```
PLOT( POLYGONS( P1, COLOUR(RGB, p1) ),    ... ,
      POLYGONS( Pn, COLOUR(RGB, pn)) )
```

Thus, the following two PLOT structures represent the same picture of a red and a green triangle.

```
> PLOT( POLYGONS( [ [0,0], [1,1], [2,0] ],
>                 COLOUR( RGB, 1, 0, 0 ) ),
>       POLYGONS( [ [0,0], [1,1], [0,1] ],
>                 COLOUR( RGB, 0, 1, 0 ) ) );

> PLOT( POLYGONS( [ [0,0], [1,1], [2,0] ],
>                 [ [0,0], [1,1], [0,1] ],
>                 COLOUR( RGB, 1, 0, 0, 0, 1, 0 ) ) );
```

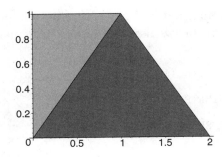

The three RGB values must be numbers between 0 and 1.

Generating Color Tables

The following procedure generates an $m \times n$ color table of RGB values. Specifically, `colormap` returns a sequence of two elements: a POLYGONS structure and a TITLE.

```
> colormap := proc(m, n, B)
>     local i, j, points, colors, flatten;
>     # points = sequence of corners for rectangles
>     points :=  seq( seq( evalf(
>             [ [i/m, j/n], [(i+1)/m, j/n],
>               [(i+1)/m, (j+1)/n], [i/m, (j+1)/n] ]
>               ), i=0..m-1 ), j=0..n-1 ):
>     # colors = listlist of RGB color values
>     colors :=  [seq( seq( [i/(m-1), j/(n-1), B],
>                    i=0..m-1 ), j=0..n-1 )] ;
>     # flatten turns the colors listlist into a sequence
>     flatten := a -> op( map(op, a) );
>     POLYGONS( points,
>               COLOUR(RGB, flatten(colors) ) ),
>     TITLE( cat( "Blue=", convert(B, string) ) );
> end proc:
```

Here is a 10×10 table of colors; the blue component is 0.

```
> PLOT( colormap(10, 10, 0) );
```

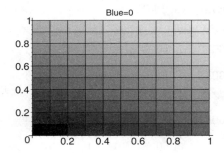

You can use animation to vary the blue component as well. The `colormaps` procedure below uses animation to generate an $m \times n \times f$ color table.

```
> colormaps := proc(m, n, f)
>     local t;
>     PLOT( ANIMATE( seq( [ colormap(m, n, t/(f-1)) ],
>                        t=0..f-1 ) ),
>           AXESLABELS("Red", "Green") );
> end proc:
```

The following gives you a $10 \times 10 \times 10$ color table.

```
> colormaps(10, 10, 10);
```

You can visualize the color scale for **HUE** coloring as follows.

```
> points := evalf( seq( [ [i/50, 0], [i/50, 1],
>                         [(i+1)/50, 1], [(i+1)/50, 0] ],
>                       i=0..49)):
```

```
> PLOT( POLYGONS(points, COLOUR(HUE, seq(i/50, i=0..49)) ),
>       AXESTICKS(DEFAULT, 0), STYLE(PATCHNOGRID) );
```

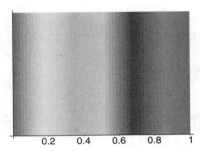

The **AXESTICKS(DEFAULT, 0)** specification eliminates the axes labeling along the vertical axis but leaves the default labeling along the horizontal axis.

You can easily see how to create a `colormapHue` procedure which creates the color scale for any color function based on **HUE** coloring.

```
> colormapHue := proc(F, n)
>    local i, points;
>    points := seq( evalf( [ [i/n, 0], [i/n, 1],
>                            [(i+1)/n, 1], [(i+1)/n, 0] ]
>                         ), i=0..n-1 ):
>    PLOT( POLYGONS( points,
>          COLOUR(HUE, seq( evalf(F(i/n)), i=0.. n-1) )),
>          AXESTICKS(DEFAULT, 0), STYLE(PATCHNOGRID) );
> end proc:
```

The basis of this color scale is $y(x) = \sin(\pi x)/3$ for $0 \leq x \leq 40$.

```
> colormapHue( x -> sin(Pi*x)/3, 40);
```

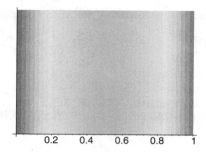

Visualizing the grayscale coloring is a simple matter of using an arbitrary procedure, F, since gray levels are simply those levels that have equal parts of red, green, and blue.

```
> colormapGraylevel := proc(F, n)
>     local i, flatten, points, grays;
>     points := seq( evalf([ [i/n, 0], [i/n, 1],
>                            [(i+1)/n, 1], [(i+1)/n, 0] ]),
>               i=0..n-1):
>     flatten := a -> op( map(op, a) );
>     grays := COLOUR(RGB, flatten(
>             [ seq( evalf([ F(i/n), F(i/n), F(i/n) ]),
>                    i=1.. n)]));
>     PLOT( POLYGONS(points, grays),
>           AXESTICKS(DEFAULT, 0) );
> end proc:
```

The identity function, $x \mapsto x$, yields the basic gray scale.

```
> colormapGraylevel( x->x, 20);
```

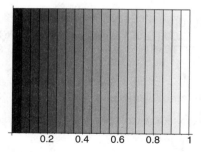

Adding Color Information to Plots

You can add color information to an existing plot data structure. The procedure addCurvecolor colors each curve in a CURVES function via the scaled y coordinates.

```
> addCurvecolor := proc(curve)
>    local i, j, N, n , M, m, curves, curveopts, p, q;
>
>    # Get existing point information.
>    curves := select( type, [ op(curve) ],
>                      list(list(numeric)) );
>    # Get all options but color options.
>    curveopts := remove( type, [ op(curve) ],
>                         { list(list(numeric)),
>                           specfunc(anything, COLOR),
>                           specfunc(anything, COLOUR) } );
>
>    # Determine the scaling.
>    # M and m are the max and min of the y-coords.
>    n :=  nops( curves );
>    N := map( nops, curves );
>    M := [ seq( max( seq( curves[j][i][2],
>           i=1..N[j] ) ), j=1..n ) ];
>    m := [ seq( min( seq( curves[j][i][2],
>           i=1..N[j] ) ), j=1..n ) ];
>    # Build new curves adding HUE color.
>    seq( CURVES( seq( [curves[j][i], curves[j][i+1]],
>                 i=1..N[j]-1 ),
>             COLOUR(HUE, seq((curves[j][i][2]
>                        - m[j])/(M[j] - m[j]),
>                     i=1..N[j]-1)),
>             op(curveopts) ), j=1..n );
> end proc:
```

For example

```
> c := CURVES( [ [0,0], [1,1], [2,2], [3,3] ],
>              [ [2,0], [2,1], [3,1] ] );
```

$$c := \mathrm{CURVES}([[0,\,0],\,[1,\,1],\,[2,\,2],\,[3,\,3]],$$
$$[[2,\,0],\,[2,\,1],\,[3,\,1]])$$

```
> addCurvecolor( c );
```

$$\mathrm{CURVES}([[0,\,0],\,[1,\,1]],\,[[1,\,1],\,[2,\,2]],\,[[2,\,2],\,[3,\,3]],$$
$$\mathrm{COLOUR}(HUE,\,0,\,\frac{1}{3},\,\frac{2}{3})),\mathrm{CURVES}([[2,\,0],\,[2,\,1]],$$
$$[[2,\,1],\,[3,\,1]],\,\mathrm{COLOUR}(HUE,\,0,\,1))$$

You can then map such a procedure over all **CURVES** structures of an existing plot structure to provide the desired coloring for each curve.

```
> addcolor := proc( aplot )
>    local recolor;
>    recolor := x -> if op(0,x)=CURVES then
```

```
>                              addCurvecolor(x)
>                    else x end if;
>     map( recolor, aplot );
> end proc:
```

Try **addcolor** on a plot of $\sin(x) + \cos(x)$.

```
> p := plot( sin(x) + cos(x), x=0..2*Pi,
>            linestyle=2, thickness=3 ):
> addcolor( p );
```

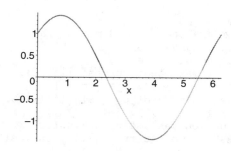

If you add color to two curves simultaneously, the two colorings are independent.

```
> q := plot( cos(2*x) + sin(x), x=0..2*Pi ):
> addcolor( plots[display](p, q) );
```

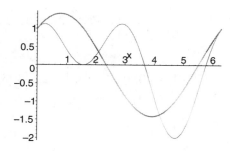

The **addcolor** procedure also works on three-dimensional space curves.

```
> spc := plots[spacecurve]( [ cos(t), sin(t), t ], t=0..8*Pi,
>                    numpoints=100, thickness=2, color=black ):
> addcolor( spc );
```

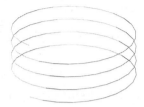

You can easily alter the coloring of an existing plot by using coloring functions. Such coloring functions should either be of the form $C_{Hue} \colon R^2 \to [0, 1]$ (for Hue coloring) or of the form $C_{RGB} \colon R^2 \to [0, 1] \times [0, 1] \times [0, 1]$. The example above uses the color function $C_{Hue}(x, y) = y / \max(y_i)$.

Creating A Chess Board Plot

The final example of programming with color shows how to make a chess board type grid with red and white squares in a three-dimensional plot. You do not simply assign a coloring function as an argument to plot3d. A coloring function, in such a case, provides colors for vertices of a grid, which does not yield color patches. You must first convert the grid or mesh into polygonal form. The rest of the procedure assigns either a red or white color to a polygon, depending on which grid area it represents.

```
> chessplot3d := proc(f, r1, r2)
>     local m, n, i, j, plotgrid, p, opts, coloring, size;
>
>     # obtain grid size
>     # and generate the plotting data structure
>     if hasoption( [ args[4..nargs] ], grid, size) then
>         m := size[1];
>         n := size[2];
>     else  # defaults
>         m := 25;
>         n := 25;
>     end if;
>
>     p := plot3d( f, r1, r2, args[4..nargs] );
>
>     # convert grid data (first operand of p)
>     # into polygon data
>     plotgrid := op( convert( op(1, p), POLYGONS ) );
>     # make coloring function - alternating red and white
>     coloring := (i, j) -> if modp(i-j, 2)=0 then
>                               convert(red, colorRGB)
>                           else
```

```
>                                    convert(white, colorRGB)
>                         end if;
>     # op(2..-1, p) is all the operands of p but the first
>     PLOT3D( seq( seq( POLYGONS( plotgrid[j + (i-1)*(n-1)],
>                              coloring(i, j) ),
>              i=1..m-1 ), j=1..n-1 ),
>           op(2..-1, p) );
> end proc:
```

Here is a chess board plot of $\sin(x)\sin(y)$.

```
> chessplot3d( sin(x)*sin(y), x=-Pi..Pi, y=-Pi..Pi,
>              style=patch, axes=frame );
```

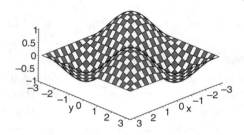

Note that **chessplot3d** works when the plotting structure from **plot3d** is either a **GRID** or **MESH** output type. The latter is the type of output that comes from parametric surfaces or from surfaces that use alternate coordinate systems.

```
> chessplot3d( (4/3)^x*sin(y), x=-1..2*Pi, y=0..Pi,
>              coords=spherical, style=patch,
>              lightmodel=light4 );
```

9.10   Conclusion

In this chapter, you have seen how you can make graphics procedures based on the commands `plot` and `plot3d`, as well as the commands found in the `plots` and `plottools` packages. However, for ultimate control, you must create `PLOT` and `PLOT3D` data structures directly; these are the primitive specifications of all Maple plots. Inside the `PLOT` and `PLOT3D` data structures you can specify points, curves, and polygons, as well as grids of values and meshes of points. You have also seen how to handle plot options, create numerical plotting procedures, work with grids and meshes, manipulate plots and animations, and apply non-standard coloring to your graphics.

10 Input and Output

Although Maple is primarily a system and language for performing mathematical manipulations, many situations arise where such manipulations require the use of data from outside of Maple, or the production of data in a form suitable for use by other applications. You may also need Maple programs to request input directly from the user and/or present output directly to the user. To meet these needs, Maple provides a comprehensive collection of input and output (I/O) commands. The *Maple I/O library* is the term which refers to these commands as a group.

10.1   A Tutorial Example

This section illustrates some of the ways you can use the Maple I/O library in your work. Specifically, the examples show how to write a table of numerical data to a file, and how to read such a table from a file. The examples refer to the following data set, given in the form of a list of lists and assumed to represent a list of (x, y) pairs, where each x is an integer and each y is a real number.

```
> A := [[0, 0],
>       [1, .8427007929],
>       [2, .9953222650],
>       [3, .9999779095],
>       [4, .9999999846],
>       [5, 1.000000000]]:
```

In a real application, this list would have been generated by a Maple command you executed or by a Maple procedure you wrote. In this example, the list was simply typed in as you see it above.

If you want to use some other program (like a presentation graphics program, or perhaps a custom C program) to process data that Maple has generated, then you often need to save the data to a file in a format that the other program recognizes. Using the I/O library, you will find it easy to write such data to a file.

```
> for xy in A do fprintf("myfile", "%d %e\n", xy[1], xy[2]) end do:

> fclose("myfile");
```

If you print the file myfile, or view it with a text editor, it looks like this:

```
0 0.000000e-01
1 8.427008e-01
2 9.953223e-01
3 9.999779e-01
4 1.000000e+00
5 1.000000e+00
```

The fprintf command wrote each pair of numbers to the file. This command takes two or more arguments, the first of which specifies the file that Maple is to write, and the second of which specifies the format for the data items. The remaining arguments are the actual data items that Maple is to write.

In the example above, the file name is myfile. The first time a given file name appears as an argument to fprintf (or any of the other output commands described later), the command creates the file if it does not already exist, and prepares (opens) it for writing. If the file exists, the new version overwrites the old one. You can override this behavior (for example, if you want to append to an already existing file) by using the fopen command, described later.

The format string, "%d %e\n", specifies that Maple should write the first data item as a decimal integer (%d), and the second data item in Fortran-like scientific notation (%e). A single space should separate the first and second data items, and a line break (\n) should follow the second data item (to write each pair of numbers on a new line). By default, as in our example, Maple rounds floating-point numbers to six significant digits for output. You can specify more or fewer digits by using options to the %e format. The section on fprintf describes these options in more detail.

When you are finished writing to a file, you must close it. Until you close a file, the data may or may not actually be in the file, because output is buffered under most operating systems. The fclose command closes a file. If you forget to close a file, Maple automatically closes it when you exit.

For a simple case like the one presented here, writing the data to a file by using the **writedata** command is easier.

```
> writedata("myfile2", A, [integer,float]):
```

The **writedata** command performs all the operations of opening the file, writing the data in the specified format, an integer and a floating-point number, and closing the file. However, **writedata** does not provide the precise formatting control that you may need in some cases. For this, use **fprintf** directly.

In some applications, you may want to read data from a file. For example, some data acquisition software may supply data that you may want to analyze. Reading data from a file is almost as easy as writing to it.

```
> A := [];
```

$$A := []$$

```
> do
>     xy := fscanf("myfile2", "%d %e");
>     if xy = 0 then break end if;
>     A := [op(A),xy];
> end do;
```

$$xy := [0, 0.]$$

$$A := [[0, 0.]]$$

$$xy := [1, .8427007929]$$

$$A := [[0, 0.], [1, .8427007929]]$$

$$xy := [2, .995322265]$$

$$A := [[0, 0.], [1, .8427007929], [2, .995322265]]$$

$$xy := [3, .9999779095]$$

$$A := [[0, 0.], [1, .8427007929], [2, .995322265],$$
$$[3, .9999779095]]$$

$$xy := [4, .9999999846]$$

$$A := [[0, 0.], [1, .8427007929], [2, .995322265],$$
$$[3, .9999779095], [4, .9999999846]]$$

$$xy := [5, 1.000000000]$$

$$A := [[0, 0.], [1, .8427007929], [2, .995322265],$$
$$[3, .9999779095], [4, .9999999846], [5, 1.000000000]]$$

$$xy := []$$

$$A := [[0, 0.], [1, .8427007929], [2, .995322265],$$
$$[3, .9999779095], [4, .9999999846], [5, 1.000000000],$$
$$[]]$$

$$xy := 0$$

```
> fclose("myfile2");
```

This example starts by initializing A to be the empty list. Upon entering the loop, Maple reads a pair of numbers at a time from the file.

The **fscanf** command reads characters from a specified file, and parses them according to the specified format (in this case, **"%d %e"**, indicating a decimal integer and a real number). It either returns a list of the resulting values or the integer 0 to indicate that it has reached the end of the file.

The first time you call **fscanf** with a given file name, Maple prepares (opens) the file for reading. If it does not exist, Maple generates an error.

The second line of the loop checks if **fscanf** returned 0 to indicate the end of the file, and breaks out of the loop if it has. Otherwise, Maple appends the pair of numbers to the list of pairs in **A**. (The syntax **A := [op(A),xy]** tells Maple to assign to **A** a list consisting of the existing elements of **A**, and the new element **xy**.)

As when you wrote to a file, you can read from a file more easily by using the **readdata** command.

```
> A := readdata("myfile2", [integer,float]);
```

$$A := [[0, 0.], [1, .8427007929], [2, .995322265],$$
$$[3, .9999779095], [4, .9999999846], [5, 1.000000000]]$$

The **readdata** command performs all the operations of opening the file, reading the data and parsing the specified format (an integer and a floating-point number), and closing the file. However, **readdata** does not provide the precise parsing control that you may need in some cases. For this, use **fscanf** directly.

These examples illustrate some of the basic concepts of Maple's I/O library, and you can do a great deal by using only the information presented in this section. However, to make more effective and efficient use of the I/O library, an understanding of a few more concepts and commands is useful. The remainder of this chapter describes the concepts of file types, modes, descriptors, and names, and presents a variety of commands for performing both formatted and unformatted file I/O.

10.2   File Types and Modes

Most of the Maple I/O library commands operate on files. This chapter uses the term *file* to denote not just files on a disk, but also Maple's user interface. In most cases, you cannot distinguish between the two from the point of view of the I/O commands. Almost any operation that you can perform on a real file you can perform on the user interface, if appropriate.

Buffered Files versus Unbuffered Files

The Maple I/O library can deal with two different kinds of files: buffered (**STREAM**) and unbuffered (**RAW**). No difference exists in how Maple uses them, but buffered files are usually faster. In buffered files, Maple collects characters in a buffer and writes them to a file all at once when the buffer is full or the file is closed. Raw files are useful when you wish to explicitly take advantage of knowledge about the underlying operating system, such as the block size on the disk. For general use, you should use buffered files, and they are used by default by most of the I/O library commands.

Commands that provide information about I/O status use the identifiers **STREAM** and **RAW** to indicate buffered and unbuffered files, respectively.

Text Files versus Binary Files

Many operating systems, including DOS/Windows and the Macintosh operating system, distinguish between files containing sequences of characters (*text files*) and files containing sequences of bytes (*binary files*). The distinction lies primarily in the treatment of the newline character. Other distinctions may exist on some platforms, but they are not visible when using the Maple I/O library.

Within Maple, the newline character, which represents the concept of ending one line and beginning a new one, is a single character (although you can type it as the two characters "\n" within Maple strings). The internal representation of this character is the byte whose value is 10, the ASCII linefeed character. Many operating systems, however, represent the concept of newline within a file using a different character, or a sequence of two characters. For example, DOS/Windows represents a newline with two consecutive bytes whose values are 13 and 10 (carriage return and line feed). The Macintosh represents a newline with the single byte with value 13 (carriage return).

The Maple I/O library can deal with files as either text files or binary files. When Maple writes to a text file, any newline characters that it writes to the file are translated into the appropriate character or character sequence that the underlying operating system uses. When Maple reads this character or character sequence from a file, it translates back into the single newline character. When Maple writes to a binary file, no translation takes place; it reads newline characters and writes them as the single byte with value 10.

When running Maple under the UNIX operating system or one of its many variants, Maple makes no distinction between text and binary files. It treats both in the same way, and no translation takes place.

Commands which can specify or query whether a file is a text file or a binary file use the identifiers **TEXT** and **BINARY**, respectively.

Read Mode versus Write Mode

At any given time, a file may be open either for reading or for writing. You cannot write to a file that is open only for reading, but you can write to and read from a file that is open for writing. If you attempt, using the Maple I/O library, to write to a file which is open only for reading, Maple closes and reopens the file for writing. If the user does not have the necessary permissions to write to the file (if the file is read-only, or resides on a read-only file system), errors occur at that point.

Commands where you can specify or query whether a file is open for reading or writing use the identifiers READ and WRITE, respectively.

The default and terminal Files

The Maple I/O library treats the Maple user interface as a file. The identifiers default and terminal refer to this file. The default identifier refers to the current input stream, the one from which Maple reads and processes commands. The terminal identifier refers to the top-level input stream, the one which was the current input stream when you first started Maple.

When Maple is run interactively, default and terminal are equivalent. Only when reading commands from a source file using the read statement does a distinction arise. In that case, default refers to the file being read; whereas, terminal refers to the session. Under UNIX, if input is redirected from a file or pipe, terminal refers to that file or pipe.

Note that only the *symbols* default and terminal are special; the *strings* "default" and "terminal" simply refer to files with those names.

10.3   File Descriptors versus File Names

The commands of the Maple I/O library refer to files in one of two ways: by name or by descriptor.

Referring to a file by name is the simpler of the two methods. The first time Maple performs an operation on the file, it opens the file, either in READ mode or in WRITE mode and as a TEXT file or a BINARY file, as appropriate to the operation that it is performing. The primary advantage of referring to files by name is simplicity. However, you will experience a slight performance penalty for using this method, especially if performing many small operations on a file (such as writing individual characters).

Referring to a file by descriptor is only slightly more complex and is a familiar concept to those who have programmed in more traditional environments. A descriptor simply identifies a file after you have opened it. Use the name of the file once to open it and create a descriptor. When you subsequently manipulate the file, use the descriptor instead of the file name. An example in section 10.4 illustrates the use of a file descriptor.

The advantages of the descriptor method include more flexibility when opening the file (you can specify whether the file is TEXT or BINARY, and if Maple should open the file in READ mode or in WRITE mode), improved performance when performing many operations on a file, and the ability to work with unbuffered files. The disadvantage is a slight increase in the amount of programming that you must do.

Which approach is best depends on the task at hand. You can perform simple file I/O tasks most easily by using names; whereas, more complex tasks can benefit from the use of descriptors.

In subsequent sections, the term *fileIdentifier* refers to either a file name or a file descriptor.

10.4   File Manipulation Commands

Opening and Closing Files

Before you can read from or write to a file, you must open it. When referring to files by name, this happens automatically with the first attempt at any operation on the file. When you use descriptors, however, you must explicitly open the file first in order to create the descriptor.

The two commands for opening files are fopen and open. The fopen command opens buffered (STREAM) files; whereas, the open command opens unbuffered (RAW) files.

Use the fopen command as follows.

```
fopen( fileName, accessMode, fileType )
```

The *fileName* specifies the name of the file to open. This name is specified as a string, and follows the conventions that the underlying operating system uses. The *accessMode* must be one of READ, WRITE, or APPEND, indicating whether you should initially open the file for reading, writing, or appending. The optional *fileType* is either TEXT or BINARY.

If you try to open the file for reading and it does not exist, fopen generates an error.

If you try to open the file for writing and it does not exist, Maple first creates it. If it does exist and you specify WRITE, Maple truncates the file to zero length; if you specified APPEND, subsequent calls to commands that write to the file append to it.

Call the open command as follows.

```
open( fileName, accessMode )
```

The arguments to open are the same as those to fopen, except that you cannot specify a fileType (TEXT or BINARY). Maple opens an unbuffered file with type BINARY.

Both fopen and open return a file descriptor. Use this descriptor to refer to the file for subsequent operations. You can still use the file's name, if you desire.

When you have finished with a file, you should tell Maple to close it. This ensures that Maple actually writes all information to the disk. It also frees up resources of the underlying operating system, which often imposes a limit on the number of files that you can open simultaneously.

Close files by using the fclose or close commands. These two commands are equivalent, and you can call them as follows.

```
fclose( fileIdentifier )
close( fileIdentifier )
```

The fileIdentifier is the name or descriptor of the file you wish to close. Once you close a file, any descriptors referring to the file are no longer valid.

```
> f := fopen("testFile.txt",WRITE):

> writeline(f,"This is a test"):

> fclose(f);

> writeline(f,"This is another test"):

Error, (in fprintf) file descriptor not in use
```

When you exit Maple or issue a restart command, Maple automatically closes any open files, whether you opened them explicitly by using fopen or open, or implicitly through a file I/O command.

Position Determination and Adjustment

Associated with each open file is the concept of its current position. This is the location within the file to which a subsequent write takes place, or from which a subsequent read takes place. Any reading or writing operation advances the position by the number of bytes read or written.

You can determine the current position within a file by using the `filepos` command. Use this command in the following manner.

```
filepos( fileIdentifier, position )
```

The *fileIdentifier* is the name or descriptor of the file whose position you wish to determine or adjust. If you give a file name, and that file is not yet open, Maple opens it in **READ** mode with type **BINARY**.

The *position* is optional. If you do not specify the *position*, Maple returns the current position. If you supply the *position*, Maple sets the current position to your specifications and returns the resulting position. In that case, the returned position is the same as the specified *position* unless the file is shorter than the specified *position*, in which case the returned position is that of the end of the file (that is, its length). You can specify the *position* either as an integer, or as the name **infinity**, which specifies the end of the file.

The following command returns the length of the file **myfile.txt**.

```
> filepos("myfile.txt", infinity);
```

$$36$$

Detecting the End of a File

The `feof` command determines whether you have reached the end of a file. Only use the `feof` command on files that you have opened as **STREAM**s, either implicitly or explicitly via `fopen`. Call `feof` in the following manner.

```
feof( fileIdentifier )
```

The *fileIdentifier* is the name or descriptor of the file that you wish to query. If you give a file name, and that file is not yet open, Maple opens it in **READ** mode with type **BINARY**.

The `feof` command returns **true** if and only if you have reached the end of the file during the most recent **readline**, **readbytes**, or **fscanf** operation. Otherwise, `feof` returns **false**. This means that if 20 bytes remain in a file and you use `readbytes` to read these 20 bytes, then `feof` still returns `false`. You only encounter the end-of-file when you attempt another `read`.

Determining File Status

The `iostatus` command returns detailed information about all the files currently in use. Call the `iostatus` command with the following syntax.

```
iostatus()
```

The `iostatus` command returns a list. The list contains the following elements:

`iostatus()[1]` The number of files that the Maple I/O library is currently using.

`iostatus()[2]` The number of active nested `read` commands (when `read` reads a file which itself contains a `read` statement).

`iostatus()[3]` The upper bound on `iostatus()[1]` + `iostatus()[2]` that the underlying operating system imposes.

`iostatus()[n]` for `n > 3`. A list giving information about a file currently in use by the Maple I/O library.

When $n > 3$, the lists that `iostatus()[n]` return each contain the following elements:

`iostatus()[n][1]` The file descriptor which `fopen` or `open` returned.

`iostatus()[n][2]` The name of the file.

`iostatus()[n][3]` The kind of file (`STREAM`, `RAW`, or `DIRECT`).

`iostatus()[n][4]` The file pointer or file descriptor that the underlying operating system uses. The pointer is in the form `FP=integer` or `FD=integer`.

`iostatus()[n][5]` The file mode (`READ` or `WRITE`).

`iostatus()[n][6]` The file type (`TEXT` or `BINARY`).

Removing Files

Many files are solely for temporary use. Often, you no longer need such files when you complete your Maple session and thus, you should remove them. Use the `fremove` command to do this.

```
fremove( fileIdentifier )
```

The *fileIdentifier* is the name or descriptor of the file you wish to remove. If the file is currently open, Maple closes it before removing it. If the file does not exist, Maple generates an error.

To remove a file without knowing whether it exists or not, use a **try/catch** statement to trap the error that **fremove** might create.

```
> try fremove("myfile.txt") catch: end try:
```

10.5   Input Commands

Reading Text Lines from a File

The **readline** command reads a single line of text from a file. Characters are read up to and including a new line. The **readline** command then discards the new line character, and returns the line of characters as a Maple string. If **readline** cannot read a whole line from the file, then it returns 0 instead of a string.

Call the **readline** command by using the following syntax.

```
readline( fileIdentifier )
```

The *fileIdentifier* is the name or descriptor of the file that you wish to read. For compatibility with earlier versions of Maple, you can omit the *fileIdentifier*, in which case Maple uses **default**. Thus **readline()** and **readline(default)** are equivalent.

If you use **-1** as the *fileIdentifier*, Maple also takes input from the **default** stream, except that Maple's command line preprocessor runs on all input lines. This means that lines beginning with "!" pass to the operating system instead of returning through **readline**, and that lines beginning with "?" translate to calls to the **help** command.

If you call **readline** with a file name, and that file is not yet open, Maple opens it in **READ** mode as a **TEXT** file. If **readline** returns 0 (indicating the end of the file) when called with a file name, it automatically closes the file.

The following example defines a Maple procedure which reads a text file and displays it on the **default** output stream.

```
> ShowFile := proc( fileName::string )
>    local line;
>    do
>       line := readline(fileName);
>       if line = 0 then break end if;
>       printf("%s\n",line);
>    end do;
> end proc:
```

Reading Arbitrary Bytes from a File

The **readbytes** command reads one or more individual characters or bytes from a file, returning either a string or a list of integers. If there are no more characters remaining in the file when you call **readbytes**, the command returns 0, indicating that you have reached the end of the file.

Use the following syntax to call the **readbytes** command.

```
readbytes( fileIdentifier, length, TEXT )
```

The *fileIdentifier* is the name or descriptor of the file that Maple is to read. The *length*, which you may omit, specifies how many bytes Maple needs to read. If you omit *length*, Maple reads one byte. The optional parameter **TEXT** indicates that the result is to be returned as a string rather than a list of integers.

You can specify the *length* as **infinity**, in which case Maple reads the remainder of the file.

If you specify **TEXT** when a byte with value 0 resides among the bytes being read, the resulting string contains only those characters preceding the 0 byte.

If you call **readbytes** with a file name, and that file is not yet open, Maple opens it in **READ** mode. If you specify **TEXT**, Maple opens it as a **TEXT** file; otherwise, Maple opens it as a **BINARY** file. If **readbytes** returns 0 (indicating the end of the file) when you call it with a file name, it automatically closes the file.

The following example defines a Maple procedure which reads an entire file, by using **readbytes**, and copies it to a new file.

```
> CopyFile := proc( sourceFile::string, destFile::string )
>    writebytes(destFile, readbytes(sourceFile, infinity))
> end proc:
```

Formatted Input

The `fscanf` and `scanf` commands read from a file, parsing numbers and substrings according to a specified format. The commands return a list of these parsed objects. If no more characters remain in the file when you call `fscanf` or `scanf`, they return 0 instead of a list, indicating that it has reached the end of the file.

Call the `fscanf` and `scanf` commands as follows.

```
fscanf( fileIdentifier, format )
scanf( format )
```

The *fileIdentifier* is the name or descriptor of the file you wish to read. A call to `scanf` is equivalent to a call to `fscanf` with `default` as the *fileIdentifier*.

If you call `fscanf` with a file name, and that file is not yet open, Maple opens it in **READ** mode as a **TEXT** file. If `fscanf` returns 0 (indicating the end of the file) when you call it with a file name, Maple automatically closes the file.

The *format* specifies how Maple is to parse the input. The *format* is a Maple string made up of a sequence of conversion specifications, that may be separated by other characters. Each conversion specification has the following format, where the brackets indicate optional components.

```
%[*] [width] [modifiers] code
```

The "%" symbol begins the conversion specification. The optional "*" indicates that Maple is to scan the object, but not return it as part of the result. It is discarded.

The optional *width* indicates the maximum number of characters to scan for this object. You can use this to scan one larger object as two smaller objects.

The optional *modifiers* are used to indicate the type of the value to be returned:

l or L The letters `l` and `L` are supported for compatibility with the C scanf function, and indicate that a "long int" or "long long" is to be returned. In Maple, these flags have no effect.

zc or Z One of these flags can precede any of the numeric formats, namely `d`, `o`, `x`, `e`, `f`, or `g`, indicating that a complex value is to be scanned. Each of the real and imaginary parts of the complex value are scanned by using the specified format with the `z` or `Z` elided.

The z format scans the real part, followed by a the character specified by c, followed by the imaginary part. The Z format scans the real part, followed by a "+" or "-" sign, followed by the imaginary part, followed by a string of character corresponding to the current setting of interface(imaginaryunit).

The z and Z options can result in one of the few conditions in which scanf will raise an exception. If scanf is part way through scanning a complex value (for example, the real part has already been successfully scanned), and is unable to finish scanning the remainder (for example, there is no imaginary part after the real part), scanf will raise an exception of the form " '%1' expected in input for complex format ", where %1 will be replaced by the expected character (for example, a comma).

The *code* indicates the type of object you wish to scan. It determines the type of object that Maple returns in the resulting list. The *code* can be one of the following:

d The next non-blank characters in the input must make up a signed or unsigned decimal integer. A Maple integer is returned.

o The next non-blank characters in the input must make up an unsigned octal (base 8) integer. The integer is converted to decimal and returned as a Maple integer.

x The next non-blank characters in the input must make up an unsigned hexadecimal (base 16) integer. The letters A through F (either capital or lower case) represent the digits corresponding to the decimal numbers 10 through 15. The integer is converted to decimal and returned as a Maple integer.

y The next non-blank characters in the input must make up an IEEE hex-dump format floating-point value. This value must consist of sixteen hexadecimal characters. The value is converted to and returned as a Maple float.

e, f, or g The next non-blank characters in the input must make up a signed or unsigned decimal number, possibly including a decimal point, and possibly followed by E or e, an optional sign, and a decimal integer indicating a power of ten. The number is returned as a Maple floating-point value.

In addition to numeric values, the e, f, and g formats also recognize the special values "inf" and "NaN". If an i or N is encountered when scanf is looking for the first digit of a number, it assumes that one of these special values has been found, and proceeds to look for the subsequent **nf** or **aN**. If the rest of the special value is not found, an exception is raised.

he, hf, or hg These are special formats for reading one or two-dimensional numeric arrays. In general, such arrays should be read by using the more sophisticated functionality provided by the {} format, but the **he**, **hf**, and **hg** formats are provided for backward compatibility with **hfarrays**, and provide some intelligence in automatically dealing with a variety of textual layouts of such arrays.

The following input must make up a one or two-dimensional array of floating-point (or integer) values. Characters encountered during scanning are categorized into three classes: numeric, separator, and terminator. All the characters that can appear within a number (the digits, decimal point, signs, E, e, D, and d) are numeric. Any white space, commas, or square brackets are separators. A square bracket not immediately followed by a comma, and any other character, are terminators. If a backslash is encountered, it and the following character are ignored completely.

The dimensions of the array are determined by the number of lines read, and the number of values in the first line. If either of these is 1, or if the number of rows multiplied by the number of columns does not equal the total number of values read, a one-dimensional array is produced.

The definition of "the first line" is "everything read up to the first line break that does not immediately follow a comma or a backslash, or up to the first closing square bracket that *is* immediately followed by a comma".

The kinds of things that can be read this way include anything that was written by the corresponding **printf**, "typical" tables of numbers, and lprinted or saved (in text form) Maple lists and lists of lists.

The result is returned as an **hfarray** of one or two dimensions.

hx The following input must make up a one or two dimensional array of floating-point numbers in IEEE hex-dump format (16 characters per number). The dimensions of the array are determined as described for the "%he", "%hf", and "%hg" formats above.

s The next non-blank characters, up to but not including the following blank characters (or the end of the string), are returned as a Maple string.

a Maple collects and parses the next non-blank characters, up to but not including the following blank characters (or the end of the string). An unevaluated Maple expression is returned.

m The next characters must be a Maple expression encoded in Maple's .m file format. Maple reads enough characters to parse a single complete expression; it ignores the *width* specification. The Maple expression is returned.

c This code returns the next character (blank or otherwise) as a Maple string. If a width is specified, that many characters (blank or otherwise) are returned as a single Maple string.

[...] The characters between "[" and "]" become a list of characters that are acceptable as a character string. Maple scans characters from the input until it encounters one that is *not* in the list. The scanned characters are then returned as a Maple string.

If the list begins with a "^" character, the list represents all those characters *not* in the list.

If a "]" is to appear in the list, it must immediately follow the opening "[" or the "^" if one exists.

You can use a "-" in the list to represent a range of characters. For example, "A-Z" represents any capital letter. If a "-" is to appear as a character instead of representing a range, it must appear either at the beginning or the end of the list.

{...}wft The characters between the left brace, "{", and the right brace, "}", are options for scanning Arrays, Matrices, or Vectors (i.e., the various classes of rtable). The optional w is an integer specifying the width to scan for each element (any width specified before the opening "{" would apply to the entire rtable being scanned, but is ignored). The character f specifies the format code, and can be any format code supported by scanf except [...] or {...}. The character t, which must be one of a, m, c, or r, specifies the type of object to be created (Array, Matrix, Vector[column], or Vector[row] respectively).

Details on rtable formatting options are described in the help page ?rtable_scanf.

M The next sequence of characters must correspond to a well formed XML element. The result is a Maple function call whose name is constructed from the XML element, whose arguments are either function calls for the child elements or the CDATA as strings, and whose attributes are equations defining the XML attributes of the object.

n The total number of characters scanned up to the "%n" is returned as a Maple integer.

Maple skips non-blank characters in the *format* but not within a conversion specification (where they must match the corresponding characters in the input). It ignores white space in the *format*, except that a space immediately preceding a "%c" specification causes the "%c" specification to skip any blanks in the input.

If it does not successfully scan any objects, Maple returns an empty list.

The **fscanf** and **scanf** commands use the underlying implementation that the hardware vendor provides for the "%o" and "%x" formats. As a result, input of octal and hexadecimal integers is subject to the restrictions of the machine architecture.

The following example defines a Maple procedure that reads a file containing a table of numbers, in which each row can have a different width. The first number in each row is an integer specifying how many real numbers follow it in that row, and commas separate all the numbers in each row.

```
> ReadRows := proc( fileName::string )
>    local A, count, row, num;
>    A := [];
>    do
>       # Determine how many numbers are in this row.
>       count := fscanf(fileName,"%d");
>       if count = 0 then break end if;
>       if count = [] then
>          error "integer expected in file"
>       end if;
>       count := count[1];
>
>       # Read the numbers in the row.
>       row := [];
>       while count > 0 do
>          num := fscanf(fileName,",%e");
>          if num = 0 then
>             error "unexpected end of file"
>          end if;
>          if num = [] then
>             error "number expected in file"
```

```
>            end if;
>            row := [op(row),num[1]];
>            count := count - 1
>        end do;
>
>        # Append the row to the accumulated result.
>        A := [op(A),row]
>    end do;
>    A
> end proc:
```

Reading Maple Statements

The `readstat` command reads a single Maple statement from the `terminal` input stream. Maple parses and evaluates the statement, and returns the result. Call the `readstat` command as follows.

```
readstat( prompt, ditto3, ditto2, ditto1 )
```

The *prompt* argument specifies the prompt that `readstat` is to use. If you omit the *prompt* argument, Maple uses a blank prompt. You can either supply or omit all of the three arguments *ditto3*, *ditto2*, and *ditto1*. If you supply them, they specify the values which Maple uses for %%%, %%, and % in the statement that `readstat` reads. Specify each of these arguments as a Maple list containing the actual value for substitution. This allows for values that are expression sequences. For example, if % is to have the value 2*n+3 and %% is to have the value a,b, then use [2*n+3] for *ditto1* and [a,b] for *ditto2*.

The response to `readstat` must be a single Maple expression. The expression may span more than one input line, but `readstat` does not permit multiple expressions on one line. If the input contains a syntax error, `readstat` returns an error describing the nature of the error, and its position in the input.

The following example shows a trivial use of `readstat` within a procedure.

```
> InteractiveDiff := proc( )
>    local a, b;
>    a := readstat("Please enter an expression: ");
>    b := readstat("Differentiate with respect to: ");
>    printf("The derivative of %a with respect to %a is %a\n",
>           a,b,diff(a,b))
> end proc:
```

Reading Tabular Data

The `readdata` command reads TEXT files containing tables of data. For simple tables, you will find this more convenient than writing your own procedure by using a loop and the `fscanf` command.

Use the following syntax to call the `readdata` command.

```
readdata( fileIdentifier, dataType, numColumns )
```

The *fileIdentifier* is the name or descriptor of the file from which `readdata` reads the data. The *dataType* must be one of `integer` or `float`, or you can omit it, in which case `readdata` assumes `float`. If `readdata` needs to read more than one column, you can specify the type of each column by using a list of data types.

The *numColumns* argument indicates how many columns of data are to be read from the file. If you omit *numColumns*, `readdata` reads the number of columns specified by the number of data types that you specified (one column if you did not specify any *dataType*).

If Maple reads only one column, `readdata` returns a list of the values read. If Maple reads more than one column, `readdata` returns a list of lists, each sublist of which contains the data read from one line of the file.

If you call `readdata` with a file name, and that file is not yet open, Maple opens it in READ mode as a TEXT file. Furthermore, if you call `readdata` with a file name, it automatically closes the file when `readdata` returns.

The following two examples are equivalent uses of `readdata` to read a table of (x, y, z)-triples of real numbers from a file.

```
> A1 := readdata("my_xyz_file.text",3);
```

$$A1 := [[1.5, 2.2, 3.4], [2.7, 3.4, 5.6], [1.8, 3.1, 6.7]]$$

```
> A2 := readdata("my_xyz_file.text",[float,float,float]);
```

$$A2 := [[1.5, 2.2, 3.4], [2.7, 3.4, 5.6], [1.8, 3.1, 6.7]]$$

10.6   Output Commands

Configuring Output Parameters by using the `interface` Command

The `interface` command is not an output command. It is a mechanism to provide communication between Maple and the user interface (called `Iris`). You can use it to configure several parameters affecting the output produced by various commands within Maple.

To set a parameter, call the `interface` command as follows.

```
interface( variable = expression )
```

The *variable* argument specifies which parameter you wish to change, and the *expression* argument specifies the value that the parameter is to have. See the following sections or `?interface` for which parameters you can set. You may set multiple parameters by giving several arguments of the form *variable = expression*, with commas separating them.

To query the setting of a parameter, use the following syntax.

```
interface( variable )
```

The *variable* argument specifies the parameter to query. The `interface` command returns the current setting of the parameter. You can query only one parameter at a time.

One-Dimensional Expression Output

The `lprint` command prints Maple expressions in a one-dimensional notation very similar to the format Maple uses for input. In most cases, you could return this output to Maple as input, and the same expression would result. The single exception is if the expression contains Maple names containing non-alphanumeric characters.

The `lprint` command is called as follows.

```
lprint( expressionSequence )
```

The *expressionSequence* consists of one or more Maple expressions. Each of the expressions is printed in turn, with three spaces separating each of them. Maple prints a new line character after the last expression.

Maple always sends the output that `lprint` produces to the `default` output stream. You can use the `writeto` and `appendto` commands, described later, to temporarily redirect the `default` output stream to a file.

The `interface` parameter `screenwidth` affects the output of `lprint`. If possible, Maple wraps the output between tokens. If a single token is too long to display (for example, a very long name or number), Maple breaks it across lines, and prints a backslash, "\", before each such break.

The following example illustrates `lprint` output, and how `screenwidth` affects it.

```
> lprint(expand((x+y)^5));

x^5+5*x^4*y+10*x^3*y^2+10*x^2*y^3+5*x*y^4+y^5
```

```
> interface(screenwidth=30);
```

```
> lprint(expand((x+y)^5));

x^5+5*x^4*y+10*x^3*y^2+10*x^2
*y^3+5*x*y^4+y^5
```

Two-Dimensional Expression Output

The `print` command prints Maple expressions in a two-dimensional notation. Depending on the version of Maple you are running, and the user interface you are using, this notation is either the standard math notation that appears in text books and other typeset mathematical documents, or an approximation of standard math notation using only text characters.

Use the following method to call the `print` command.

```
print( expressionSequence )
```

The *expressionSequence* consists of one or more Maple expressions. Maple prints each expression, in turn, with commas separating them.

The output produced by `print` is always sent to the `default` output stream. You can use the `writeto` and `appendto` commands, described later, to temporarily redirect the `default` output stream to a file.

Several `interface` parameters affect the output of `print`. They are set using the syntax

```
interface( parameter = value )
```

They include:

prettyprint This selects the type of output that `print` is to produce. If you set `prettyprint` to 0, `print` produces the same output as `lprint`. If you set `prettyprint` to 1, `print` produces a simulated math notation using only text characters. If you set `prettyprint` to 2, and the version of Maple you are running is capable of it, `print` produces output using standard math notation. The default setting of `prettyprint` is 2.

indentamount This specifies the number of spaces that Maple uses to indent the continuation of expressions that are too large to fit on a single line. This parameter takes effect only when you set `prettyprint` (see above) to 1, and/or when Maple is printing procedures. The default setting of `indentamount` is 4.

labelling or labeling You can set this to `true` or `false`, indicating whether or not Maple should use labels to represent common subexpressions in large expressions. The use of labels can make large expressions easier to read and comprehend. The default setting of `labelling` is `true`.

labelwidth This indicates the size that a subexpression must have in order for Maple to consider it for labeling (if `labelling` is `true`). The size is the approximate width, in characters, of the expression when printed with `print` and `prettyprint = 1`.

screenwidth This indicates the width of the screen in characters. When `prettyprint` is 0 or 1, Maple uses this width to decide when to wrap long expressions. When `prettyprint` is 2, the user interface must deal with pixels instead of characters, and determines the width automatically.

verboseproc Use this parameter when printing Maple procedures. If you set `verboseproc` to 1, Maple only prints user defined procedures; Maple shows system defined procedures in a simplified form giving only the arguments, and possibly a brief description of the procedure. If you set `verboseproc` to 2, Maple prints all procedures in full. Setting `verboseproc` to 3 prints all procedures in full, and prints the contents of a procedure's remember table in the form of Maple comments after the procedure.

When you use Maple interactively, it automatically displays each computed result. The format of this display is the same as if you used the `print` command. Therefore, all the `interface` parameters that affect the `print` command also affect the display of results.

The following example illustrates `print` output, and how `prettyprint`, `indentamount`, and `screenwidth` affect it.

```
> print(expand((x+y)^6));
```

$$x^6 + 6\,x^5\,y + 15\,x^4\,y^2 + 20\,x^3\,y^3 + 15\,x^2\,y^4 + 6\,x\,y^5 + y^6$$

```
> interface(prettyprint=1);
> print(expand((x+y)^6));
```

```
 6       5          4  2        3  3        2  4          5
x   + 6 x   y + 15 x   y  + 20 x   y  + 15 x   y  + 6 x y

        6
    + y
```

```
> interface(screenwidth=35);
> print(expand((x+y)^6));
```

```
 6       5          4  2        3  3
x   + 6 x   y + 15 x   y  + 20 x   y

        2  4        5      6
    + 15 x   y  + 6 x y  + y
```

```
> interface(indentamount=1);
> print(expand((x+y)^6));
```

```
 6       5          4  2        3  3
x   + 6 x   y + 15 x   y  + 20 x   y

      2  4        5      6
  + 15 x   y  + 6 x y  + y
```

```
> interface(prettyprint=0);
> print(expand((x+y)^6));
```

```
x^6+6*x^5*y+15*x^4*y^2+20*x^3*y^3+
15*x^2*y^4+6*x*y^5+y^6
```

Writing Maple Strings to a File

The `writeline` command writes one or more Maple strings to a file. Each string appears on a separate line. Call the `writeline` command as follows.

```
writeline( fileIdentifier, stringSequence )
```

The *fileIdentifier* is the name or description of the file to which you want to write, and *stringSequence* is the sequence of strings that `writeline` should write. If you omit the *stringSequence*, then `writeline` writes a blank line to the file.

Writing Arbitrary Bytes to a File

The `writebytes` command writes one or more individual characters or bytes to a file. You may specify the bytes either as a string or a list of integers.

The following syntax calls the `writebytes` command.

```
writebytes( fileIdentifier, bytes )
```

The *fileIdentifier* is the name or descriptor of the file to which `writebytes` is writing. The *bytes* argument specifies the bytes that `writebytes` writes. This can be either a string or a list of integers. If you call `writebytes` with a file name, and that file is not yet open, Maple opens it in WRITE mode. If you specify the *bytes* as a string, Maple opens the file as a TEXT file; if you specify the *bytes* as a list of integers, Maple opens the file as a BINARY file.

The following example defines a Maple procedure which reads an entire file and copies it to a new file using `writebytes`.

```
> CopyFile := proc( sourceFile::string, destFile::string )
>    writebytes(destFile, readbytes(sourceFile, infinity));
> end proc:
```

Formatted Output

The `fprintf` and `printf` commands write objects to a file, using a specified format.

Call the `fprintf` and `printf` commands as follows.

```
fprintf( fileIdentifier, format, expressionSequence )
printf( format, expressionSequence )
```

The *fileIdentifier* is the name or descriptor of the file to which Maple is to write. A call to `printf` is equivalent to a call to `fprintf` with `default` as the *fileIdentifier*. If you call `fprintf` with a file name, and that file is not yet open, Maples opens it in `WRITE` mode as a `TEXT` file.

The *format* specifies how Maple is to write the elements of the *expressionSequence*. This Maple string is made up of a sequence of formatting specifications, possibly separated by other characters. Each format specification has the following syntax, where the brackets indicate optional components.

```
%[flags][width][.precision][modifiers]code
```

The "%" symbol begins the format specification. One or more of the following flags can optionally follow the "%" symbol:

+ A signed numeric value is output with a leading "+" or "−" sign, as appropriate.

− The output is left justified instead of right justified.

blank A signed numeric value is output with either a leading "−" or a leading blank, depending on whether the value is negative or non-negative.

0 The output is padded on the left (between the sign and the first digit) with zeroes. If you also specify a "−", the "0" is ignored.

{} The braces enclose a set of detailed formatting options for printing an `rtable`. These are described in more detail in the help page `?rtable_printf`.

The optional *width* indicates the minimum number of characters to output for this field. If the formatted value has fewer characters, Maple pads it with blanks on the left (or on the right, if you specify "−").

The optional *precision* specifies the number of digits that appear after the decimal point for floating-point formats, or the maximum field width for string formats.

You may specify both *width* and/or *precision* as "*", in which case Maple takes the *width* and/or *precision* from the argument list. The *width* and/or *precision* arguments must appear, in that order, before the argument that is being output. A negative *width* argument is equivalent to the appearance of the "-" flag.

The optional *modifiers* are used to indicate the type of the· value to be printed:

l or L The letters l and L are supported for compatibility with the C **printf** function, and indicate that a "long int" or "long long" is to be formatted. In Maple, these flags have no effect.

zc or Z One of these flags can precede any of the numeric formats, namely d, o, x, e, f, or g, indicating that a complex value is to be formatted. Each of the real and imaginary parts of the complex value are formatted using the specified format, with the z or Z elided. The z format prints the real part, followed by a the character specified by c, followed by the imaginary part. The Z format prints the value in the form x+yi, where x is the real part, y is the imaginary part, and i is the current setting of **interface(imaginaryunit)**. If y is negative, a "-" is output instead of a "+". If a supplied value is not complex, it is treated as a complex value with a zero imaginary part.

The *code* indicates the type of object that Maple is to write. The *code* can be one of the following.

d Formats the object as a signed decimal integer.

o Formats the object as an unsigned octal (base 8) integer.

x or X Formats the object as an unsigned hexadecimal (base 16) integer. Maple represents the digits corresponding to the decimal numbers 10 through 15 by the letters "A" through "F" if you use "X", or "a" through "f" if you use "x".

e or E Formats the object as a floating-point number in scientific notation. One digit will appear before the decimal point, and *precision* digits will appear after the decimal point (six digits if you do not specify a *precision*). This is followed by the letter "e" or "E", and a signed integer specifying a power of 10. The power of 10 will have a sign and at least three digits, with leading zeroes added if necessary.

If the value being formatted is infinity, -infinity, or undefined, the output is "Inf", "-Inf", or "NaN" respectively.

f Formats the object as a fixed-point number. The number of digits specified by the *precision* will appear after the decimal point.

If the value being formatted is infinity, -infinity, or undefined, the output is "Inf", "-Inf", or "NaN" respectively.

g or G Formats the object using "d", "e" (or "E" if you specified "G"), or "f" format, depending on its value. If the formatted value does not contain a decimal point, Maple uses "d" format. If the value is less than 10^{-4} or greater than $10^{precision}$, Maple uses "e" (or "E") format. Otherwise, Maple uses "f" format.

If the value being formatted is infinity, -infinity, or undefined, the output is "Inf", "-Inf", or "NaN" respectively.

y or Y The floating-point object is formatted in byte-order-independent IEEE hex dump format (16 characters wide). At least 16 characters will always be output, regardless of the specified width. The precision is ignored. The digits corresponding to the decimal numbers 10 through 15 are represented by the letters "A" through "F" if uppercase Y was specified, or "a" through "f" if lowercase y was specified.

c Outputs the object, which must be a Maple string containing exactly one character, as a single character.

s Outputs the object, which must be a Maple string of at least *width* characters (if specified) and at most *precision* characters (if specified).

a or A Outputs the object, which can be any Maple object, in correct Maple syntax. Maple outputs at least *width* characters (if specified) and at most *precision* characters (if specified). *Note:* truncating a Maple expression by specifying a *precision* can result in an incomplete or syntactically incorrect Maple expression in the output.

The "%a" and "%A" formats are identical, except that "%A" will omit any quotes that would normally appear around Maple symbols that require them.

q or Q These are similar to "%a" or "%A", except that "%q" or "%Q" will consume all remaining arguments and print them as an expression sequence, with each element formatted in "%a" or "%A" format respectively. No additional format specifiers can appear after "%q" or "%Q", since there will be no arguments left to format.

m The object, which can be any Maple object, is output in Maple's ".m" file format. Maple outputs at least *width* characters (if specified), and at most *precision* characters (if specified). *Note:* truncating a Maple ".m" format expression by specifying a *precision* can result in an incomplete or incorrect Maple expression in the output.

% A percent symbol is output verbatim.

Maple outputs characters that are in *format* but not within a format specification verbatim.

All of the formats apply to Arrays (type **Array**), Matrices (type **Matrix**), Vectors (type **Vector**), and hfarrays (type **hfarray**), all of which are objects of type **rtable**.

If no rtable-specific formatting options are specified (via the {...} option, see **?rtable_printf**), the **%a**, **%A**, **%m**, and **%M** format codes will print a representation of the rtable structure itself. For example, **%a** would print a **Matrix**, **Vector**, or **Array** call.

If no additional rtable-specific formatting options are specified for a format code *other than* **%a**, **%A**, **%m**, and **%M**, or if an empty rtable option sequence (i.e., just {}) is specified for *any* format code, the following default formatting is applied:

One-dimensional objects are formatted as one long line, with the elements separated by at least one space.

Objects of N dimensions, where $N > 1$, are formatted as a sequence of $(N-1)$-dimensional objects separated by $N-2$ blank lines. Therefore, two-dimensional objects are formatted in the obvious way, three-dimensional objects are formatted as a series of two-dimensional objects separated by blank lines, and so on.

Any of the floating-point formats can accept integer, rational, or floating-point objects; Maple converts the objects to floating-point values and outputs them appropriately.

The **fprintf** and **printf** commands do *not* automatically start a new line at the end of the output. If you require a new line, the *format* string must contain a new line character, "\n". Output from **fprintf** and **printf** is *not* subject to line wrapping at **interface(screenwidth)** characters.

The "%o", "%x", and "%X" formats use the underlying implementation that the hardware vendor provides. As a result, output of octal and hexadecimal values is subject to the restrictions of the machine architecture.

Writing Tabular Data

The `writedata` command writes tabular data to `TEXT` files. In many cases, this is more convenient than writing your own output procedure by using a loop and the `fprintf` command.

Call the `writedata` command in the following manner.

```
writedata( fileIdentifier, data, dataType, defaultProc )
```

The *fileIdentifier* is the name or descriptor of the file to which `writedata` writes the data.

If you call `writedata` with a filename, and that file is not yet open, Maple opens it in `WRITE` mode as a `TEXT` file. Furthermore, if you call `writedata` with a file name, the file automatically closes when `writedata` returns.

The *data* must be a vector, matrix, list, or list of lists.[1] If the *data* is a vector or list of values, `writedata` writes each value to the file on a separate line. If the *data* is a matrix or a list of lists of values, `writedata` writes each row or sublist to the file on a separate line, with tab characters separating the individual values.

The *dataType* is optional, and specifies whether `writedata` is to write the values as integers, floating-point values (the default), or strings. If you specify `integer`, the values must be numeric, and `writedata` writes them as integers (Maple truncates rational and floating-point values to integers). If you specify `float`, the values must be numeric, and `writedata` writes them as floating-point values (Maple converts integer and rational values to floating-point). If you specify `string`, the values must be strings. When writing matrices or lists of lists, you can specify the *dataType* as a list of data types, one corresponding to each column in the output.

The optional *defaultProc* argument specifies a procedure that `writedata` calls if a data value does not conform to the *dataType* you specified (for example, if `writedata` encounters a non-numeric value when the *dataType* is `float`). Maple passes the file descriptor corresponding to the *fileIdentifier*, along with the non-conforming value, as an argument to the *defaultProc*. The default *defaultProc* simply generates the error, `Bad data found`. A more useful *defaultProc* might be the following.

```
> UsefulDefaultProc := proc(f,x) fprintf(f,"%a",x) end proc:
```

---

[1] For information about how to read and write rtable-based Matrices and Vectors, see the help pages `?ImportMatrix` and `?ImportVector`.

This procedure is a sort of "catch-all"; it is capable of writing any kind of value to the file.

The following example computes a 5 by 5 Hilbert matrix, and writes its floating-point representation to a file.

```
> writedata("hilbertFile.txt",linalg[hilbert](5)):
```

Examining the file shows:

1	.5	.3333333333	.25	.2
.5	.3333333333	.25	.2	.1666666667
.3333333333	.25	.2	.1666666667	.1428571429
.25	.2	.1666666667	.1428571429	.125
.2	.1666666667	.1428571429	.125	.1111111111

Flushing a Buffered File

I/O buffering may result in a delay between when you request a write operation and when Maple physically writes the data to the file. This is to capitalize on the greater efficiency of performing one large write instead of several smaller ones.

Normally, the I/O library chooses when to write to a file automatically. In some situations, however, you may desire to ensure that the data you write has actually made it into the file. For example, under UNIX, a common procedure is to run a command, such as "tail -f fileName", in another window in order to monitor the information as Maple is writing it. For cases such as these, the Maple I/O library provides the fflush command.

Call the fflush command using the following syntax.

```
fflush( fileIdentifier )
```

The fileIdentifier is the name or descriptor of the file whose buffer Maple is to flush. When you call fflush, Maple writes all information that is in the buffer but not yet in the physical file to the file. Typically, a program would call fflush whenever something significant is written (for example, a complete intermediate result or a few lines of output).

Note that you do not need to use fflush; anything you write to a file will physically be written no later than when you close the file. The fflush command simply forces Maple to write data on demand, so that you can monitor the progress of a file.

Redirecting the `default` Output Stream

The `writeto` and `appendto` commands redirect the `default` output stream to a file. This means that any operations that write to the `default` stream write to the file you specify instead.

You can call the `writeto` and `appendto` commands as follows.

```
writeto( fileName )
appendto( fileName )
```

The *fileName* argument specifies the name of the file to which Maple is to redirect the output. If you call `writeto`, Maple truncates the file if it already exists, and writes subsequent output to the file. The `appendto` command appends to the end of the file if the file already exists. If the file you specify is already open (for example, it is in use by other file I/O operations), Maple generates an error.

The special *fileName* `terminal` (specified as a name, not a string) causes Maple to send subsequent `default` output to the original `default` output stream (the one that was in effect when you started Maple). The calls `writeto(terminal)` and `appendto(terminal)` are equivalent.

Issuing a `writeto` or `appendto` call directly from the Maple prompt is not the best choice of action. When `writeto` or `appendto` are in effect, Maple also writes any error messages that may result from subsequent operations to the file. Therefore, you cannot see what is happening. You should generally use the `writeto` and `appendto` commands within procedures or files of Maple commands that the `read` command is reading.

10.7 Conversion Commands

C or Fortran Generation

Maple provides commands to translate Maple expressions into two other programming languages, C and Fortran. Conversion to other programming languages is useful if you have used Maple's symbolic techniques to develop a numeric algorithm, which then may run faster as a C or Fortran program than as a Maple procedure.

Perform a conversion to Fortran or C by using the `fortran` or `C` commands in the `codegen` package, respectively. There are also several support commands for code generation, which can be found in the `codegen` package.

Call the `fortran` and `C` commands using the following syntax.

```
codegen[fortran]( expression, options )
codegen[C]( expression, options )
```

The *expression* can take one of the following forms:

1. A single algebraic expression: Maple generates a sequence of C or Fortran statements to compute the value of this expression.

2. A list of expressions of the form `name= expression`: Maple generates a sequence of statements to compute each *expression* and assigns it to the corresponding *name*.

3. A named array of expressions: Maple generates a sequence of C or Fortran statements to compute each expression and assigns it to the corresponding element of the array.

4. A Maple procedure: Maple generates a C function or Fortran subroutine.

The **fortran** command uses the `'fortran/function_name'` command when translating function names to their Fortran equivalents. This command takes three arguments: the Maple function name, the number of arguments, and the precision, and returns a single Fortran function name. You can override the default translations by assigning values to the remember table of `'fortran/function_name'`.

```
> 'fortran/function_name'(arctan,1,double) := datan;
```

$$\text{fortran/function\_name}(\text{arctan}, 1, \mathit{double}) := \mathit{datan}$$

```
> 'fortran/function_name'(arctan,2,single) := atan2;
```

$$\text{fortran/function\_name}(\text{arctan}, 2, \mathit{single}) := \mathit{atan2}$$

When translating arrays, the C command re-indexes all array indices to begin with 0, since the base of C arrays is 0. The **fortran** command re-indexes arrays to begin with 1, but only when Maple is translating a procedure.

Here Maple symbolically calculates the anti-derivative.

```
> f := unapply( int( 1/(1+x^4), x), x );
```

$$f := x \rightarrow \frac{1}{8}\sqrt{2}\ln(\frac{x^2 + x\sqrt{2} + 1}{x^2 - x\sqrt{2} + 1}) + \frac{1}{4}\sqrt{2}\arctan(x\sqrt{2} + 1)$$
$$+ \frac{1}{4}\sqrt{2}\arctan(x\sqrt{2} - 1)$$

The `fortran` command generates a Fortran routine.

```
> codegen[fortran](f, optimized);
```

```
c The options were    : operatorarrow
      doubleprecision function f(x)
      doubleprecision x

      doubleprecision t1
      doubleprecision t12
      doubleprecision t16
      doubleprecision t2
      doubleprecision t3
      doubleprecision t8

        t1 = sqrt(2.D0)
        t2 = x**2
        t3 = x*t1
        t8 = log((t2+t3+1)/(t2-t3+1))
        t12 = atan(t3+1)
        t16 = atan(t3-1)
        f = t1*t8/8+t1*t12/4+t1*t16/4
        return
      end
```

Now translate the same expression to C.

```
> codegen[C](f, optimized);
```

```
/* The options were    : operatorarrow */
double f(x)
double x;
{
  double t1;
  double t12;
  double t16;
  double t2;
  double t3;
  double t8;
  {
    t1 = sqrt(2.0);
    t2 = x*x;
    t3 = x*t1;
    t8 = log((t2+t3+1.0)/(t2-t3+1.0));
    t12 = atan(t3+1.0);
    t16 = atan(t3-1.0);
    return(t1*t8/8.0+t1*t12/4.0+t1*t16/4.0);
```

```
    }
  }
```

LaTeX Generation

Maple supports conversion of Maple expressions to the LaTeX typesetting language. Conversion to typesetting languages is useful when you need to insert a result in a scientific paper.

You can perform conversion to LaTeX by using the `latex` command. Call the `latex` command as follows.

```
latex( expression, fileName )
```

The *expression* can be any mathematical expression. Maple-specific expressions, such as procedures, are not translatable. The *fileName* is optional, and specifies that Maple writes the translated output to the file you specified. If you do not specify a *fileName*, Maple writes the output to the `default` output stream (your session).

The `latex` command knows how to translate most types of mathematical expressions, including integrals, limits, sums, products, and matrices. You can expand the capabilities of `latex` by defining procedures with names of the form `'latex/functionName'`. Such a procedure is responsible for formatting calls to the function called *functionName*. You should produce the output of such formatting functions with `printf`. `latex` uses `writeto` to redirect the output when you specify a *fileName*.

The `latex` command does not generate the commands that LaTeX requires to put the typesetting system into mathematics mode (`$...$`, for example).

The following example shows the generation of LaTeX for an equation for an integral and its value. Notice the use of `Int`, the inert form of `int`, to prevent evaluation of the left hand side of the equation that Maple is formatting.

```
> Int(1/(x^4+1),x) = int(1/(x^4+1),x);
```

$$\int \frac{1}{x^4+1}\,dx = \frac{1}{8}\sqrt{2}\ln(\frac{x^2+x\sqrt{2}+1}{x^2-x\sqrt{2}+1})$$
$$+\frac{1}{4}\sqrt{2}\arctan(x\sqrt{2}+1)+\frac{1}{4}\sqrt{2}\arctan(x\sqrt{2}-1)$$

```
> latex(%);
```

```
\int \! \left( {x}^{4}+1 \right) ^{-1}{dx}=1/8
\,\sqrt {2}\ln  \left( {\frac {{x}^{2}+x\sqrt
{2}+1}{{x}^{2}-x\sqrt {2}+1}} \right) +1/4\,
\sqrt {2}\arctan \left( x\sqrt {2}+1 \right) +
1/4\,\sqrt {2}\arctan \left( x\sqrt {2}-1
\right)
```

You can also export a whole Maple worksheet in LATEX format by choosing **Export As** from the **File** menu, then **LaTeX**. For more information, see Section 7.3 of the *Learning Guide*.

Conversion between Strings and Lists of Integers

The `readbytes` and `writebytes` commands described in sections 10.5 and 10.6 can work with either Maple strings or lists of integers. You can use the `convert` command to convert between these two formats as follows.

```
convert( string, bytes )
convert( integerList, bytes )
```

If you pass `convert(...,bytes)` a string, it returns a list of integers; if you pass it a list of integers, it returns a string.

Due to the way strings are implemented in Maple, the character corresponding to the byte-value 0 cannot appear in a string. Therefore, if *integerList* contains a zero, `convert` returns a string of only those characters corresponding to the integers preceding the occurrence of 0 in the list.

Conversion between strings and lists of integers is useful when Maple must interpret parts of a stream of bytes as a character string, while it must interpret other parts as individual bytes.

In the following example, Maple converts a string to a list of integers. Then, it converts the same list, but with one entry changed to 0, back to a string. Notice that the string is truncated at the location of the 0.

```
> convert("Test String",bytes);
```

$$[84, 101, 115, 116, 32, 83, 116, 114, 105, 110, 103]$$

```
> convert([84,101,115,116,0,83,116,114,105,110,103],bytes);
```

"Test"

Parsing Maple Expressions and Statements

The `parse` command converts a string of valid Maple input into the corresponding Maple expression. The expression is simplified, but not evaluated.

Use the `parse` command as follows.

```
parse( string, options )
```

The *string* argument is the string that needs parsing. It must describe a Maple expression (or statement, see below) by using the Maple language syntax.

You may supply one or more *options* to the `parse` command:

`statement` This indicates that `parse` is to accept statements in addition to expressions. However, since Maple does not allow the existence of unevaluated statements, `parse` does evaluate the *string* if you specify `statement`.

`nosemicolon` Normally, `parse` supplies a terminating semicolon, ";" if the string does not end in a semicolon or a colon, ":". If you specify `nosemicolon`, this does not happen, and Maple generates an `unexpected end of input` error if the string is incomplete. The `readstat` command, which uses `readline` and `parse`, makes use of this facility to allow multi-line inputs.

If the *string* passed to `parse` contains a syntax error, `parse` generates an error (which you can trap with `traperror`) of the following form.

```
incorrect syntax in parse:
        errorDescription (errorLocation)
```

The *errorDescription* describes the nature of the error (for example, '+' unexpected, or `unexpected end of input`). The *errorLocation* gives the approximate character position within the string at which Maple detected the error.

When you call `parse` from the Maple prompt, Maple displays the parsed result depending on whether the call to `parse` ends in a semicolon or a colon. Whether the *string* passed to `parse` ends in a semicolon or a colon does not matter.

```
> parse("a+2+b+3");
```

$$a + 5 + b$$

```
> parse("sin(3.0)"):
> %;
```

$$.1411200081$$

Formatted Conversion to and from Strings

The `sprintf` and `sscanf` commands are similar to `fprintf`/`printf` and `fscanf`/`scanf`, except that they read from or write to Maple strings instead of files.

Call the `sprintf` command using the following syntax.

```
sprintf( format, expressionSequence )
```

The *format* specifies how Maple is to format the elements of the *expressionSequence*. This Maple string is made up of a sequence of formatting specifications, possibly separated by other characters. See 10.6.

The `sprintf` command returns a string containing the formatted result.

Call the `sscanf` command as follows.

```
sscanf( sourceString, format )
```

The *sourceString* provides the input for scanning. The *format* specifies how Maple is to parse the input. A sequence of conversion specifications (and possibly other anticipated characters) make up this Maple string. See 10.5. The `sscanf` command returns a list of the scanned objects, just as `fscanf` and `scanf` do.

The following example illustrates `sprintf` and `sscanf` by converting a floating-point number and two algebraic expressions into a floating-point format, Maple syntax, and Maple .m format, respectively. This string is then parsed back into the corresponding objects using `sscanf`.

```
> s := sprintf("%4.2f %a %m",evalf(Pi),sin(3),cos(3));
```

$$s := \text{``}3.14 \ \sin(3) \ \text{-}\%\$cosG6\#\backslash\text{``}\backslash \ \text{``}\$\text{''}$$

```
> sscanf(s,"%f %a %m");
```

$$[3.14, \sin(3), \cos(3)]$$

10.8   A Detailed Example

This section provides an example that uses several of the I/O facilities described in this chapter to generate a Fortran subroutine in a text file. In this example, you can find all of the required Maple commands typed on the command line. In general, for such a task you would write a procedure or, at the very least, a file of Maple commands.

Suppose you wish to compute values of the function $1 - \mathrm{erf}(x) + \exp(-x)$ for many points on the interval [0,2], accurate to five decimal places. By using the **numapprox** package from the Maple library, you can obtain a rational approximation for this function as follows.

```
> f := 1 - erf(x) + exp(-x):
> approx := numapprox[minimax](f, x=0..2, [5,5]);
```

$$
\begin{aligned}
approx := &\, (1.872569003 + (-2.480756984+ \\
&(1.455338215 + (-.4103981070 + .04512734455\,x)\,x)\,x \\
&)x)/(.9362855506 + (-.2440826049+ \\
&(.2351099626 + (.00115111416 - .01091329716\,x)\,x)\,x \\
&)x)
\end{aligned}
$$

You can now create the file and write the subroutine header to the file.

```
> file := "approx.f77":
```

```
> fprintf(file, "real function f(x)\nreal x\n"):
```

Before you can write the actual Fortran output to the file, you must close the file. Otherwise, the **fortran** command attempts to open the file in **APPEND** mode, which results in an error if the file is already open.

```
> fclose(file):
```

Now you can write the actual Fortran statements to the file.

```
> codegen[fortran](['f'=approx], filename=file):
```

Finally, you add the remainder of the Fortran subroutine syntax.

```
> fopen(file, APPEND):
> fprintf(file, "return\nend\n"):
> fclose(file):
```

If you now examine the file, it looks like this:

```
real function f(x)
real x
    f = (0.187258E1+(-0.2480777E1+(0.1455351E1+
    #(-0.4104024E0+0.4512788E-1*x)*x)*x)*x)/(0.9
    #362913E0+(-0.2440864E0+(0.235111E0+(0.11504
    #53E-2-0.1091373E-1*x)*x)*x)*x)
return
end
```

This subroutine is now ready for you to compile and link into a Fortran program.

10.9 Notes to C Programmers

If you have experience programming in the C or C++ programming languages, many of the I/O commands described in this chapter will seem familiar. This is not coincidental, as the Maple I/O library design purposely emulates the C standard I/O library.

In general, the Maple I/O commands work in a similar manner to their C counterparts. The differences that arise are the result of differences between the Maple and C languages, and how you use them. For example, in the C library, you must pass the **sprintf** function a buffer into which it writes the result. In Maple, strings are objects that you can pass around as easily as numbers, so the **sprintf** command simply returns a string that is sufficiently long to hold the result. This method is both easier to work with and less error prone, as it removes the danger of writing past the end of a fixed length buffer.

Similarly, the **fscanf**, **scanf**, and **sscanf** commands return a list of the parsed results instead of requiring you to pass references to variables. This method is also less error prone, as it removes any danger of passing the wrong type of variable or one of insufficient size.

Other differences include the use of a single command, `filepos`, to perform the work of two C functions, `ftell` and `fseek`. You can do this in Maple, since functions can take a variable number of arguments.

In general, if you have C or C++ programming experience, you should have very little trouble using the Maple I/O library.

10.10   Conclusion

This chapter has revealed the details of importing and exporting data and code into and out of Maple. Most commands discussed in this chapter are more primitive than those commands which you are likely to use, such as `save` and `writeto`. The aforementioned Maple commands ensure that you are properly equipped to write specialized exporting and importing procedures. Their basis is similar to the commands found in the popular C programming language, although they have been extended to allow easy printing of algebraic expressions.

Overall, this book provides an essential framework for understanding Maple's programming language. Each chapter is designed to teach you to use a particular area of Maple effectively. However, a complete discussion of Maple can not fit into a single book. The Maple help system is an excellent resource and complements this volume. While this book teaches fundamental concepts and provides a pedagogical introduction to topics, the help system provides the details on each command and feature. It explains such things as the options and syntax of Maple commands and serves as a resource for use of the Maple interface.

Also, numerous authors have published many books about Maple. These include not only books, such as this one, on the general use of Maple, but also books directed toward the use of Maple in a particular field or application. Should you wish to consult books that parallel your own area of interest, this book will still serve as a handy reference and guide to Maple programming.

11 Using Compiled Code in Maple

It is possible to call routines written in C or Fortran by using Maple's external calling facility. Maple makes extensive use of this facility to call NAG and other numerical libraries. You can augment the rich suite of functions in Maple by writing your own libraries. There are also third party external libraries available to extend the power of Maple. External functions can be used to improve performance because compiled code is usually much faster than interpreted code.

Maple's external calling facility is very extensive, allowing a user to translate most data from a Maple format to a hardware format for use in an external program. To balance power and flexibility with ease of use, the external calling application program interface (API) is divided into three methods. All use the same basic interface, but each has very different back-end support routines.

Using any of the methods, a user can call a C routine. Using Methods 1 and 3, a user can call a Fortran routine. Method 2 is not applicable to Fortran routines (as discussed below). The structure of the procedure that defines the external call depends on the routine, and thus whether it was written in C or Fortran. However, the choice to use C or Fortran routines is dependent on only the availability of routines that perform the desired function or, in the case of custom routines, the preference of the developer writing the external library.

Method 1: Calling External Functions   In most cases, compiled functions use only standard hardware types like integers, floating-point numbers, strings, pointers (to strings, integers, and floating-point numbers), matrices, and vectors. In these cases, Maple can automatically translate between its internal representation and the hardware representation. Because this method does not require the use of a compiler, it is efficient and easy to use. This method of *directly calling* the external code allows the use of an external library without modification.

Method 2: Wrapper Generation   Method 1 is limited by its use of only standard data types. When dealing with more complicated compound types or passing functions or records as parameters, a compiled *wrapper* is needed. Because Fortran does not use these data structures, this method applies only to C routines. The wrapper performs the conversion between Maple's internal representation and the hardware representation. Maple automatically generates and compiles wrappers, which are based on your specifications, to interface with libraries of compiled code. This allows you to use a greater diversity of external libraries than you can by simply directly calling the external function. External calls that use these wrappers require that a C compiler is installed.

Method 3: Customizing Wrappers   For flexibility beyond that available by either of the other methods, an external API is provided for users who want to augment existing wrappers or write *custom wrappers*. The user can write the wrapper in C or Fortran as desired. This powerful method also allows direct access to Maple data structures from the wrapper.

This chapter provides a technical overview of Maple's external calling mechanism, and provides a context in which to explain the external calling facilities.

11.1   Method 1: Calling External Functions

To illustrate how Maple's external calling facility is used, start by looking at a trivial example of a function written in C. Consider the following code that adds two numbers and returns the result. Obviously, such a function would never be used since Maple's + operator exists, but working through this example will demonstrate the steps that are required to use compiled code in Maple.

```
int add( int num1, int num2 )
{
     return num1+num2;
}
```

There are 3 basic steps required to call an external function.

Step 1: DLL Creation First, this function needs to be compiled into a Dynamic Link Library (Windows XXX.DLL), or Shared Library (Unix libXXX.so or Macintosh XXX.ShLib). For the rest of this chapter, the compiled library will be referred to as a DLL. If the sources are downloaded from the internet or purchased, a DLL may already have been built. Otherwise, consult the compiler's documentation for help on how to build a DLL. When building the DLL ensure that you *export* the function that Maple is intended to be able to call. In this case, the function name is *add*.

This is the only step that requires the user to have knowledge of a specific compiler. For the remaining steps, it does not matter if the function was written in C or Fortran.

Maple expects that the external library functions are compiled by using the `_stdcall` calling convention, which is the default under UNIX but must be specified explicitly on Windows.

Step 2: Function Specification To make the appropriate argument conversions, Maple requires some details about the function that it is going to call. At a minimum, Maple needs to know the following:

- name of the function,

- type of parameters the function passes and returns, and

- name of the DLL containing the function.

The specification of the parameter types are independent of the compiler. The same specification can be used regardless of the language that was used to compile the DLL. The example uses the C type *int*. In Maple, this is specified as `integer[4]`. The 4 in the square brackets denotes the number of bytes used to represent the integer. Most C compilers use 4-byte *ints*, but some older compilers may use 2-byte *ints*. Maple's type specification is flexible enough to support both types of compiler integer sizes. See Table 11.1 for a map of the most common type relations.

Since `num1` and `num2` are both *ints*, they can be specified as the following in Maple.

```
num1::integer[4]
num2::integer[4]
```

The return type does not have a name so the keyword `RETURN` is used.

```
RETURN::integer[4]
```

Using all of this information, the complete function can be defined by calling the Maple function `define_external`.

```
> myAdd := define_external(
>         'add',
>         'num1'::integer[4],
>         'num2'::integer[4],
>         'RETURN'::integer[4],
>         'LIB'="mylib.dll"
>     );
```

It is important to specify the function exactly, and to ensure that the arguments are in the correct order. Failure to do this may result in strange behavior or program crashes when executing step 3.

Step 3: Function Invocation Executing the `define_external` call for `myAdd` returns a Maple procedure that translates Maple types to hardware types that can work with an external function. This procedure can be used the same way as any other procedure in Maple.

```
> myAdd(1,2);
```

$$3$$

```
> a := 33:
> b := 22:
> myAdd(a,b);
```

$$55$$

```
> r:= myAdd(a,11);
```

$$r := 44$$

Procedures generated in this manner contain run-time information and thus cannot be saved. The `define_external` command must be reissued after exiting or restarting Maple.

The following subsections provide additional information for Step 2, the function specification.

External Definition

The `define_external` function constructs and returns another function which can be used to make the actual call. The `define_external` function is called as follows.

```
define_external( functionName, arg1::type1, ...,
                argN::typeN, options, 'LIB'=dllName )
define_external( functionName, 'MAPLE',
                options, 'LIB'=dllName )
```

The *functionName* parameter specifies the name of the actual external function to be called. This name can be specified as a Maple string or name.

The parameters *arg1* through *argN* describe the arguments of the function to be called. These should be specified in the order they appear in the documentation or source code for the external function, without regard to issues such as actual passing order (left to right versus right to left). The intent is that the Maple procedure returned by `define_external` will have the same calling sequence as the actual external function when used in the language for which it was written. The only exception is that one argument may be given the name RETURN. This specifies the type returned by the function rather than a parameter passed to the function. For more information about how each *argi* is specified, see the section on *type specification*.

The *options* are used to specify argument passing conventions, libraries, calling methods, etc. See the appropriate sections of this chapter for details.

If instead of the *arg* parameters, the single word MAPLE is specified, the external function is assumed to accept the raw Maple data structures passed without conversion. This assumes that the wrapper has been manually generated and compiled into a shared library. Various support functions for writing such external functions are described in Section 11.3. Using MAPLE instead of specifying arguments is the basis of method 3.

The location of the DLL containing the function to be called is specified by using the *LIB* option to `define_external`. The *dllName* is a string that specifies the filename of the library in which the function is to be found. The format of this name is highly system dependent. Likewise, whether a full pathname is required depends on the system. In general, the name should be in the same format as would be specified to a compiler on the same system.

Type Specification

Step two of the introductory example indicated how to specify types using Maple notation. Maple uses its own notation to provide a generic well-defined interface for calling compiled code in any language.

The format of each *arg* parameter is as follows.

```
argumentIdentifier :: dataDescriptor
```

The return value description is also described by using a data descriptor, with the name **RETURN** as the *argumentIdentifier*. If the function returns no value, no **RETURN** parameter is specified. Also, if no parameters are passed, no argument identifiers are required.

Scalar Data Formats

External libraries generally deal with scalar data supported directly by the underlying machine. All array, string, and structured formats are built up from these. The data descriptors used to represent scalar formats usually contain a type name and size. The size represents the number of bytes needed to represent the given hardware type. Table 11.1 lists the basic type translations for standard C and Fortran compilers.

Structured Data Formats

In addition to the basic types listed in Table 11.1, Maple also recognizes some compound types that can be derived from the basic types, such as arrays and pointers. These compound types are listed in Table 11.2.

Character String Data Formats   Strings are similar to both scalar and array data. A string in C is an array of characters, but it is often manipulated as if it were an object. A string in Maple is an atomic object, but it can be manipulated as if it were an array of characters.

Parameter *n* in *string[n]* indicates that the called function is expecting a fixed size string. Otherwise, a pointer to a character buffer (**char***) will be used.

Strings are implicitly passed by reference (only a pointer to the string is passed), but any changes made to the string are not copied back to Maple unless the string is declared with a size.

Table 11.1 Basic Type Translations

Maple Data Descriptor	C Type	Fortran Type
integer[1]	char	BYTE
integer[2]	short	INTEGER*2
integer[4]	int	INTEGER
	long[1]	INTEGER*4
integer[8]	long[1]	INTEGER*8
	long long	INTEGER*8
float[4]	float	REAL
		REAL*4
float[8]	double	DOUBLE PRECISION
		REAL*8
char[1]	char	CHARACTER
boolean[1]	char	LOGICAL*1
boolean[2]	short	LOGICAL*2
boolean[4]	int	LOGICAL
	long	LOGICAL*4
boolean[8]	long	LOGICAL*8
	long long	LOGICAL*8

[1] Type *long* is typically (but not necessarily) 4-bytes on 32-bit machines and 8-bytes on 64-bit machines. Use the *sizeof* operator or consult your compiler manual to verify *sizeof(long)*.

Table 11.2 Compound Types

Maple Data Descriptor	C Type	Fortran Type
ARRAY(datatype=typename, order=..., etc.)	char	BYTE
string[n]	char x[n]	CHARACTER*2
complex[4]	struct { float r, i; }	COMPLEX COMPLEX*8
complex[8]	struct { double r, i; }	DOUBLE COMPLEX COMPLEX*16
REF(typename)	TYPENAME*	NA

Array Data Formats An array of data is a homogeneous, n-rectangular structure matching the Maple `rtable` formats. Any `datatype` that is accepted by Maple's `Array`, `Matrix`, or `Vector` constructor will be accepted.

The *options* are used to specify array conventions. They are the same optional arguments that can be passed to the `Array` constructor in Maple. The only significant difference is that indexing functions must be specified with `indfn=` (and are not allowed when using wrapper-generated external calling). These options override any defaults normally assumed by the `Array` constructor.

datatype=... Only hardware datatypes are allowed. This field is required, but the equation form of entry is not necessary. For example, simply specifying `integer[4]` is sufficient.

order=... This may be left unspecified for vectors since Fortran and C representation is the same. Otherwise, this will default to `Fortran_order` when calling a Fortran library and `C_order` when calling a C library.

storage=... If this is not specified, the default is full rectangular storage

subtype=... This is optional and restricts the subtype to `Array`, `Matrix`, `Vector[row]`, or `Vector[column]`.

indfn=(..., ...) This specifies the indexing functions that the `Array`, `Matrix`, or `Vector` must have.

Other Compound Types There are other types, including records (structs), and procedures that are supported when using wrapper generated external linking. These data descriptors are described in section 11.2.

Specifying Argument Passing Conventions

Different programming languages have different conventions for parameter passing. C always uses *pass-by-value*; *pass-by-reference* must be done explicitly by passing an address. Fortran uses pass-by-reference. Pascal uses either, depending on how the parameter was declared.

Maple's external calling mechanism currently supports both C and Fortran calling conventions. Automatic wrapper generation is only supported for C, but an external API exists for both C and Fortran. The default convention used is C. To use Fortran calling, specify the name Fortran as a parameter to `define_external`.

```
> f := define_external('my_func','FORTRAN', ...);
```

Some other compiler implementations (such as Pascal, C++, and Java) may be made to work with C external calling by using the correct definitions and order of passed parameters.

11.2   Method 2: Wrapper Generation

There are some types in Maple that do not lend well to automatic "on the fly" conversions. Two of these types are procedures (callbacks), and records (structs). Maple provides an alternate mechanism for handling this kind of data.

For a description of the steps required to use compiled code in Maple, refer to Section 11.1. The same three basic steps (DLL creation, function specification, and function invocation as described on pages 533-534) are used in this method. The information in this section extends the basic information by describing the use of wrappers.

Specifying the keyword WRAPPER in the call to define_external will cause Maple to generate code to do the necessary data translations. Maple will compile this code into a shared library and dynamically link to the new library. Subsequently invoking the procedure returned by define_external will call the newly generated conversion routine before calling the external function in the library you provided.

The C code generated by Maple "wraps" the Maple data structures by translating them to hardware equivalent types. Hence, the code file is called the *wrapper*, and the library generated from this code is called the *wrapper library*.

Additional Types and Options

Generating a wrapper file allows Maple to translate more complicated types that are difficult to handle without compilation technology. It also allows greater flexibility when dealing with pointers and passed data that do not exactly fit the required type.

Table 11.3 (located at the end of the chapter) lists additional types are supported when the keyword WRAPPER is specified.

Structured Data Formats

A structure is a non-homogeneous collection of members, corresponding to a *struct* in C, or a *record* in Pascal. A *union* is similar, except that all the members start at the same memory address.

Each *member :: descriptor* pair describes one member of the structure or union. The descriptor is any of the types described in this chapter.

The *options* are used to specify what kind of datatype the wrapper should expect for conversion purposes. The following two options are supported.

TABLE Tables will be used as the corresponding Maple type. Using tables is the default behavior, and they are friendlier to use than lists. When tables are used, the *member* names will correspond to table indices.

LIST Lists will be used as the corresponding Maple type. Lists are primarily used in a read-only basis. Lists cannot be modified in-place, so making updates to a list structure in external code requires a copy to be made. When structures must be passed back to Maple, or if they contain pointer types, it is better to use tables.

Lists and tables cannot be used interchangeably. Once the wrapper has been generated, it will accept only the declared type, not both.

Enumerated Types

Maple's external calling mechanism does not directly support enumerated types (such as *enum* in C). Instead, use the `integer[n]` type with `n` of an appropriate size to match the size of the enumerated type of the compiler with which the external function was compiled (usually this is the same size as the *int* type).

Procedure Call Formats

Some languages, like C, support passing functions as arguments. A Maple procedure can be passed to an external function in the same way. The wrapper will set up a C style procedure to call Maple to execute the passed procedure with the given arguments. This C callback is given to the external call to be used like any other C function.

Each *member :: descriptor* pair describes one parameter of the procedure. The *descriptor* is any of the types described in this chapter.

It is not permitted to declare a procedure that itself takes a procedure parameter. In other words, a callback cannot itself call back to the external code.

Call by Reference

Unless modified as described below, each argument is passed by value. The `REF` modifier can be used to override this.

```
argumentIdentifer :: REF( dataDescriptor, options )
```

The **REF** modifier can take the following options.

ANYTHING This option must be first in the list of options. Use this option to declare the equivalent of a C *void** parameter. The wrapper code will attempt to convert passed arguments to simple types, (4-byte integer, 8-byte float, complex, or string), when encountered. If no conversion to one of these types is possible, then **NULL** is passed to the external function.

CALL_ONLY This option specifies that although the object is to be passed by reference, any changes made by the external function will not be written back to the Maple symbol that was passed. This can be used both to protect the objects being passed (see section on *array options*), and to reduce overhead (as no translation back to Maple data structures need be made).

RETURN_ONLY This option specifies that no data is actually passed to the external function. Instead, only a reference to the allocated space is passed, and the external function is expected to fill the space with data. The result is converted back into an appropriate Maple object.

Array Options

If an **ARRAY** argument is declared as **CALL_ONLY** and an **Array**, **Matrix**, or **Vector** with proper settings is passed to the external function (so that no copying is required), then **CALL_ONLY** will have no effect and thus will not prevent the called function from overwriting the original array. To prevent this from occurring, the option **COPY** can be included in the **ARRAY** descriptor.

The **ARRAY** descriptor accepts extra options when used with wrapper generation. These options can be specified as follows.

```
ARRAY( dim1, ..., dimN, datatype=typename,
       order=..., ..., options )
```

The *dim1* through *dimN* parameters are each integer ranges, specifying the range of each dimension of the array. Any of the upper or lower bounds may be the name of another argument, in which case the value of that argument will specify the corresponding array bound at run-time.

The *options* are used to specify how an array should be passed. The following are valid options.

COPY Do not operate *in-place* on the given array. That is, make a copy first, and use the copy for passing to and from the external function.

NO_COPY This ensures that a copy of the data is never made. Usually, when using a wrapper generated external call, if the `Array`, `Matrix`, or `Vector` is of the wrong type, (say the order is wrong), then a copy is made with the correct properties before passing it to the external function. Also, the "returned" array will have the properties of the copy. If `NO_COPY` is specified, and an `Array`, `Matrix`, or `Vector` with incorrect options is passed, an exception is raised. Arrays are always passed by reference. If no options are given (via a `REF` descriptor), they are passed by using the `CALL_ONLY` behavior of `REF` with the noted exception described at the beginning of this section.

Non-Passed Arguments

Sometimes it will be necessary to pass additional arguments to the Maple wrapper that should not be passed on to the external function. For example, consider the following hypothetical C function:

```
int sum( int *v1, int *v2 )
```

This function takes two integer vectors, `v1` and `v2`, and adds the elements of `v2` to `v1`, stopping when it finds an entry that is zero. It might be nice for the generated wrapper to make sure the vectors are the same size. The Maple definition for this function is as follows.

```
> Sum := define_external( 'sum',
>         v1 :: ARRAY(1..size,integer[4]),
>         v2 :: ARRAY(1..size,integer[4]),
>         size :: NO_PASS(integer[4]),
>         RETURN :: integer[4],
>         LIB="libsum.dll");
```

The `NO_PASS` modifier indicates that the size argument should not be passed to the external function. The `Sum` function could then be called by the following statement,

```
> Sum(v1,v2,op(1,v1));
```

where `v1` and `v2` are vectors. Maple will pass the vector data, or a copy of the vector data, and pass it to the external `sum` function. It will not pass the `size` element to the external function, but `size` will be used for argument checking (since the `NO_CHECK` option was not specified).

Note that this option can only be used for top-level arguments. That is, it is invalid to declare a callback procedure's arguments as `NO_PASS`.

Argument Checking and Efficiency Considerations

It is intended that the time and space costs of calling an external function not be any higher than the costs for calling an equivalent built-in function with the same degree of argument type checking. Clearly, the amount of type checking done by a generated Maple-language wrapper exceeds that done by most internal functions, so there will be some additional overhead.

The `define_external` function has an option `NO_CHECK` which, if used, will disable the type checking done by the Maple-language wrapper. For frequently called external functions that perform simple operations this can significantly improve performance. However, there is a risk associated with using the `NO_CHECK` option. If you pass an object of the wrong type, the generated C-language wrapper might misinterpret what it has received, resulting in erroneous translations to external types, and hence unpredictable behavior of the external function.

Conversions

When the procedure returned by `define_external` is actually called, the Maple arguments that are passed are converted to the corresponding arguments of the external function. Likewise, the value returned from the external function is converted back to the corresponding Maple type.

The following table describes each of the external types and the Maple types that can be converted into that type. The first listed Maple type is the one that a result of the corresponding external type would be converted into.

External Type	Allowed Maple Type(s)
`boolean[n]`	`boolean`
`integer[n]`	`integer`
`float[n]`	`float, rational, integer, numeric`
`complex[n]`	`complex, numeric, float, rational, integer`
`char[n]`	one-character `string`
`string[n]`	`string, symbol,` 0
`ARRAY()`	`Array, Vector, Matrix, name,` 0
`STRUCT()`	`list, table`
`UNION()`	`table`
`PROC()`	`procedure`

For `STRUCT`s, either lists or tables are valid for a particular declaration. Once declared, only one of the types–a list or a table–will be acceptable. They cannot be used interchangeably unless the wrapper is regenerated. For `UNION`s, only tables are permitted, and the table must contain exactly one entry when passed (corresponding to one of the members of the union).

If an argument of an incompatible type is passed, an error occurs, and the external function will not be called. Likewise, if a value is passed that would be out of range for the specified type (e.g., integer too large), an error occurs. When passing floating-point values, precision in excess of that supported by the external type is discarded, provided the magnitude of the value is within the range of the external type.

Arguments that were declared as REFerences may be passed either a name, a zero, or the declared kind of Maple expression. If a name is passed, it is evaluated, and the value is passed by reference to the external function. After the external function returns, the revised value is converted back to the type specified for the argument and assigned back to the name. If the name passed has no value, then either NULL is passed, or a pointer to newly allocated space for the structure is passed. This behavior is determined by the presence or absence of ALLOC in the REF declaration. If a zero is passed, NULL is passed to the external function. If any other Maple expression is passed, its value is passed by reference, and the revised value is discarded.

Compiler Options

To compile the wrapper library, Maple requires the use of a C compiler installed on the same machine that is running Maple. Maple will generate a system command to call the compiler. The compiler needs to be well known to the system. It should be in the system PATH and all associated environment variables need to be set.

The compile and link commands are completely customizable provided that your compiler has a command-line interface available. Default configurations are provided, which should make most cases work "out of the box." Maple is preprogrammed to use the vendor-supplied C compiler to compile wrappers on most platforms.[1]

All default compile and link options are stored in a module that can be obtained by using the command define_external('COMPILE_OPTIONS'). When the module returned by this command is modified, the modification will affect all wrapper generation commands via define_external for the remainder of the session. All of the names exported by the compile options module can also be specified as a parameter to define_external. When specified as a parameter, the effect lasts only for the duration of that call.

The compile and link commands are assembled by calling the COMPILE_COMMAND

---

[1]Under Microsoft Windows, Maple uses the Microsoft C Compiler.

and `LINK_COMMAND` procedures defined in the compile options module. These procedures make use of the definitions in the compile options module to formulate a command string that will be executed using `ssystem`.[2]

To customize the compile and link commands to suit your situation, any of the following options can be modified. All option values must be strings or `NULL`, except for `COMPILE_COMMAND` and `LINK_COMMAND`, which must be procedures or `NULL`.

COMPILER This specifies the name of the compiler executable.

CFLAGS This specifies miscellaneous flags passed to the compiler.

COMPILE_ONLY_FLAG This is the flag to indicate that the file is only to be compiled. On most platforms it is "-c", which will tell the compiler to generate an object file, but not link it to form any executable or library. Linking will happen in a separate command.

COBJ_FLAG This is the flag used by the compiler to specify the object filename. The compiler command uses `COBJ_FLAG || FILE || OBJ_EXT` to name the object file. On most platforms it is "-o".

LOBJ_FLAG This is the flag used by the linker to specify the target library name. The link command uses `LOBJ_FLAG || FILE || DLL_EXT` to name the shared library.

FILE This is the base name of the file to be compiled. The file extension should not be included in this name. For example, if you want to compile "foo.c", set `FILE="foo"` and `FILE_EXT=".c"`. When `FILE` is set to `NULL` the system generates a file name based on the function name.

FILE_EXT This is the program file extension. If you want to compile "foo.c", set `FILE_EXT=".c"`, and `FILE="foo"`.

OBJ_EXT This is the object file extension. Common extensions are ".o" and ".obj".

DLL_EXT This is the dynamic library extension. Common extensions are ".dll" and ".so".

INC_FLAG This precedes directories in the `INC_PATH`. On most platforms it is "-I".

---

[2]If using the Microsoft C compiler, the `LINK_COMMAND` is set to `NULL` since the `COMPILE_COMMAND` does both the compiling and linking.

INC_PATH This specifies the directories to search for header files. Use an expression sequence to specify more than one directory. For example, INC_PATH=("/usr/local/maple/extern/include", "/users/jdoe/include").

COMPILE_COMMAND This is set to the procedure that generates the compiler command. The procedure must return a string. Unless you are using an unusual compiler, it should not be necessary to change the default.

LINKER This specifies the name of the linker executable.

LINK_FLAGS This specifies miscellaneous flags passed to the linker, including those that tell the linker to build a dynamic (shared) library.

LIB_FLAG This precedes directories in the LIB_PATH. On most platforms it is "-L".

LIB_PATH This specifies the directories to search for libraries. Use an expression sequence to specify more than one directory. For example, LIB_PATH=("/usr/local/maple/extern/lib","/users/jdoe/lib").

LIB This names the library which contains the external function you want to call. This option must be specified in every call to define_external.

LIBS This specifies other libraries that need to be linked with the wrapper library to resolve all external symbols. Use an expression sequence to specify more than one library. For example, LIBS=("/usr/local/maple/extern/lib/libtest.so","/users/jdoe/libdoe.so").

SYS_LIBS This specifies system libraries that need to be linked with the wrapper library to resolve all external symbols. Use an expression sequence to specify more than one library. For example, LIBS=("-lc","-lm").

EXPORT_FLAG This flag is used in combination with FUNCTION to name the function to be exported from the shared library. This is unassigned or set to NULL on platforms that export all symbols by default.

FUNCTION This is the name of the external function defined in the wrapper library. The system will generate a FUNCTION name if this is left unassigned or set to NULL.

LINK_COMMAND This is set to the procedure that generates the linker command. The procedure must return a string. Set this to NULL if the compile command also does the linking.

A common use of these options as parameters to `define_external` with a standard compiler would be to specify the filename. For example, the following will generate a wrapper file named "foo.c".

```
> f := define_external('myfunc','WRAPPER','FILE'="foo",'LIB'=
>                       "mylib.dll"):
```

To use a non-standard compiler or to alter compile flags, it may be easier to assign directly to the compile options module. The following example shows how to setup the GNU compiler on a machine running Solaris.

```
> p := define_external('COMPILE_OPTIONS'):
> p:-COMPILER := "gcc";
> p:-COBJ_FLAG := "-o ":
> define_external('mat_mult','WRAPPER','LIB'="libcexttest.so"):
```

The tricky part in the above example is that gcc likes to have a space between -o and the object name. Modifying the **COBJ_FLAG** allows this to be easily done. All other option default values were acceptable.

The best way see what commands are actually being executed is to set the `infolevel` for `define_external` to 3 or higher. Repeating the above example you might see the following.

```
> p := define_external('COMPILE_OPTIONS'):
> p:-COMPILER := "gcc";
> p:-COBJ_FLAG := "-o ":
> infolevel[define_external] := 3:
> define_external('mat_mult','WRAPPER','LIB'="libcexttest.so"):
```

```
"COMPILE_COMMAND"
"gcc  -g -c -I/user/local/maple/extern/include -o \
 mwrap_mat_mult.o mwrap_mat_mult.c"
"LINK_COMMAND"
"ld -znodefs -G -dy -Bdynamic
 -L/user/local/maple/bin/bin.SUN_SPARC_SOLARIS \
 -omwrap_mat_mult.so mwrap_mat_mult.o -lc -lmaplec"
```

An alternate way to see the compile and link commands is to call the command-builder procedures directly. Make sure to set or unassign the variables that will be filled in, otherwise they will be left blank.

```
> p := define_external('COMPILE_OPTIONS'):
> p:-COMPILER := "gcc";
> p:-COBJ_FLAG := "-o ":
> p:-COMPILE_COMMAND();
```

"gcc -g -c -I/u/maple/extern/include -o .o .c"

```
> unassign('p:-FILE');
> p:-COMPILE_COMMAND();
```

"gcc -g -c -I/u/maple/extern/include -o FILE.o FILE.c"

The following example shows two calls to **define_external** separated by the **restart** command. The first call does not use the WRAPLIB option and thus generates quad.c and compiles the wrapper library quad.dll. The second call uses the WRAPLIB option in order to reuse the existing quad.dll. No compilation or wrapper generation is done in the second call.

```
> quadruple_it := define_external('quadruple_it',
>                 WRAPPER,FILE="quad",
>                 x::float[4],
>                 RETURN::float[4],
>                 LIB="test.dll"):
> quadruple_it(2.2);
```

$$8.80000019073486328$$

```
> restart;
> quadruple_it := define_external('quadruple_it',
>                 WRAPPER,FILE="quad",
>                 x::float[4],
>                 RETURN::float[4],
>                 WRAPLIB="quad.dll",
>                 LIB="test.dll"):
> quadruple_it(2.2);
```

$$8.80000019073486328$$

When DLLs are created and compiled at runtime it is important not to duplicate the name of a previously generated DLL without restarting Maple (either by closing Maple down or issuing the **restart** command). Maple will maintain an open connection with the first DLL opened with any given name. Attempting to create a new DLL of the same name without restarting may lead to unexpected results. The Maple command **dlclose** can be used to avoid restarting, but subsequently calling any external function in that closed DLL without reissuing the **define_external** command will likely crash Maple.

Evaluation Rules

External functions follow normal Maple evaluation rules in that the arguments are evaluated during a function call. It therefore may be necessary to quote assigned names when passing by-reference. For example, consider the following function that multiplies a number by two in-place.

```
void double_it( int *i )
{
        if( i == NULL ) return;

        *i *= 2;
}
```

In Maple, the wrapperless definition of this function might appear as follows.

```
> double_it := define_external('double_it', i::REF(integer[4]),
>                              LIB="libtest.dll");
```

When an integer is passed to this function, a pointer to the hardware conversion is sent to the external routine. In this case, the result will be lost since there is no way to refer back to it from Maple.

```
> double_it(3);
```

The solution is to name the value you want to pass out. The name needs to be quoted in order to prevent evaluation and thus have only the value passed out.

```
> double_it(n);  # n is evaluated so 3 gets passed
> n;
```

$$3$$

```
> double_it('n');  # used unevaluation quotes to pass the 'n'
> n;
```

$$6$$

For numeric data, the string "NULL" can be passed as a parameter to represent the address 0 (the C NULL). For strings, since "NULL" is a valid string, the integer 0 represents address 0.

```
> double_it("NULL");
>
> concat := define_external('concat',
>       RETURN::string, a::string, b::string,
>       LIB="libtest.dll"):
> concat("NULL","x");
```

                        "NULLx"

```
> concat(0,0);
```

                          0

In the `concat` example above, the C code might look like the following. Note that this function does not clean up memory as it should.

```
char * concat( char* a, char *b )
{
    char *r;

    if( !a || !b ) return( NULL );

    r = (char*)malloc((strlen(a)+strlen(b)+1)*sizeof(char));

    strcpy(r,a);
    strcat(r,b);

    return( r );
}
```

11.3   Method 3: Customizing Wrappers

For complete control over data conversions, Maple allows modification of existing wrappers and creation of custom wrappers. There is an extensive API of functions available to external programs called from Maple using `define_external`.

To use this method, you must be familiar with the steps required to use compiled code in Maple, described in Section 11.1. For this method, you do not perform a function specification because Maple passes one data structure containing all the passed information. Therefore, there are only two basic steps (DLL creation and function invocation as described on pages 533-534) in addition to wrapper generation. Wrappers were introduced in Section 11.2.

External Function Entry Point

Maple will look up the symbol name given as the first argument to `define_external` in the DLL specified in the `LIB=` argument. Maple also looks up the `MWRAP_symbolName` in the wrapper library. This `MWRAP_symbolName` function prototype has the following format.

```
ALGEB MWRAP_quadruple_it(
    MKernelVector kv,
    FLOAT32 (*fn) ( FLOAT32 a1 ),
    ALGEB fn_args
);
```

The prototype above was taken from the wrapper `quad.c` described in the previous section. The first argument `kv` is a handle to the Maple kernel function vector. The second argument `fn` is a function pointer assigned the symbol looked up in the external DLL. In this case, `fn` will be assigned the `quadruple_it` external function. The last argument is a Maple expression sequence data structure containing all the arguments passed to the function during any given call to the Maple procedure generated by the `define_external` command.

The above entry point is the format used when wrappers are automatically generated, and when `WRAPLIB` is specified. An alternate external entry point that excludes the function pointer is available when the parameter `MAPLE` is specified instead of `WRAPPER` or `WRAPLIB`.

```
ALGEB MWRAP_quadruple_it(
    MKernelVector kv,
    ALGEB fn_args
);
```

The API function prototypes for manipulating Maple data structures can be found in `$MAPLE/extern/include` where `$MAPLE` is the path of your Maple installation. The header file `maplec.h` should be included when writing custom C wrappers. One of the header files, `maplefortran.hf` or `maplefortran64bit.hf`, should be included when writing custom Fortran wrappers. Other header files, `mplshlib.h`, and `mpltable.h` contain macros, types, and data structures that are needed for direct manipulation of Maple data structures.

Maple uses directed acyclic graphs (dags) to represent all objects such as integers, floating point numbers, sums, modules, procedures, etc. (See Appendix A for more details about Maple's internal representation of objects.) These dags have the type **ALGEB** in C wrappers, and **INTEGER** or **INTEGER*8** in Fortran wrappers. Fortran 77 has no user type definition semantics so **ALGEB** pointers must be "faked" by using machine word-sized integers. If the machine word size is 64-bit (e.g., as on a DEC Alpha), then the header `maplefortran64bit.hf` must be used and **INTEGER*8** must be used as the dag datatype. Execute the Maple command `kernelopts(wordsize)` to see if you should be using 32-bit or 64-bit integer-dag types in Fortran. When working with C, the datatype is **ALGEB** regardless of the machine word size.

For the most part, treat these dags as black boxes. In other words, you do not have to know the internal details of dags to manipulate and work with them. The only exception is the argument sequence passed to the wrapper entry point. This is an expression seqence (**EXPSEQ**) dag, and can be treated as an array of dags starting at index 1 (not 0). Thus, `fn_args[1]` is the first parameter passed to the external function. Use `MapleNumArgs` to determine the number of arguments passed. Note that the Fortran API uses a slightly different naming convention. The equivalent Fortran call is `maple_num_args`. The C API names will be used for the remainder of this chapter. Refer to the API listing to find equivalent Fortran names.

The easiest way to start writing custom wrappers is to inspect automatically generated wrappers. Consider the **add** function that was introduced at the beginning of this chapter. Use the **WRAPPER** option to tell `define_external` to generate a wrapper. Also use the **NO_COMPILE** option to tell `define_external` not to compile the generated wrapper. The name of the generated file will be returned.

```
> myAdd := define_external(
>       'add',
>       'WRAPPER',
>       'NO_COMPILE',
>       'num1'::integer[4],
>       'num2'::integer[4],
>       'RETURN'::integer[4]
> );
```

$$myAdd := \text{"mwrap\_add.c"}$$

The file `mwrap_add.c` will look something like the following.

```
/* MWRAP_add Wrapper
```

```
    Generated automatically by Maple
    Do not edit this file. */

#include <stdio.h>
#include <stdlib.h>
#include <string.h>
#include <mplshlib.h>
#include <maplec.h>

MKernelVector mapleKernelVec;
typedef void *MaplePointer;
ALGEB *args;

/* main - MWRAP_add */
ALGEB MWRAP_add( MKernelVector kv,
        INTEGER32 (*fn) ( INTEGER32 a1, INTEGER32 a2 ),
        ALGEB fn_args )
{
    INTEGER32 a1;
    INTEGER32 a2;
    INTEGER32 r;
    ALGEB mr;
    int i;
    mapleKernelVec = kv;
    args = (ALGEB*) fn_args;

    if( MapleNumArgs(mapleKernelVec,(ALGEB)args) != 2 )
        MapleRaiseError(mapleKernelVec,"Incorrect number
        of arguments");

    /* integer[4] */
    a1 = MapleToInteger32(mapleKernelVec,args[1]);

    /* integer[4] */
    a2 = MapleToInteger32(mapleKernelVec,args[2]);

    r = (*fn)(a1, a2);

    mr = ToMapleInteger(mapleKernelVec,(long) r);
    return( mr );
}
```

The generated wrapper is human readable, and thus a good starting point for creating your own wrapper. There may be some extra variables and declarations used since the wrapper generation is generic and may be heavy handed at times. For example, the use of **args** rather than **fn_args** avoids the need for a cast with **args[1]**, but it also is a static global which is useful when working with callbacks which may need access to the argument sequence outside the main entry point.

Remember that the **add** function simply added the arguments **a1** and **a2** and returned the result. This can be done directly in the wrapper. By removing the second argument **fn** so the **MAPLE** option can be used, plus inlining the **a1+a2** functionality and cleaning up the code, the wrapper may look like the following.

```
/* Program to add two numbers from Maple */

#include <stdio.h>
#include <stdlib.h>
#include <maplec.h>

/* main entry point - MWRAP_add */
ALGEB myAdd( MKernelVector kv, ALGEB fn_args )
{
    INTEGER32 a1;     /* INTEGER32 => int (defined in mpltable.h) */
    INTEGER32 a2;
    INTEGER32 r;

    if( MapleNumArgs(kv,fn_args) != 2 )
        MapleRaiseError(kv,"Incorrect number of arguments");

    /* convert from Maple integer to C int */
    a1 = MapleToInteger32(kv,((ALGEB*)fn_args)[1]);

    /* convert from Maple integer to C int */
    a2 = MapleToInteger32(kv,((ALGEB*)fn_args)[2]);

    r = a1 + a2;

    return( ToMapleInteger(kv,(long) r) );
}
```

This program first checks to make sure there were exactly two arguments passed in the Maple function call. It then converts the two arguments to hardware integers and adds them together. The result is converted back to a Maple integer and returned.

This program can be compiled into a DLL using your favorite C compiler. Ensure that you link with the Maple API shared library. The DLL can be placed into the Maple **bin.$SYSTEM** directory, or somewhere else in the PATH. When using DLLs outside of **bin.$SYSTEM** directory, you may have to specify the full path to the DLL in the **LIB** argument to **define_external**. Unix developers may need to set their load-library-path.

Table 11.4 (located at the end of the chapter) lists the Maple API Libraries for C and Fortran.

After compiling the DLL, the function can be used from within Maple. No type desciptors are needed in the **define_external** call since Maple does no conversion on arguments passed to the custom wrapper.

```
> myAdd := define_external('myAdd','MAPLE','LIB'=
>                     "myAdd.dll"):
> myAdd(2,3);
```

                              5

```
> myAdd(2.2,1);

  Error, (in myAdd) integer expected for integer[4] parameter

> myAdd(2^80,2^70);

  Error, (in myAdd) integer too large in context
```

The equivalent Fortran wrapper would look like the following.

```
  Program to add two numbers from Maple


  INTEGER FUNCTION myAdd(kv, args)

  INCLUDE "maplefortran.hf"
  INTEGER kv
  INTEGER args

  INTEGER arg
```

```
        INTEGER a1, a2, r
        CHARACTER ERRMSG*20
        INTEGER ERRMSGLEN

        ERRMSGLEN = 20

        IF ( maple_num_args(kv, args) .NE. 2 ) THEN
            ERRMSG = 'Incorrect number of arguments'
            CALL maple_raise_error( kv, ERRMSG, ERRMSGLEN )
            myAdd = to_maple_null( kv )
            RETURN
        ENDIF

        arg = maple_extract_arg( kv, args, 1 )
        a1 = maple_to_integer32(kv, arg)

        arg = maple_extract_arg( kv, args, 2 )
        a2 = maple_to_integer32(kv, arg)

        r = a1 + a2

        myAdd = to_maple_integer( kv, r )

        END
```

Once compiled into a DLL, the same syntax can be used in Maple to access the function. The only difference is the additional keyword 'FORTRAN' in the `define_external` call.

```
> myAdd := define_external('myAdd','MAPLE','FORTRAN','LIB'=
>                          "myAdd.dll"):
> myAdd(2,3);
```

$$5$$

External API

An external API is provided for users who want to augment existing wrappers or write their own custom wrappers. This section describes the functions available when linking with the Maple API library (see Table 11.4) and including either `maplec.h` or `maplefortran.hf`.

Argument Checking The following C function can be used to query the number of arguments contained in the argument expression sequence passed as the last argument to the external function entry point. The expression sequence passed to this entry point can be queried directly (e.g., `((ALGEB*)expr)[1]`). If `n = MapleNumArgs(kv,expr)`, then the last argument is `((ALGEB*)expr[n]`.

```
M_INT MapleNumArgs( MKernelVector kv, ALGEB expr );
```

The arguments passed to the Fortran entry point cannot be queried directly. The `maple_extract_arg` function must be used to get at the argument data (e.g., `arg1 = maple_extract_arg(kv,args,1)`). If `n = maple_num_args(kv,s)`, then the last argument is `maple_extract_arg(kv,args,n)`.

```
INTEGER maple_num_args( kv, s )
INTEGER maple_extract_arg( kv, s, i )
```

The following functions indicate the type of the given Maple object.

```
M_BOOL IsMapleAssignedName( MKernelVector kv, ALGEB s );
M_BOOL IsMapleComplexNumeric( MKernelVector kv, ALGEB s );
M_BOOL IsMapleNumeric( MKernelVector kv, ALGEB s );
M_BOOL IsMapleInteger( MKernelVector kv, ALGEB s );
M_BOOL IsMapleInteger8( MKernelVector kv, ALGEB s );
M_BOOL IsMapleInteger16( MKernelVector kv, ALGEB s );
M_BOOL IsMapleInteger32( MKernelVector kv, ALGEB s );
M_BOOL IsMapleInteger64( MKernelVector kv, ALGEB s );
M_BOOL IsMapleName( MKernelVector kv, ALGEB s );
M_BOOL IsMapleNULL( MKernelVector kv, ALGEB s );
M_BOOL IsMaplePointer( MKernelVector kv, ALGEB s );
M_BOOL IsMaplePointerNULL( MKernelVector kv, ALGEB s );
M_BOOL IsMapleProcedure( MKernelVector kv, ALGEB s );
M_BOOL IsMapleRTable( MKernelVector kv, ALGEB s );
M_BOOL IsMapleString( MKernelVector kv, ALGEB s );
M_BOOL IsMapleTable( MKernelVector kv, ALGEB s );
M_BOOL IsMapleUnassignedName( MKernelVector kv, ALGEB s );
M_BOOL IsMapleUnnamedZero( MKernelVector kv, ALGEB s );
```

Equivalent Fortran functions are as follows. The C functions, `IsMaplePointer`, `IsMaplePointerNULL`, `IsMapleUnassignedName`, and `IsMapleUnnamedZero` are not available in the Fortran API.

```
INTEGER is_maple_assigned_name( kv, s )
```

```
INTEGER is_maple_complex_numeric( kv, s )
INTEGER is_maple_numeric( kv, s )
INTEGER is_maple_integer( kv, s )
INTEGER is_maple_integer8( kv, s )
INTEGER is_maple_integer16( kv, s )
INTEGER is_maple_integer32( kv, s )
INTEGER is_maple_integer64( kv, s )
INTEGER is_maple_name( kv, s )
INTEGER is_maple_null( kv, s )
INTEGER is_maple_procedure( kv, s )
INTEGER is_maple_rtable( kv, s )
INTEGER is_maple_string( kv, s )
INTEGER is_maple_table( kv, s )
INTEGER is_maple_unassigned_name( kv, s )
```

These functions all return TRUE (1) when the Maple dag s fits the description given by the function name. If s is not of the correct type, FALSE (0) is returned. Maple's NULL is not the same as a C *Pointer-NULL*. The former case is the empty expression sequence in the Maple language. The latter case is a pointer variable set to the address zero. Since there is no concept of real pointers in the Maple Language, the idea of *Pointer-NULL* in this context means the Maple integer zero, or an unassigned Maple name. The IsMaple...Numeric routines use the Maple type numeric definition. All other checks use the dag type definition. For example, type(t[1],name) returns true in Maple, but IsMapleName checks for a NAME dag and will return FALSE since t[1] is internally represented as a TABLEREF dag. Integer query routines with the bit size specified in the name will check to make sure the given Maple object s is a Maple integer and also that it could fit into the specified number of bits if converted to a hardware integer.

Conversions From Maple Objects The following functions return the specified type when given a dag s that can be converted to that type.

```
COMPLEXF32 MapleToComplexFloat32( MKernelVector kv, ALGEB s );
COMPLEXF64 MapleToComplexFloat64( MKernelVector kv, ALGEB s );
CXDAG MapleToComplexFloatDAG( MKernelVector kv, ALGEB s );
FLOAT32 MapleToFloat32( MKernelVector kv, ALGEB s );
FLOAT64 MapleToFloat64( MKernelVector kv, ALGEB s );
INTEGER8 MapleToInteger8( MKernelVector kv, ALGEB s );
INTEGER16 MapleToInteger16( MKernelVector kv, ALGEB s );
INTEGER32 MapleToInteger32( MKernelVector kv, ALGEB s );
```

```
INTEGER64 MapleToInteger64( MKernelVector kv, ALGEB s );
M_BOOL MapleToM_BOOL( MKernelVector kv, ALGEB s );
M_INT MapleToM_INT( MKernelVector kv, ALGEB s );
void* MapleToPointer( MKernelVector kv, ALGEB s );
char* MapleToString( MKernelVector kv, ALGEB s );
```

The following are the equivalent Fortran routines. Note that complex and string conversion are done by reference. That is, the third argument passed to the function will be set to the converted value rather than the function returning the value. Equivalent functions for `MapleToComplexFloatDAG` and `MapleToPointer` are not available.

```
SUBROUTINE maple_to_complex_float32( kv, s, c )
SUBROUTINE maple_to_complex_float64( kv, s, c )
REAL maple_to_float32( kv, s )
DOUBLEPRECISION maple_to_float64( kv, s )
INTEGER maple_to_integer8( kv, s )
INTEGER maple_to_integer16( kv, s )
INTEGER maple_to_integer32( kv, s )
INTEGER*8 maple_to_integer64( kv, s )
INTEGER maple_to_m_bool( kv, s )
INTEGER maple_to_m_int( kv, s )
INTEGER maple_to_string( kv, s, string )
```

Floating Point numbers may lose precision during the conversion to hardware size data.

Conversion from a **STRING** dag to an integer will return the ASCII value of the first character in that string. Conversion from a Maple **Boolean** to an integer will return 1 for **true** or 0 for **false**.

Conversions from a **STRING** dag to a string should not be modified in-place. A copy should be made if any modifications are necessary.

The `MapleToPointer` conversion returns the pointer value stored in a Maple **BINARY** dag.

Conversions To Maple Objects The following functions return a dag of the specified dag type when given a dag the corresponding hardware data.

```
ALGEB ToMapleBoolean( MKernelVector kv, long b );
ALGEB ToMapleChar( MKernelVector kv, long c );
ALGEB ToMapleComplex( MKernelVector kv, double re,
        double im );
ALGEB ToMapleComplexFloat( MKernelVector kv, ALGEB re,
```

```
                      ALGEB im );
      ALGEB ToMapleExpressionSequence( MKernelVector kv, int
              nargs, /* ALGEB arg1, ALGEB arg2, */ ... );
      ALGEB ToMapleInteger( MKernelVector kv, long i );
      ALGEB ToMapleInteger64( MKernelVector kv, INTEGER64 i );
      ALGEB ToMapleFloat( MKernelVector kv, double f );
      ALGEB ToMapleName( MKernelVector kv, char *n, M_BOOL
              is_global );
      ALGEB ToMapleNULL( MKernelVector kv );
      ALGEB ToMapleNULLPointer( MKernelVector kv );
      ALGEB ToMaplePointer( MKernelVector kv, void *v );
      ALGEB ToMapleRelation( MKernelVector kv, const char *rel,
                              ALGEB lhs, ALGEB rhs );
      ALGEB ToMapleString( MKernelVector kv, char *s );
      ALGEB ToMapleUneval( MKernelVector kv, ALGEB s );
```

The equivalent Fortran routines are as follows. The Fortran API does not support ToMapleExpressionSequence, ToMapleNULLPointer, ToMaplePointer, ToMapleRelation, and ToMapleUneval.

```
      to_maple_boolean( kv, b )
      to_maple_char( kv, c )
      to_maple_complex( kv, re, im )
      to_maple_complex_float( kv, re, im )
      to_maple_integer( kv, i )
      to_maple_integer64( kv, i )
      to_maple_float( kv, f )
      to_maple_name( kv, s, s_len )
      to_maple_null( kv )
      to_maple_string( kv, s, s_len )
```

ToMapleBoolean is three valued. When b is zero, it return Maple's false dag. If n is -1, Maple's FAIL dag is returned. If n is non-zero (and not -1), Maple's true dag is returned.

ToMapleChar returns a single character Maple string dag.

ToMapleComplex converts the pair of doubles, re and im, to the Maple expression re + I*im, and returns this dag.

ToMapleComplexFloat converts a pair of FLOAT dags to the same structure.

ToMapleExpressionSequence create and returns a Maple expression sequence and fills it with the N algebraics, arg1, arg2, ..., argN.

ToMapleName returns a Maple NAME dag with the name n. If is_global is set to TRUE, the name will be global in Maple's name space. Otherwise, if is_global is FALSE, the name will be a unique exported local.

ToMapleNULL returns Maple's NULL dag (an empty EXPSEQ).

ToMapleNULLPointer returns Maple's zero dag. This is the wrapper representation of a NULL pointer passed to a procedure. This is not to be confused with the value returned by ToMapleNULL.

ToMapleString copies the character string s to a Maple STRING dag and returns it. When using the Fortran API, the length of the given string must also be passed.

Rectangular Table (Vector, Matrix, Array) Manipulation *Rtables* are the container class of Vector, Matrix, and Array data structures in Maple. The basic access functions are as follows.

```
ALGEB RTableCreate( MKernelVector kv, RTableSettings *s,
        void *pdata, M_INT *bounds );
void* RTableDataBlock( MKernelVector kv, ALGEB rt );
M_INT RTableNumElements( MKernelVector kv, ALGEB rt );
M_INT RTableNumDimensions( MKernelVector kv, ALGEB rt );
M_INT RTableLowerBound( MKernelVector kv, ALGEB rt,
        M_INT dim );
M_INT RTableUpperBound( MKernelVector kv, ALGEB rt,
        M_INT dim );
M_BOOL RTableIsReal( MKernelVector kv, ALGEB rt );
```

The Fortran API contains the following functions.

```
SUBROUTINE copy_to_array( kv, rt, a, num_rdims,
            rbounds, num_fdims, fbounds, data_type )
SUBROUTINE copy_to_rtable( kv, a, rt, num_fdims,
            fbounds, num_rdims, rbounds, data_type )
INTEGER convert_to_rtable( kv, a, num_rdims,
            rbounds, num_fdims, fbounds, data_type )
INTEGER rtable_num_elements( kv, s )
INTEGER rtable_num_dimensions( kv, s )
INTEGER rtable_lower_bound( kv, s, dim )
INTEGER rtable_upper_bound( kv, s, dim )
INTEGER rtable_is_real( kv, s )
```

RtableDataBlock returns a pointer to the data block of a given rtable. The returned value should be casted to the known data type of the rtable. The data block can be manipulated directly instead of using `RtableAssign` or `RtableSelect`. Users who directly manipulate the data block must be aware of the storage type, order, data type, and presence of indexing functions to do this properly.

In Fortran, there is no way to return an `ARRAY` pointer. To work with an array created in Maple, the data-block must be copied to a pre-allocated Fortran data block using the `copy_to_array` function. It copies the contents of the rtable `rt` to the `ARRAY`, `a`. See `maplefortran.hf` for a complete explanation of the parameters that are passed. To copy an array back to Maple, the `copy_to_rtable` function can be used.

`RtableCreate` returns a newly created `RTABLE` as specified by:

1. The definitions given in the `RtableSettings` structure `s`.

2. A pointer to an existing block of data. If `pdata` is `NULL`, then a data block is allocated and initialized to `s->fill`. When providing an already created block of data, it is important that `s->foreign` is set to `TRUE`. Size, storage, data type, order, and indexing functions should all be considered when managing your own data block. Usually, let Maple create the data-block, then use `RtableDataBlock` to gain access to it.

3. The bounds array, `bounds`. An `m x n` matrix would have `bounds = 1,m,1,n` (i.e.,. both the upper and lower bounds must be specified).

The Fortran equivalent function is `convert_to_rtable`. It creates an rtable from an existing Fortran array. The data is not copied in; instead, the rtable maintains a pointer to the external data.

`RtableNumElements` returns the number of elements in a given rtable. This may be different in sparse versus dense rtables.

1. For dense rtables, return the number of elements of storage allocated for this rtable.

2. If `rt` is in NAG-sparse format, then this returns the number of elements in the data vector specified for the rtable, (which is the same as the length of each index vector). Note that the number returned here represents the number of data elements that are actually filled in, not the number of elements allocated. Some of the elements may have the value zero.

3. For Maple-sparse rtables, this always returns zero.

`RtableNumDimensions` returns the number of dimensions in a given rtable.

RtableUpperBound and RtableLowerBound give the upper and lower bound of the *dim*th dimension of the RTABLE, rt. For a 2 x 3 matrix, RtableLowerBound(rt,1) will return 1 since the first dimension bounds are 1..2, and the lower bound is 1.

RtableIsReal checks the elements of the RTABLE rt to see if they are all real or not. If there are imaginary numbers present this returns FALSE. If there are only real numbers, this returns TRUE. Note that this routine will return immediately when given a non-complex hardware type.

In addition to the above functions, there is an extensive C API for working rtable data types.

```
void RTableAppendAttribute( MKernelVector kv, RTableSettings
        *s, char *name );
void RTableAppendIndFn( MKernelVector kv, RTableSettings
        *s, ALGEB indfn );
void RTableGetDefaults( MKernelVector kv, RTableSettings
        *s );
void RTableGetSettings( MKernelVector kv, RTableSettings
        *s, ALGEB rt );
M_INT RTableIndFn( MKernelVector kv, ALGEB rt, M_INT num );
ALGEB RTableIndFnArgs( MKernelVector kv, ALGEB rt, M_INT num );
void RTableSetAttribute( MKernelVector kv, RTableSettings
        *s, char *name );
void RTableSetIndFn( MKernelVector kv, RTableSettings *s,
        ALGEB indfn );
void RTableSetType( MKernelVector kv, RTableSettings *s,
        M_INT id, char *name );
RTableData RTableSelect( MKernelVector kv, ALGEB rt, M_INT
        *index );
RTableData RTableAssign( MKernelVector kv, ALGEB rt, M_INT
        *index, RTableData val );
void RTableSparseCompact( MKernelVector kv, ALGEB rt );
NAG_INT* RTableSparseIndexRow( MKernelVector kv, ALGEB rt,
        M_INT dim );
ALGEB RTableSparseIndexSort( MKernelVector kv, ALGEB rt,
        M_INT by_dim );
void RTableSparseSetNumElems( MKernelVector kv, ALGEB rt,
        M_INT num );
M_INT RTableSparseSize( MKernelVector kv, ALGEB rt );

ALGEB RTableCopy( MKernelVector kv, RTableSettings *s,
```

```
                ALGEB rt );
    ALGEB RTableCopyImPart( MKernelVector kv, RTableSettings
                *s, ALGEB rt );
    ALGEB RTableCopyRealPart( MKernelVector kv, RTableSettings
                *s, ALGEB rt );
    ALGEB RTableZipReIm( MKernelVector kv, RTableSettings *s,
                ALGEB rt_re, ALGEB rt_im );
```

Most **Rtable** access functions use the **RtableSettings** structure defined in **mpltable.h**. This struct corresponds directly to the options available to the **rtable** constructor in Maple.[3]

RtableAppendAttribute appends the **name** attribute to the list of attributes in the **RtableSettings** structure.

RtableAppendIndFn appends the indexing function, **infn** to the list of indexing functions in the **RtableSettings** structure. Note that **infn** must be a valid Maple name or table-reference. For example,

```
RTableAppendIndFn(kv,&settings,ToMapleName(kv,"symmetric",
    TRUE));
RTableAppendIndFn(kv,&settings,EvalMapleStatement(kv,
    "triangular[upper]"));
```

RtableGetDefaults fills the **RtableSettings** structure **s** with standard default values. These defaults are as follows:

```
        data_type = RTABLE_DAG
        maple_type = 'anything' (Maple name 'anything')
        subtype = RTABLE_ARRAY
        storage = RTABLE_RECT
        p1 = -1, p2 = -1
        order = RTABLE_FORTRAN
        read_only = FALSE
        foreign = FALSE
        num_dimensions = -1
        index_functions = 'NULL' (Maple NULL)
        attributes = 'NULL' (Maple NULL)
        transpose = FALSE
        fill = 0
```

RtableGetSettings fills the **RtableSettings** structure **s** with the settings held by the **RTABLE**, rt.

---

[3]For more information, see **?rtable**.

RtableIndFn returns the *i*th indexing function code. The indexing codes are defined in `mpltable.h` in the form `RTABLE_INDEX_XXXX`. If there are no indexing functions, this will give an error for any value of `i`. If there is one indexing function, then `rtableIndFun(rt,1)` will return the code for the only indexing function. Use `MapleNumArgs` to find out how many indexing functions there are.

RtableIndFnArgs returns the argument expression sequence for indexing function 'num' in rtable 'rt'. If no arguments exist, Maple 'NULL' is returned. The result can be further converted to a hardware type using the `MapleToXXX` function(s). The number of arguments returned can be determined using `MapleNumArgs`. Note that some knowledge about the indexing functions is required in order to convert the return value to the appropriate hardware type. For example, `RTableIndFnArgs(kv,rt,1)` of a `band[b1,b2]` rtable will return the `b1` part of the expression sequence `(b1,b2)`. The user must know that `b1` and `b2` are always integers. Conversely, `c` in `constant[c]` will always be the same type as the rtable's datatype. Thus for `float[8]` rtables, `MapleToFloat64` should be used to do the conversion to a hardware type.

RtableSetAttribute sets all the attributes of the `RtableSettings` structure `s` to the single `NAME` attribute, `name`.

RtableSetIndFn sets all the indexing functions of the `RtableSettings` structure `s` and resets it to the single indexing function `infn`.

RtableSetType sets the `data_type` field in the given `RtableSettings` structure `s` to `id`, and when `id=RTABLE_DAG`, sets the `maple_type` to `name`. For example, to set the data type to `float[8]`, `RTableSetType(kv,&s,RTABLE_FLOAT,NULL)` would be called. To set the type to `numeric`, `RTableSetType(kv,&s,RTABLE_DAG,"numeric")` would be called. Basic type ids are defined in `mpltable.h`. To set compound types, the `RtableSettings` data structure can be manipulated directly as follows:

```
settings.data_type = RTABLE_DAG;
settings.maple_type = EvalMapleStatement(kv,
                          "complex(numeric)");
```

RtableSelect returns the value `rt[index]`, where `rt` is an `RTABLE`, and `index` is an integer array.

RtableAssign assigns the value `val` to `rt[index]`. This function should be used instead of assigning directly to the rtable data-block whenever the given rtable has an indexing function or unusual storage format (e.g., sparse). The `index` is an integer array. For example, the following code assigns the value `3.14` to the `[2,1]` element of the given `datatype=float[8]` rtable.

```
RTableData val;
M_INT *index;

index[0] = 2;
index[1] = 1;
val.float64 = 3.14;

RTableAssign(kv,rt,index,val);
```

RtableSparseCompact removes any zeros in the sparse rtable data block. This should be called after an external routine that modifies the sparse data block directly.

RtableSparseIndexRow returns the vector of indices for the ith dimension of **rt**. The **rt** must be a NAG sparse rtable.

RtableSparseIndexSort sorts the Nth index vector for the NAG sparse rtable **rt**. This is done in-place; and the other index vectors are adjusted accordingly so that the index/value mapping is preserved.

RtableSparseSetNumElems sets the number of non-zero entries in the NAG sparse rtable **rt** to N. This should only be done if the number of elements has actually changed.

RtableSparseSize returns the number of entries allocated to store data in the NAG sparse rtable **rt**. This is not necessarily the same as **RtableNumElems**.

RtableCopy returns a copy of the rtable **rt** with new settings as given by the **RtableSettings** structure s.

RtableCopyImPart returns a copy of the imaginary part of the rtable **rt** with new settings as given by the **RtableSettings** structure s. The copy returned is purely real, but contains only the imaginary parts of the given rtable.

RtableCopyRealPart returns a copy of the real part of the rtable **rt** with new settings as given by the **RtableSettings** structure s.

RtableZipReIm combines two real RTABLEs, **rt_re** and **rt_im**, into a complex rtable of the form **rt_re + I*rt_im**. The settings of the new rtable that is returned are determined by the **RtableSettings** structure s.

List Manipulation   To work with Maple lists, the following API functions can be used. These functions are only available using the C API.

```
ALGEB MapleListAlloc( MKernelVector kv, M_INT num_members );
void MapleListAssign( MKernelVector kv, ALGEB list,
        M_INT i, ALGEB val );
```

```
ALGEB MapleListSelect( MKernelVector kv, ALGEB list,
        M_INT i );
```

MapleListAlloc creates a **LIST** dag with space for **num_members** elements. This list must be filled up before it can be passed back to Maple.

MapleListAssign sets the *i*th element of the given list to the value **val**. That is, **list[i] := val**.

MapleListSelect returns the *i*th element of the given **list**.

Table Manipulation   To work with Maple tables, the following API functions can be used. These functions are only available using the C API.

```
ALGEB MapleTableAlloc( MKernelVector kv );
void MapleTableAssign( MKernelVector kv, ALGEB table,
        ALGEB ind, ALGEB val );
ALGEB MapleTableSelect( MKernelVector kv, ALGEB table,
        ALGEB ind );
void MapleTableDelete( MKernelVector kv, ALGEB table,
        ALGEB ind );
M_BOOL MapleTableHasEntry( MKernelVector kv, ALGEB table,
        ALGEB ind );
```

MapleTableAlloc creates a **TABLE** dag. The table is initially empty.

MapleTableAssign sets the **ind** element of the given **table** to the value **val**. That is, **table[ind] := val**, where **ind** can be a **NAME** or an expression sequence of numbers, or any other valid index into a Maple table.

MapleTableSelect returns the **ind** element of the given **table**.

MapleTableDelete removes the **ind** element from the **table**.

MapleTableHasEntry queries the **table** to see if it contains an element at index **ind**. If it does, **TRUE** is returned; otherwise, **FALSE** is returned.

Data Selection   The following functions are available when using the C API only and deal with selecting from various kinds of Maple data structures.

```
ALGEB MapleSelectImaginaryPart( MKernelVector kv, ALGEB s );
ALGEB MapleSelectRealPart( MKernelVector kv, ALGEB s );
ALGEB MapleSelectIndexed( MKernelVector kv, ALGEB s, M_INT
        dim, M_INT *ind );
```

MapleSelectImaginaryPart and **MapleSelectRealPart** return the imaginary and real parts of a complex number dag, respectively.

`MapleSelectIndexed` returns a value from any indexable object in Maple (`list`, `array`, `set`, etc.). The index is specified by filling in the `ind` array with the desired index. The second parameter `dim` is the number of dimensions in the array `s` (also the number of elements in `ind`).

For example, to lookup `a[1,2,3]`, the following code could be used (assuming `arg1` points to the array `a`).

```
ALGEB val;
M_INT ind[3];

ind[0] = 1;
ind[1] = 2;
ind[2] = 3;

val = k->selectIndexed(arg1, 3, ind);
```

Unique Data   The following function is available only in the C API.

```
ALGEB MapleUnique( MKernelVector kv, ALGEB s );
```

This function processes the given Maple expression `s`, and returns the unique copy of that expression from Maple's simpl table. For example, if you create the number `num` = one-billion, then you compute the number `val` = 2*500-million. An address comparison of `num` and `val` will not indicate equality. After calling simplify as in `num = MapleUnique(kv,num);`, both `num` and `val` will point to the same memory.

Error Handling   The following functions will raise a Maple-style error message.

```
void MapleRaiseError( MKernelVector kv, char *msg );
void MapleRaiseError1( MKernelVector kv, char *msg,
        ALGEB arg1 );
void MapleRaiseError2( MKernelVector kv, char *msg,
        ALGEB arg1, ALGEB arg2 );
```

The Fortran equivalent is:

```
SUBROUTINE maple_raise_error( kv, msg, len )
```

These functions display the message `msg`, stop execution, and return to Maple's input loop. A call to `MapleRaiseError` does not return.

The character string `msg` may contain wildcards of the form `%N`, where `N` is a non-zero integer. These wildcards will be replaced by the extra argument, `arg1` or `arg2`, before displaying the message. If `%-N` is specified, then the optional argument will be displayed with `st`, `nd`, `rd`, or `th` appended to it. For example:

```
MapleRaiseError2(kv, "the %-1 argument, '%2', is not valid",
                 ToMapleInteger(i), args[i]);
```

This, if invoked, will raise the error, *"the 4th argument, 'foo', is not valid"*, assuming `i=4`, and `args[i]` is set to the Maple name `foo`.[4]

The only option not allowed is `%0` since the function cannot know how many optional arguments are left to parse.

The C API also provides a mechanism for trapping errors raised by Maple.

```
void* MapleTrapError( MKernelVector kv, void *(*proc)
        P(( void *data )), void *data, M_BOOL *errorflag );
```

`MapleTrapError` executes the C function `proc`, passing it the data, `data`. If an error occurs, `errorflag` is set to `TRUE` and `traperror` returns immediately. If no error occurs, the result of `proc(data)` is returned and `errorflag` is `FALSE`.

For example, the following code attempts to execute a Maple procedure. If an error occurs, a separate branch of code is taken.

```
typedef struct {
   MKernelVector k;
   ALGEB fn, arg1, arg2;
} CallbackArgs;

void *tryCallback( void *data )
{
 /* calls the maple procedure 'fn' with arguments 'arg1' */
 /* and 'arg2' */
 return (void*)
     EvalMapleProc( ((CallbackArgs*)data)->k,
       ((CallbackArgs*)data)->fn, 2,
       ((CallbackArgs*)data)->arg1,
       ((CallbackArgs*)data)->arg2);
```

---

[4]For more information, see `?error`.

```
}

void MainProc( MKernelVector k, ALGEB fn )
{
M_BOOL errorflag;
ALGEB result;
CallbackArgs a;

a.k = k;
a.fn = fn;
a.arg1 = ToMapleFloat(k,3.14);
a.arg2 = ToMapleInteger(k,44);

result = (ALGEB)MapleTrapError(k,tryCallback,&a,&errorflag);
if( errorflag ) {
    /* do something */
}
else {
    /* do something else */
}
}
```

Hardware Float Evaluation The following procedures evaluate a Maple Procedure or statement using hardware floats.

```
double MapleEvalhf( MKernelVector kv, ALGEB s );
double EvalhfMapleProc( MKernelVector kv, ALGEB fn,
                        int nargs, double *args );
```

The equivalent Fortran functions are as follows.

```
DOUBLEPRECISION maple_evalhf( kv, s)
DOUBLEPRECISION evalhf_maple_proc( kv, fn, nargs, args )
```

`MapleEvalhf` applies `evalhf` to the given dag `s`. Then `evalhf` will either evaluate an expression using hardware floats to produce a hardware float result, or it will return the handle to an `evalhfable` rtable that can be used as a parameter to `EvalhfMapleProc`.

`EvalhfMapleProc` calls the `evalhf` computation engine directly to evaluate the given procedure `fn` without converting the hardware float parameters to software floats. The procedure `fn` is a valid Maple `PROC` dag, `nargs` is the number of parameters to pass to `fn`, and `args` is the list of parameters. Note that `args` starts at 1; `args[1]` is the first parameter, `args[nargs]` is the last, and `args[0]` is not used.

Setting up a callback may require the use of static local variables in the wrapper module so that the callback will have access to the kernel vector (unless it is passed via a **data** parameter that the callback receives). The following is an example of a wrapper that uses **EvalhfMapleProc** to evaluate a function that takes an **hfarray** and some numeric values.

```
#include "maplec.h"

static MKernelVector kv;              /* kernel vector */
static ALGEB fn;                      /* function handle */
static double hfparams[HF_MAX_PARAMS+1]; /* parameters */

void callback( int N, double X, double Y[] )
{
 hfparams[1] = (double)N;
 hfparams[2] = X;
 /* hfparams[3] is already set */
 EvalhfMapleProc(kv,fn,3,hfparams);
}

/* main wrapper function called from Maple */
ALGEB test( MKernelVector k, ALGEB args )
{
  /* skip arg checking for the sake of brevity */

  kv = k;                             /* save kernel vector */
  /* get the hfarray handle */
  hfparams[3] = MapleEvalhf(DAG(args[1]));
  fn = DAG(args[2]);        /* save the function handle */

  do_stuff(callback);       /* start the routine that */
                            /* calls callback() */
  return( k->toMapleNULL() );
}
```

In Maple, the external routine would be accessed just like any other, except an error will be raised if the given procedure is not able to use **evalhf**.

```
> f := proc(n,x,y) y[1] := n*sin(x); end:
> y := Vector([1,2],datatype=float[8]):
```

```
> p := define_external('test',MAPLE,LIB="libtest.so"):
> p(y,f):
```

General Evaluation   The following procedures evaluate a Maple procedures or statements. These routines are not available in the Fortran API.

```
ALGEB MapleEval( MKernelVector kv, ALGEB s );
ALGEB EvalMapleProc( MKernelVector kv, ALGEB fn, int nargs,
          /* ALGEB arg1, ALGEB arg2, */ ... );
ALGEB EvalMapleStatement( MKernelVector kv, char *statement );
```

EvalMapleProc is a callback to Maple. The first argument **fn** is a Maple PROC or FUNCTION dag, which will be evaluated with the arguments, **arg1 .. argN**. For example, consider the following Maple function.

```
> f := proc(x) x^2; end:
```

If this function is passed to the external function as **args[1]**, then the following code would execute the given function at **x := 3.14**.

```
ALGEB a1, MapleResult;
double CResult;

a1 = ToMapleFloat(kv,3.14);
MapleResult = EvalMapleProc(kv,args[1],1,a1);
CResult = MapleToFloat64(kv,MapleResult);
```

EvalMapleStatement enables you to enter a single parsable Maple statement and have it evaluated. For example, the following call will evaluate the integral x^3 in the range **x = 0..1**.

```
ALGEB MapleResult;
double CResult;

MapleResult = EvalMapleStatement(kv,"int(x^3,x=0..1)");
CResult = mapleToFloat64(kv,MapleResult);
```

MapleEval evaluates a Maple expression. It is especially useful for getting at the value of an assigned name.

Assignment to Maple Variables   The following assignment functions are available only when using the C API.

```
ALGEB MapleAssign( MKernelVector kv, ALGEB lhs, ALGEB rhs );
ALGEB MapleAssignIndexed( MKernelVector kv, ALGEB lhs,
              M_INT dim, M_INT *ind, ALGEB rhs );
```

MapleAssign sets the value dag **rhs** to the name dag **lhs**. This is equivalent to the Maple statement

> lhs := rhs;

MapleAssignIndexed sets the value **rhs** to the indexed variable **lhs**. The second parameter **dim** tells the number of dimensions in the array (or 1 if **lhs** is a table). The third parameter **ind** is a hardware array of indices.

For example, to make the assignment a[1][2][3] = 3.14, the following code could be used (assuming **arg1** points to the array **a**).

```
ALGEB rhs;
M_INT ind[3];

ind[0] = 1;
ind[1] = 2;
ind[3] = 3;

rhs = ToMapleFloat(kv,3.14);
MapleAssignIndexed(kv,arg1,3,ind,rhs);
```

User Information The MapleUserInfo command displays "msg" when infolevel['name'] is set to **level**. This command is only available in the C API.

```
void MapleUserInfo( MKernelVector kv, int level, char
        *name, char *msg );
```

Memory Management The following functions are available only when using the C API.

```
void* MapleAlloc( MKernelVector kv, M_INT nbytes );
void MapleDispose( MKernelVector kv, ALGEB s );
void MapleGcAllow( MKernelVector kv, ALGEB a );
void MapleGcProtect( MKernelVector kv, ALGEB a );
```

MapleAlloc allocates **nbytes** bytes of memory and returns a pointer to it. Garbage collection of this memory is handled by Maple. Note that to allocate this memory, a new **BINARY** dag structure is created, and a pointer to the data part of the dag is returned.

The following code snapshot might be seen in a wrapper that converts a integer reference (a name) in Maple to C.

```
ALGEB arg1;
INTEGER32 *i;

i = MapleAlloc(kv,sizeof(INTEGER32));
*i = MapleToInteger32(kv,arg1);
```

MapleDispose frees the memory allocated to the structure s. This should only be used on data structures created using MapleAlloc, or those that were created externally and are guaranteed not to be pointed to by any other Maple structure. Maple's garbage collector will reclaim any memory not pointed to by any other data structure, so in typical cases it is not necessary to use MapleDispose.

MapleGcProtect prevents the algebraic a from being collected by Maple's garbage collector. The memory pointed to by a will not be freed until Maple exits, or a call to MapleGcAllow is issued. Any dags that must persist between external function invocations should be protected. This includes any external global or static ALGEB variables that will be referred to in a later external call. Failure to protect such a persistent variable will lead to unexpected results if Maple's garbage collector cleans it up between function calls.

MapleGcAllow allows the algebraic structure a to be collected by Maple's garbage collector. Any algebraic structure that is not referenced by another algebraic structure will automatically be destroyed and its memory reclaimed. Algebraics are protected from garbage collection if they are used somewhere (i.e., the value of a global name, part of an array's data, etc). The normal state of an algebraic is to have garbage collection enabled on it.

11.4   System Integrity

The Maple kernel has no control over the quality or reliability of external functions. If an external function performs an illegal operation, such as accessing memory outside of its address space, that operation will most likely result in a segmentation fault. The external routine will crash, taking Maple along with it.

If an external routine accesses memory outside of its address space but inside Maple's address space, the external routine will likely not crash, but Maple will have become corrupted, resulting in inexplicable behavior or a crash later in the Maple session. Similarly, an external routine that deals directly with Maple data structures can corrupt Maple by misusing the data structure manipulation facilities.

Therefore, external calling is a feature to use at your own risk. Whether an external routine is one that you have written, or is one supplied by a third party to which you have declared an interface (via `define_external`), Maple must rely on the integrity of the external routine when it is called.

11.5 Conclusion

This chapter outlined the three methods for using compiled C or Fortran routines in Maple. You can extend the power of Maple by using your own or third party libraries.

Table 11.3 Wrapper Compound Types

Maple Data Descriptor	C Type	Fortran Type
STRUCT(member1 :: descriptor1, ..., memberN :: descriptorN, options)	struct { type1 member1; ...., typeN memberN; }	NA
UNION(member1 :: descriptor1, ..., memberN :: descriptorN, options)	union { type1 member1; ...., typeN memberN; }	NA
PROC(member1 :: descriptor1, ..., memberN :: descriptorN, RETURN :: descriptorR)	typeR (*proc) (type1 member1, ..., typeN, memberN);	NA

Table 11.4 Maple API Libraries for C and Fortran

Operating System	Binary Directory	Load Library Environment Variable	C Maple API Library	Fortran Maple API Library
Microsoft Windows	bin.wXX[1]	NA	maplec.lib (maplec.dll)	maplefortran.lib (maplefortran.dll)
MacOS	NA	NA	maplec.ShLib	maplefortran.ShLib
Solaris	bin.SUN_SPARC_SOLARIS	LD_LIBRARY_PATH	libmaplec.so	libmaplefortran.so
HP-UX	bin.HP_RISC_UNIX	SHLIB_PATH	libmaplec.sl	libmaplefortran.sl
IRIX	bin.SGI_MIPS_UNIX	LD_LIBRARY_PATH	libmaplec.so	libmaplefortran.so
AIX	bin.IBM_RISC_UNIX	LIBPATH	libmaplec.a	libmaplefortran.a
OSF1/True64	bin.DEC_ALPHA_UNIX	LD_LIBRARY_PATH	libmaplec.so	libmaplefortran.so
Linux	bin.IBM_INTEL_LINUX	LD_LIBRARY_PATH	libmaplec.so	libmaplefortran.so

[1] For Microsoft Windows, the binary directory name depends on the platform. It is one of: `bin.w95`, `bin.wnt`, `bin.w2000`, and `bin.wme`.

A Internal Representation and Manipulation

The following is a list of the structures currently implemented in Maple.

AND	*ASSIGN*	*BINARY*	*BREAK*	*CATENATE*
COMPLEX	*CONTROL*	*DCOLON*	*DEBUG*	*EQUATION*
ERROR	*EXPSEQ*	*FLOAT*	*FOR*	*FOREIGN*
FUNCTION	*GARBAGE*	*HASH*	*HASHTAB*	*HFLOAT*
IF	*INEQUAT*	*INTNEG*	*INTPOS*	*LESSEQ*
LESSTHAN	*LEXICAL*	*LIST*	*LOCAL*	*MEMBER*
MODDEF	*MODULE*	*NAME*	*NEXT*	*NOT*
OR	*PARAM*	*POWER*	*PROC*	*PROD*
RANGE	*RATIONAL*	*READ*	*RETURN*	*RTABLE*
SAVE	*SERIES*	*SET*	*STATSEQ*	*STOP*
STRING	*SUM*	*TABLE*	*TABLEREF*	*TRY*
UNEVAL	*USE*	*ZPPOLY*		

Each of these structures, along with the constraints on its length and contents, is described in the following sections.

A.1 Internal Organization

Maple appears to the user as an interactive calculator. The user interface reads input, parses it, and then calls the math engine for each complete statement encountered. Maple will read and evaluate an infinite number of statements until a `quit` statement is evaluated, or the user interface is shut down.

Maple consists of three main components: a kernel, a library, and a user interface. The kernel and library together are known as the math engine .

The kernel is written in the C language and is responsible for low-level operations such as arbitrary precision arithmetic, file I/O, execution of the Maple language, and the performance of simple mathematical operations such as differentiation of polynomials.

Most of Maple's mathematical knowledge is represented in the Maple library, which is written in the Maple language. The library is stored in an archive, and pieces of it are loaded and interpreted by the kernel on demand.

The user interface is the part of Maple that the user sees, and is conceptually separate from the math engine. The same math engine can be used with different user interfaces. Usually, Maple is provided with a graphical user interface (GUI) and a text based interface. The GUI is more useful for interactive use, especially when working with plots or large matrices. The textual interface is practical for batch processing, or solving large problems where you wish to devote all the resources of your machine to computation.

The internal functions in Maple are divided into four distinct groups:

1. **Evaluators**   The evaluators are the main functions responsible for evaluation. There are six types of evaluations: statements, algebraic expressions, boolean expressions, name forming, arbitrary precision floating-point arithmetic, and hardware floating-point arithmetic. The user interface calls only the statement evaluator, but thereafter, there are many interactions between evaluators. For example, the statement,

$$\textbf{if } \texttt{a > 0} \textbf{ then } \texttt{b||i := 3.14/a} \textbf{ end if}$$

is first analyzed by the statement evaluator, which calls the Boolean evaluator to resolve the **if** condition. Once completed (for example, with a **true** result), the statement evaluator is invoked again to do the assignment, for which the name-forming evaluator is invoked with the left-hand side of the assignment, and the expression evaluator with the right-hand side. Since the right hand side involves floating-point values, the expression evaluator calls the arbitrary precision floating-point evaluator.

Normally, the user will not specifically invoke any of the evaluators, but in some circumstances, when a non-default type of evaluation is needed, the user can directly call **evalb** (the Boolean evaluator), evaln (the name-forming evaluator), evalf (the arbitrary precision floating-point evaluator), or evalhf (the hardware floating-point evaluator).

2. **Algebraic Functions** These are commonly called basic functions. Some examples are: taking derivatives (diff), dividing polynomials (divide), finding coefficients of polynomials (coeff), series computation (series), mapping a function (map), expansion of expressions (expand), and finding indeterminates (indets).

3. **Algebraic Service Functions** These functions are algebraic in nature, but serve as subordinates of the functions in the above group. In most cases, these functions cannot be explicitly called by the user. Examples of such functions are the internal arithmetic packages, the basic simplifier, and retrieval of library functions.

4. **Data Structure Manipulation Functions** These are like the algebraic functions, but instead of working on mathematical objects (polynomials, sets, etc.), they work on data structures (expression sequences, sums, products, lists, etc.). Examples of such functions are operand selection (op), operand substitution (subsop), searching (has), and length determination (length),

5. **General Service Functions** Functions in this group are at the lowest hierarchical level. That is, they may be called by any other function in the system. They are general purpose, and not necessarily specific to symbolic or numeric computation. Some examples are: storage allocation and garbage collection, table manipulation, internal I/O, and exception handling.

The flow of control need not remain internal to the Maple kernel. In many cases, where appropriate, a decision is made to call functions written in Maple and residing in the library. For example, many uses of the expand function will be handled in the kernel. However, if an expansion of a sum to a large power is required, then the internal expand will call the external Maple library function `expand/bigpow` to resolve it. Functions such as diff, evalf, series, and type make extensive use of this feature.

Thus, for example, the basic function diff does not know how to differentiate any function. All of that knowledge resides in the Maple library in procedures named `diff/functionName`. This is a fundamental feature of Maple since it permits flexibility (changing the library), personal tailoring (by defining your own handling functions), readability (much of

Maple's knowledge is visible at the user level), and it allows the kernel to remain small by unloading non-essential functions to the library.

A.2   Internal Representations of Data Types

The parser and some internal functions are responsible for building all of the data structures used internally by Maple. All of the internal data structures have the same general format:

$$\boxed{\text{Header}\ \mid\ Data_1\ \mid\ \ldots\ \mid\ Data_n}$$

The header field, stored in one or more machine words, encodes the length of the structure and its type. Additional bits are used to record simplification status, garbage collection information, persistent store status, and various information about specific data structures (e.g., whether or not a **for** loop contains a **break** or **next**).

The length is encoded in 26 bits on 32-bit architectures, resulting in a maximum single object size of $67,108,863$ words ($268,435,452$ bytes, or 256 megabytes). On 64-bit architectures, the length is stored in 32 bits, for a maximum object size of $4,294,967,295$ words ($34,359,738,360$ bytes, or 32 gigabytes).

Every structure is created with its own length, and that length will not change during the existence of the structure. Furthermore, the contents of most data structures are never changed during execution, because it is unpredictable how many other data structures may be referring to it, and relying on it not to change. The normal procedure to modify a structure is to copy it, and then to modify the copy. Structures that are no longer used will eventually be reclaimed by the garbage collector.

The following figures describe each of the 58 structures currently implemented in Maple, along with the constraints on their length and contents. The 6-bit numeric value identifying the type of structure is of little interest, so symbolic names will be used.

Logical AND

$$\boxed{\text{AND}\ \mid\ {}^{\wedge}expr\ \mid\ {}^{\wedge}expr}$$

Maple syntax: expr **and** expr
Length: 3

Assignment Statement

ASSIGN	$^\wedge name$	$^\wedge expr$

Maple syntax: `name := expr`
Length: 3

The name entry should evaluate to an assignable object: a NAME, FUNCTION, or TABLEREF structure.

Binary Object

BINARY	data	...

Maple syntax: none
Length: arbitrary

The BINARY structure can hold any arbitrary data. It is not used directly as a Maple object, but is used as storage for large blocks of data inside other Maple objects (currently only RTABLEs). It is also sometimes used as temporary storage space during various kernel operations.

Break Statement

BREAK

Maple syntax: `break`
Length: 1

Name Concatenation

CATENATE	$^\wedge name$	$^\wedge expr$

Maple syntax: `name || expr`
Length: 3

If the name entry is one of NAME, CATENATE, LOCAL, or PARAM, and if the expr entry evaluates to an integer, NAME, or STRING, then the result is a NAME. If the name entry is a STRING or CATENATE that will resolve to a STRING, and if the expr entry evaluates to an integer, NAME, or STRING, then the result is a STRING. If expr is a RANGE, then the result is to generate an EXPSEQ of NAMEs or STRINGs.

Complex Value

$$\boxed{\text{COMPLEX} \mid {}^{\wedge}re \mid {}^{\wedge}im}$$

$$\boxed{\text{COMPLEX} \mid {}^{\wedge}im}$$

Maple syntax: Complex(re,im) or re + im * I
Length: 2 or 3

The *re* and *im* fields must point to INTPOS, INTNEG, RATIONAL, or FLOAT structures, one of the NAMEs infinity or undefined, or a SUM structure representing -infinity. In the length 3 case, if either *re* or *im* is a FLOAT, the other must be a FLOAT as well.

Communications Control Structure

$$\boxed{\text{CONTROL} \mid {}^{\wedge}integer}$$

Maple syntax: none
Length: 2

This is an internal structure used in kernel to user-interface communication. Such a structure will never reach the user level, or even the mathematical parts of the kernel.

Type Specification or Test

$$\boxed{\text{DCOLON} \mid {}^{\wedge}expr \mid {}^{\wedge}type - expr}$$

Maple syntax: expr :: typeExpr
Length: 3

This structure has three interpretations depending on the context in which it is used. When it appears in the header of a procedure definition, it is a typed parameter declaration. When it appears in the **local** section of a procedure or on the left hand side of an assignment, it is a type assertion. When it appears elsewhere (specifically in a conditional expression), it is a type test.

Debug

$$\boxed{\text{DEBUG} \mid {}^{\wedge}expr \mid {}^{\wedge}expr \mid \dots}$$

Maple syntax: none
Length: 2 or more

This is another internal-only structure. It is used by the kernel when printing error traceback information to transmit that information up the call stack.

Equation or Test for Equality

$$\boxed{\text{EQUATION}} \;\boxed{^{\wedge}expr} \;\boxed{^{\wedge}expr}$$

Maple syntax: `expr = expr`
Length: 3

This structure has two interpretations depending on the context in which it is used. It can be either a test for equality, or a statement of equality (not to be confused with an assignment).

Error Statement

$$\boxed{\text{ERROR}} \;\boxed{^{\wedge}expr}$$

Maple syntax: `error "msg", arg, ... arg`
Length: 2

This represents the Maple **error** statement. The *expr* is either a single expression (if only a message was specified in the **error** statement), or an expression sequence (if arguments were also specified). The actual internal tag used for the **ERROR** structure is **MERROR**, to prevent collision with a macro defined by some C compilers.

Expression Sequence

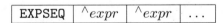

Maple syntax: `expr, expr, ...`
Length: 1 or more

Expression sequences are available to the user as a data structure, and are also used to pass arguments to procedures. Effectively, procedures take a single argument that is an expression sequence. An expression sequence may be of length 1 (i.e., an empty sequence), which is represented by the Maple symbol **NULL**, or in some contexts (such as parameters to a function call) as nothing at all.

Floating-Point Number

FLOAT	$^\wedge integer1$	$^\wedge integer2$	$^\wedge attrib - expr$

Maple syntax: `1.2`, `1.2e3`, `Float(12,34)`, `Float(infinity)`
Length: 2 (or 3 with attributes)

A floating-point number is interpreted as $integer1 * 10^{integer2}$. A floating-point number may optionally have attributes, in which case the length of the structure will be 3, and the third word will point to a Maple expression. This suggests that several floating-point numbers with the same value but different attributes can exist simultaneously.

The *integer2* field can optionally be one of the names **undefined** or **infinity**, in which case the **FLOAT** structure represents an undefined floating-point value (not-a-number, or NaN, in IEEE terminology), or a floating-point infinity. When *integer2* is **undefined**, *integer1* can take on different small integer values, allowing the existence of different NaNs. When *integer2* is **infinity**, *integer1* must be 1 or -1.

For/While Loop Statement

FOR	$^\wedge name$	$^\wedge from-$ expr	$^\wedge by-$ expr	$^\wedge to-$ expr	$^\wedge cond-$ expr	$^\wedge stat-$ seq

FOR	$^\wedge name$	$^\wedge in - expr$	$^\wedge cond - expr$	$^\wedge stat - seq$

Maple syntax:

```
for name from fromExpr by byExpr to toExpr
        while condExpr do
                statSeq
        od
```

Maple syntax:

```
for name in inExpr
        while condExpr do
                statSeq
        od
```

Length: 7 or 5

The *name* follows the same rules as in **ASSIGN**, except that it can also be the empty expression sequence (**NULL**), indicating that there is no controlling variable for the loop.

The *from-expr*, *by-expr*, *to-expr*, and *cond-expr* entries are general expressions. All are optional in the syntax of `for` loops and can thus be filled in with default values (1, 1, `NULL`, and `true` respectively) by the parser.

The *stat-seq* entry can be a single Maple statement or expression, a `STATSEQ` structure, or `NULL` indicating an empty loop body. An additional bit in the `FOR` structure's header is used to indicate whether the *stat-seq* contains any `break` or `next` statements.

Foreign Data

FOREIGN	...

Maple syntax: none
Length: 1 or more

This is similar to the `BINARY` structure, except that it is for use by components of Maple outside the kernel, such as the user interface. A `FOREIGN` structure is exempt from garbage collection, and it is up to the external component to free it when it is done with it.

Function Call

FUNCTION	$^\wedge name$	$^\wedge expr - seq$	$^\wedge attrib - expr$

Maple syntax: `name( exprSeq )`
Length: 2 (or 3 with attributes)

This structure represents a function invocation (as distinct from a procedure definition that is represented by the `PROC` structure). The *name* entry follows the same rules as in `ASSIGN`, or it may be a `PROC` structure. The *expr-seq* entry gives the list of actual parameters, and is always an expression sequence (possibly of length 1, indicating no parameters).

Garbage

GARBAGE	...

Maple syntax: none
Length: 1 or more

This structure is used internally by Maple's garbage collector as a temporary object type for free space.

Hardware Float

HFLOAT	*floatword*

HFLOAT	*floatword*	*floatword*

Maple syntax: none

Length: 2 on 64-bit architectures, 3 on 32-bit architectures

This structure is used to hold a hardware floating-point value. The one or two words (always 8 bytes) after the header hold the actual double-precision floating-point value. HFLOAT objects are currently not available directly to the user, but they are used internally to more efficiently transfer hardware floating-point values between RTABLEs of such values, and Maple's I/O facilities (for example, the printf and scanf families of functions).

If Statement

IF	$^\wedge cond-$ *expr*	$^\wedge stat-$ *seq*	$^\wedge cond-$ *expr*	$^\wedge stat-$ *seq*	... ...	... ...	$^\wedge stat-$ *seq*

Maple syntax:

```
      if condExpr then
            statSeq
      elif condExpr then
            statSeq
      ...
      else statSeq
      end if
```

Length: 3 or more

This structure represents the if ... then ... elif ... else ... end if statement in Maple. If the length is even, the last entry is the body of an else clause. The remaining entries are interpreted in pairs, where each pair is a condition of the if or elif clause, followed by the associated body.

Not Equal or Test for Inequality

INEQUAT	$^\wedge expr$	$^\wedge expr$

Maple syntax: `expr < expr`
Length: 3

This structure has two interpretations, depending on the context in which it is used. It can be either a test for inequality or a statement of inequality (not to be confused with an assignment).

Negative Integer

INTNEG	*integer*	*integer*	...

Maple syntax: -123
Length: 2 or more

This data structure represents a negative integer of arbitrary precision. See the comments below about the representation of integers.

Positive Integer

INTPOS	*integer*	*integer*	...

Maple syntax: 123
Length: 2 or more

This data structure represents a positive integer of arbitrary precision. Integers are represented internally in a base dependent on the host machine. On 32-bit architectures, this base is $10,000$. On 64-bit architectures, the base is $1,000,000,000$. The base is chosen such that the square of the base is still representable in a machine integer. Each *integer* field represents either 4 or 9 digits. The least significant digits are represented first. For example, on a 32-bit platform, the integer $123,456,789,638,747$ is represented as:

INTPOS	8747	8963	4567	123

Small integers are not represented by data structures at all. Instead of a pointer to an INTPOS or INTNEG structure, a small integer is represented by the bits of what would normally be a pointer. The least significant bit is 1, which makes the value an invalid pointer (since pointers must be word-aligned). Such an integer is called an *immediate integer*.

The range of integers representable in this way is $-1,073,741,823$ to $1,073,741,823$ (i.e., about $+/-10^9$) on 32-bit architectures, and $-4,611,686,018,427,387,903$ to $4,611,686,018,427,387,903$ (i.e., about

$+/-4*10^{18}$) on 64-bit architectures. (These numbers may not seem "small", but consider that Maple's maximum integer magnitude is about $10^{268,435,448}$ on 32-bit architectures and $10^{38,654,705,646}$ on 64-bit architectures.)

Less Than or Equal

LESSEQ	$^\wedge expr1$	$^\wedge expr2$

Maple syntax: `expr1 <= expr2, expr2 = expr1`
Length: 3

This structure has two interpretations, depending on the context. It can be interpreted as a relation (i.e., an inequation), or as a comparison (e.g., in the condition of an `if` statement, or the argument to a call to `evalb`). Maple does not have a greater-than-or-equal structure. Any input of that form is turned around into a LESSEQ structure.

Less Than

LESSTHAN	$^\wedge expr$	$^\wedge expr$

Maple syntax: `expr1 < expr2, expr2 expr1`
Length: 3

Like the LESSEQ structure above, this structure has two interpretations, depending on the context. It can be interpreted as a relation (i.e., an inequation), or as a comparison (e.g., in the condition of an `if` statement, or the argument to a call to `evalb`).

Maple does not have a greater-than structure. Any input of that form is turned around into a LESS structure.

Lexically Scoped Variable within an Expression

LEXICAL	*integer*

Maple syntax: `name`
Length: 2

This represents an identifier within an expression in a procedure that is not local to that procedure, but is instead declared in a surrounding procedure scope. The *integer* field identifies which lexically scoped variable of the current procedure is being referred to. The *integer*, multiplied by 2, is an index into the *lexical-seq* structure referred to by the PROC DAG of the procedure. Specifically, |integer| * 2 - 1 is the index to the NAME of the identifier, and |integer| * 2 is the index to a description (LOCAL, PARAM, or LEXICAL) relative to the surrounding scope. The value of *integer* can be positive or negative. If positive, the original identifier was a local variable of a surrounding procedure; if negative, it was a parameter of a surrounding procedure.

List

LIST	$^\wedge expr - seq$	$^\wedge attrib - expr$

Maple syntax: [expr, expr, ...]
Length: 2 (or 3 with attributes)

The elements of the *expr-seq* are the elements of the list. The list can optionally have attributes.

Local Variable within an Expression

LOCAL	*integer*

Maple syntax: name
Length: 2

This indicates a local variable when it appears within an expression in a procedure or module. The *integer* is an index into the procedure's *local-seq*. At procedure execution time, it is also an index into the internal data structure holding the active locals on the procedure activation stack, and holds private copies of the NAMEs of the local variables (private copies in the sense that these NAMEs are not the same as the global NAMEs of the same name).

Member

MEMBER	$^\wedge module$	$^\wedge name$

Maple syntax: module :- name
Length: 3

This structure represents a module member access in an expression. MEMBER objects typically do not persist when a statement is simplified. Instead, they are replaced by the actual member that they refer to (an instance of a NAME).

Module Definition

MODDEF	param-seq	local-seq	option-seq	export-seq	stat-seq	desc-seq	...

global-seq	lexical-seq	mod-name

Maple syntax:

> **module** modName ( )
> > **description** descSeq;
> > **local** localSeq;
> > **export** exportSeq;
> > **global** globalSeq;
> > **option** optionSeq;
> > statSeq
> **end module**

Length: 10

The *param-seq* points to an expression sequence describing the formal parameters of the module. Currently, Maple doesn't support parameterized modules, so this field always points to the sequence containing just an instance of the name `thismodule`.

The *local-seq* points to an expression sequence listing the explicitly and implicitly declared local variables. Each entry is a `NAME`. The explicitly declared variables appear first. Within the module, locals are referred to by `LOCAL` structures, the local variable number being the index into the *local-seq*.

The *export-seq* points to an expression sequence listing the exported module members. Each entry is a `NAME`. Within the module, exports are referred to by `LOCAL` structures, the local variable number being the number of elements in the *local-seq*, plus the index into the *export-seq*.

The *option-seq* points to an expression sequence of options to the module (for modules, options are the same thing as attributes). Each entry is a `NAME` or `EQUATION` specifying an option. Typical options are `load= ...` and `unload= ...`

The *stat-seq* field points to a single statement or a statement sequence (`STATSEQ`). If the module has an empty body, this is a pointer to `NULL` instead.

The *desc-seq* field points to an expression sequence of NAMEs or STRINGs. These are meant to provide a brief description of what the module does, and are displayed even when `interface(verboseproc)` is less than 2.

The *global-seq* field points to a list of the explicitly declared global variables in the module (those that appeared in the `global` statement). This information is never used at run-time, but it is used when simplifying nested modules and procedures to determine the binding of lexically scoped identifiers (for example, an identifier on the left-hand side of an assignment in a nested procedure can be global if it appears in the `global` statement of a surrounding context). This information is also used at printing time, so that the `global` statement will contain exactly the global identifiers that were declared in the first place.

The *lexical-seq* field points to an expression sequence of links to identifiers in the surrounding scope, if any. The sequence consists of pairs of pointers. The first pointer of each pair is to the globally unique NAME of the identifier; this is needed at simplification and printing time. The second pointer is a pointer to a LOCAL, PARAM, or LEXICAL structure which is understood to be relative to the surrounding scope. When a module definition is evaluated, the *lexical-seq* is updated by replacing each of the second pointers with a pointer to the actual object represented. The name pointers are not touched, so that the actual identifier names are still available. The *lexical-seq* for a module contains entries for any surrounding-scope identifiers used by that module or by any procedures or modules contained within it.

The *mod-name* field points to the optional name of the module. If a module name was specified when the module was declared, the name will appear there. If no module name was specified, this field will contain NULL.

Module Instance

MODULE	$^\wedge export - seq$	$^\wedge mod - def$	$^\wedge local - seq$

Maple syntax: none
Length: 4

Executing a module definition (MODDEF) results in a module instance. Each local or exported member of the module is instantiated and belongs to that instance of the module. The *export-seq* field points to an expression sequence of names of the instantiated exports (as opposed to the global names, as stored in the module definition). The *mod-def* field points back to the original module definition. The *local-seq* field points to an expression sequence of names of the instantiated local variables of the module.

Identifier

NAME	$^\wedge$*assigned–expr*	$^\wedge$*attrib–expr*	*characters*	*characters*	. . .

Maple syntax: name
Length: 4 or more

The *assigned-expr* field points to the assigned value of the name. If the name has no assigned value, this field is a null pointer (not a pointer to NULL). The next field points to an expression sequence of attributes of the name. If there are no attributes, this field points to the empty expression sequence (NULL). The remaining fields contain the characters making up the name, stored 4 or 8 per machine word (for 32-bit and 64-bit architectures respectively). The last character is followed by a zero-byte. Any unused bytes in the last machine word are also zero. The maximum length of a name is 268,435,447 characters on 32-bit architectures and 34,359,738,351 characters on 64-bit architectures.

Next Statement

NEXT

Maple syntax: next
Length: 1

Logical NOT

NOT	$^\wedge$*expr*

Maple syntax: not expr
Length: 2

Logical OR

OR	$^\wedge$*expr*	$^\wedge$*expr*

Maple syntax: expr or expr
Length: 3

Procedure Parameter within an Expression

$$\boxed{\text{PARAM} \mid \textit{integer}}$$

Maple syntax: **name**
Length: 2

This indicates a parameter when it appears within a procedure. The *integer* is an index into the procedure's *param-seq*. Several special PARAM structures exist:

$$\boxed{\text{PARAM} \mid 0}$$

This represents the Maple symbol **nargs**, the number of arguments passed when the procedure was called.

$$\boxed{\text{PARAM} \mid -1}$$

This represents the Maple symbol **args**, the entire sequence of arguments passed when the procedure was called.

$$\boxed{\text{PARAM} \mid -2}$$

This represents the Maple symbol **procname**, referring to the currently active procedure.

At procedure execution time, the *integer* (if positive) is used as an index into the internal data structure **Actvparams** which is part of the Maple procedure activation stack, and holds pointers to the values (which are also Maple structures, of course) of the actual parameters passed to the procedure.

Power

$$\boxed{\text{POWER} \mid {}^{\wedge}\textit{expr} \mid {}^{\wedge}\textit{expr}}$$

Maple syntax: $expr^{\wedge}expr$
Length: 3

This structure is used to represent a power when the exponent is not an integer, rational, or floating-point value. When the exponent is numeric, the POWER structure is converted to a length 3 PROD structure.

Procedure Definition

PROC	$^\wedge param-$ seq	$^\wedge local-$ seq	$^\wedge option-$ seq	$^\wedge rem-$ table	$^\wedge stat-$ seq	$^\wedge desc-$ seq	...

$^\wedge global-$ seq	$^\wedge lexical-$ seq

Maple syntax:

> **proc** (paramSeq)
>   **description** descSeq;
>   **local** localSeq;
>   **export** exportSeq;
>   **global** globalSeq;
>   **option** optionSeq;
>   statSeq
> **end proc**

Length: 9

The *param-seq* points to an expression sequence describing the formal parameters of the procedure. Each entry is either a NAME or a DCOLON (which in turn contains a NAME and an expression specifying a type). Within the procedure, parameters are referred to by PARAM structures, the parameter number being the index into the *param-seq*.

The *local-seq* points to an expression sequence listing the explicitly and implicitly declared local variables. Each entry is a NAME. The explicitly declared variables appear first. Within the procedure, locals are referred to by LOCAL structures, the local variable number being the index into the *local-seq*.

The *option-seq* field points to an expression sequence of options to the procedure (for procedures, options are the same thing as attributes). Each entry is a NAME or EQUATION specifying an option. Typical options are **remember**, **operator**, and `Copyright ... `.

The *rem-table* field points to a hash table containing remembered values of the procedure. Entries in the table are indexed by the procedure arguments, and contain the resulting value. If there is no remember table, this field contains a pointer to NULL, the empty expression sequence.

The *stat-seq* field points to a single statement or a statement sequence (STATSEQ). If the procedure has an empty body, this is a pointer to NULL instead. For each procedure that is built into the kernel, there is a wrapper PROC that has the option **builtin** in its *option-seq*, and a single Maple integer pointed to by its *stat-seq*. The integer gives the built-in function number.

The *desc-seq* field points to an expression sequence of NAMEs or STRINGs. These are meant to provide a brief description of what the procedure does, and are displayed even when `interface(verboseproc)` is less than 2.

The *global-seq* field points to a list of the explicitly declared global variables in the procedure (those that appeared in the global statement). This information is never used at run-time, but it is used when simplifying nested procedures to determine the binding of lexically scoped identifiers. For example, an identifier on the left-hand side of an assignment in a nested procedure can be global if it appears in the global statement of a surrounding procedure. This information is also used at procedure printing time, so that the `global` statement will contain exactly the same global identifiers that were declared in the first place.

The *lexical-seq* field points to an expression sequence of links to identifiers in the surrounding scope, if any. The sequence consists of pairs of pointers. The first pointer of each pair is to the globally unique NAME of the identifier; this is needed at simplification and printing time. The second pointer is a pointer to a LOCAL, PARAM, or LEXICAL structure which is understood to be relative to the surrounding scope. When a procedure is evaluated (not necessarily called), the *lexical-seq* is updated by replacing each of the second pointers with a pointer to the actual object represented. The name pointers are not touched, so that the actual identifier names are still available. The *lexical-seq* for a procedure contains entries for any surrounding-scope identifiers used by that procedure or by any procedures contained within it.

Product, Quotient, Power

PROD	$^\wedge expr$	$^\wedge expon$	$^\wedge expr$	$^\wedge expon$	...	...

Maple syntax: `expr ^ expon * expr ^ expon ...`
Length: $2n + 1$

This structure is interpreted as pairs of factors and their numeric exponents. Rational or integer expressions to an integer power are expanded. If there is a rational constant in the product, this constant will be moved to the first entry by the simplifier. A simple power, such as `a^2`, is represented as a PROD structure. More complex powers involving non-numeric exponents are represented as POWER structures.

Range

RANGE	$^\wedge expr$	$^\wedge expr$

Maple syntax: expr .. expr
Length: 3

Rational

RATIONAL	$^\wedge integer$	$^\wedge pos - integer$

Maple syntax: 1/2
Length: 3

This structure is one of the basic numeric objects in Maple. Note that this is not a division operation, but only a representation for rational numbers. Both fields must be integers (INTPOS, INTNEG or an immediate integer) and the second must be positive.

Read Statement

READ	$^\wedge expr$

Maple syntax: read expr
Length: 2

The Maple read statement. The expression must evaluate to either a string or symbol (STRING or NAME structure), and specifies the name of the file to read.

Return Statement

RETURN	$^\wedge expr - seq$

Maple syntax: return "msg", arg, ... arg
Length: 2

The Maple return statement. The expression sequence is evaluated, giving the value(s) to return.

Rectangular Table

RTABLE	$^\wedge data$	$^\wedge maple-$ $type$	$^\wedge ind-$ fn	$^\wedge attrib$	$flags$	$num-$ $elems$	...

L_1	U_1	$\ldots$	$\ldots$	L_N	U_N	P_1	P_2

Maple syntax: `rtable(...)`

Length: `2n + p`, `2n + p`, or `2n + p`, where **n** is the number of dimensions (0 to 63), and **p** is 0, 1, or 2, depending on the number of P_i parameters.

The *data* field points to either a block of memory (for dense and NAG-sparse RTABLEs), or to a HASHTAB structure (for Maple-sparse RTABLEs). The data block is either an object of type BINARY, or memory allocated directly from the operating system's storage manager when the block would be too large to be allocated as a Maple data structure. If the data block is a BINARY object, the *data* pointer points to the first data word, not to the object header.

The *maple-type* field points to a Maple structure specifying the data type of the elements of an RTABLE of Maple objects. If the RTABLE contains hardware objects, the *maple-type* field points to the Maple NAME **anything**.

The *ind-fn* pointer points to either an empty expression sequence (NULL), or an expression sequence containing at least one indexing function and a pointer to a copy of the RTABLE structure. The copy of the RTABLE is identical to the original, except that its *ind-fn* field refers to one less indexing function (either NULL, or another expression sequence containing at least one indexing function and a pointer to another copy of the RTABLE with one less indexing function again).

The *attrib* pointer points to an expression sequence of zero or more arbitrary attributes, which can be set by the **setattribute** function, and queried by **attributes**.

The *flags* field is a bit field containing the following sub-fields:

- data type - 4 bits - indicates one of several hardware datatypes or that a Maple data type (as specified by *maple-type*) is being used.

- sub type - 2 bits - indicates if the RTABLE is an Array, Matrix, or Vector.

- storage - 4 bits - describes the storage layout (e.g. sparse, upper triangular, etc.)

- order - 1 bit - indicates C or Fortran ordering of RTABLE elements.

- read only - 1 bit - indicates the RTABLE is to be read-only once created.

- foreign - 1 bit - indicates that the space pointed to by the *data* field does not belong to Maple, so Maple should not garbage collect it.

- number of dimensions - 6 bits - the number of dimensions of the RTABLE, from 0 to 63.

The *num-elems* field indicates the total number of elements of storage allocated for the data. For a Maple-sparse RTABLE, *num-elems* is not used. For a NAG-sparse RTABLE, *num-elems* specifies the number of elements currently allocated, some of which might not be in use.

The remaining fields specify the upper and lower bounds of each dimension, and are stored directly as signed machine integers. The limits on bounds are $-2,147,483,648$ to $2,147,483,647$ for 32-bit architectures and $-9,223,372,036,854,775,808$ to $9,223,372,036,854,775,807$ for 64-bit architectures. The total number of elements cannot exceed the upper limit numbers either.

Save Statement

SAVE	$^\wedge expr - seq$

Maple syntax: `save expr, expr, ...`
Length: 2

The Maple `save` statement. The expression sequence gives a list of names of objects to save, and either a file name or repository name in which to save them. The file or repository name can be specified as a NAME or STRING.

Series

SERIES	$^\wedge expr$	$^\wedge expr$	*integer*	$^\wedge expr$	*integer*	...	...

Maple syntax: none
Length: $2n + 2$

This is the internal representation of a series in Maple. There is no input syntax for a series; one can only arise from a computation. The first expression has the general form x-a, where x denotes the variable of the series used to do that expansion, and a denotes the point of expansion. The remaining entries are interpreted as pairs of coefficients and exponents. The exponents are integers, *not* pointers to integers or immediate integers. The exponents appear in increasing order. A coefficient O(1) (a function call to the function O, with parameter 1) is interpreted specially by Maple as an order term.

Set

$$\boxed{\text{SET} \mid {}^{\wedge}expr - seq \mid {}^{\wedge}attrib - expr}$$

Maple syntax: $\{expr, expr, ...\}$
Length: 2 (or 3 with attributes)

The entries in the set's expression sequence are sorted in order of increasing memory address. This is an arbitrary but consistent order, necessary for efficiently working with sets.

Statement Sequence

$$\boxed{\text{STATSEQ} \mid {}^{\wedge}stat \mid {}^{\wedge}stat \mid ...}$$

Maple syntax: `stat; stat; ...`
Length: 3 or more

This structure represents a sequence of two or more statements, and can be used wherever a single statement (e.g., ASSIGN, IF, FOR) can appear. A statement sequence, containing only a single statement, is replaced by that statement. A statement sequence containing no statements is replaced by the empty expression sequence (NULL). Nested STATSEQ structures are flattened. All of the above transformations are made by the simplifier.

Stop Maple

$$\boxed{\text{STOP}}$$

Maple syntax: `quit`, `done`, or `stop`
Length: 1

String

$$\boxed{\text{STRING} \mid reserved \mid {}^{\wedge}attrib - expr \mid characters \mid characters \mid ...}$$

Maple syntax: `"This is a string"`
Length: 4 or more

A Maple string is structurally similar to a NAME, except that it has no *assigned-value* field. The *attrib-expr* field points to an expression sequence of attributes of the string. If there are no attributes, this field points to the empty expression sequence (NULL). The remaining fields contain the characters making up the string, stored 4 or 8 per machine word (for 32-bit and 64-bit architectures respectively). The last character is followed by a zero-byte. Any unused bytes in the last machine word are also zero.

The maximum length of a string is $268,435,447$ characters on 32-bit architectures and $34,359,738,351$ characters on 64-bit architectures.

Sum, Difference

SUM	$^\wedge expr$	$^\wedge factor$	$^\wedge expr$	$^\wedge factor$	...	...

Maple syntax: expr * factor + expr * factor ...
Length: $2n + 1$

This structure is interpreted as pairs of expressions and their numeric factors. Rational or integer expressions with an integer factor are expanded and the factor replaced with 1. If there is a rational constant in the sum, this constant will be moved to the first entry by the simplifier. Simple products, such as a*2, are represented as SUMs. More complex products involving non-numeric factors are represented as PROD structures.

Table

TABLE	$^\wedge index - func$	$^\wedge array - bounds$	$^\wedge hash - tab$

Maple syntax: N/A
Length: 4

This is a general table type, as created by the table and array functions in Maple. The *index-func* will point to either a NAME or a PROC. For general tables, the *array-bounds* field points to the empty expression sequence (NULL). For arrays (not to be confused with Arrays, which are implemented as RTABLEs), the *array-bounds* field refers to an expression sequence of RANGEs of integers. The *hash-tab* field points to a HASHTAB structure containing the elements.

Table Reference

TABLEREF	$^\wedge name$	$^\wedge expr - seq$	$^\wedge attrib - expr$

Maple syntax: name [expr]
Length: 3 (or 4 with attributes)

This data structure represents a table reference, or indexed name. The *name* entry follows the same rules as for ASSIGN, or it may be a TABLE structure. (The parser will not generate a TABLEREF with a TABLE structure for the *name* entry, but this can arise internally.) The expression sequence contains the indices.

Try Statement

TRY	$^\wedge try-$ $stat-$ seq	$^\wedge catch-$ $-str$	$^\wedge catch-$ $stat-$ seq	...	...	$^\wedge final-$ $stat-$ seq

Maple syntax:

> **try** tryStat
> > **catch** "catchStr": catchStat
> > ...
> > **finally** finalStat;
> **end try**

Length: 3 or more

This structure represents a try statement, and can have an arbitrary length, depending on how many catch blocks there are within it, and whether or not it has a finally block. The *catch-strs* point to the catch string of the corresponding catch block. If no catch string was specified, the *catch-str* points to NULL. Empty *catch-stat-seqs* are also represented by pointers to NULL, as is an empty (but present) finally block.

The actual internal tag used for the TRY structure is MTRY, to prevent collision with a macro defined by some C exception handling libraries.

Unevaluated Expression

UNEVAL	$^\wedge expr$

Maple syntax: ' expr '
Length: 2

Use Statement

USE	$^\wedge bindings$	$^\wedge statseq$

Maple Syntax:

> **use** bindings in
>   statseq
> **end use**

Length: 3

The *bindings* component points to an expression sequence of equations whose left hand sides are symbols, and the *statseq* component points to a sequence of statements that form the body of the **use** statement. The right hand sides of the binding equations can be arbitrary expressions.

The **use** statement introduces a new binding contour and binds the names that appear on the left hand side of the equations in *bindings*. For convenience, on input, a module 'm' can appear among the *bindings*, and is treated as if it were the sequence e1 = m:-e1, e2 = m:-e2, ..., where the ei are the exports of 'm'. Within the sequence *statseq* of statements, the symbols appearing on the left hand side of the equations in *bindings* are bound to the corresponding right hand sides. The previous bindings of those symbols are restored upon exit from the **use** statement. Bindings are resolved during automatic simplification.

Polynomials with Integer Coefficients modulo n

ZPPOLY	$^\wedge indet$	mod	$coef0$	$coef1$	...

ZPPOLY	$^\wedge indet\_seq$	mod	$^\wedge zppoly0$	$^\wedge zppoly1$	...

Maple Syntax: modp1(ConvertIn(expr, indet), n);
Maple Syntax: modp2(ConvertIn(expr, indet1, indet2), n);

Length: **degree(zppoly)** $+2$ (for the zero polynomial)
Length: **degree(zppoly)** $+3$ (otherwise)

This is the internal representation of univariate and bivariate polynomials modulo some integer. The **modp1()** and **modp2()** front ends provide a suite of functions to work on this data structure operating in the domain of polynomials in one or two variables with integer coefficients modulo n, written $Zn[x]$ or $Zn[x, y]$, respectively. *indet_seq* is an expression sequence of the indeterminates of the polynomial (x), or (x,y). *mod* is the integer modulus of the integer domain. In a univariate polynomial the coefficients are stored in the following order.

    (coef0*indet^0 + coef1*indet^1 + ... + coefi*indet^i) mod n

A bivariate polynomial contains pointers to univariate ZPPOLY structures representing the coefficients of the first indeterminate.

(coef0(indet2)*indet1^0 + coef1(indet2)*indet1^1 + ...) mod n

where each `coefi` is a univariate polynomial in `indet1` mod n.

All coefficients are stored including zero coefficients. The leading coefficient is always non-zero.

A.3   The Use of Hashing in Maple

An important factor in achieving Maple's overall performance is the use of hash table based algorithms for critical functions. Tables are used in both simplification and evaluation, as well as for less critical functions. For simplification, Maple keeps a single copy of each expression, or subexpression, during a session. This is done by keeping all objects in a table. In procedures, the `remember` option specifies that the result of each computation of the procedure is to be stored in a "remember table" associated with the procedure. Finally, tables are available to the user as one of Maple's data types.

All of the table searching is done by hashing. The algorithm used is direct chaining, except that the chains are dynamic vectors instead of the typical linked lists. The two data structures used to implement hash tables are `HASHTAB` and `HASH`.

Hash Table

HASHTAB	$^\wedge hash-chain$	$^\wedge hash-chain$	...

Maple syntax: none
Length: $2^n + 1$

This is an internal data structure with no Maple syntax equivalent. It is used in the representation of tables within Maple. Each entry points to a hash chain (a `HASH` structure), or is a null pointer if no entry has been created in that bucket yet. The size of a `HASHTAB` structure depends on the type of table and the platform, but is always a power of 2 plus one.

Hash Chain

HASH	key	$^\wedge expr$	key	$^\wedge expr$	...	...

Maple syntax: none

Length: $2n + 1$

Each table element is stored as a pair of consecutive entries in a hash bucket vector. The first entry of this pair is the hash key, and the second is a pointer to a stored value. In some cases (e.g., procedure remember tables, user defined tables), the key is also a pointer. In other cases, the key is a hashed value (e.g., the simplification table, the symbol table). The key cannot have the value zero (or the null pointer) since this is used to indicate the bottom of the bucket.

The Simplification Table

By far, the most important table maintained by the Maple kernel is the *simplification table*. All simplified expressions and subexpressions are stored in the simplification table. The main purpose of this table is to ensure that simplified expressions have a unique instance in memory. Every expression, which is entered into Maple or generated internally, is checked against the simplification table and, if found, the new expression is discarded and the old one is used. This task is done by the simplifier which recursively simplifies (applies all the basic simplification rules) and checks against the table. Garbage collection deletes the entries in the simplification table that cannot be reached from a global name or from a "live" local variable.

The task of checking for equivalent expressions within thousands of subexpressions would not be feasible if it were not done with the aid of hashing. Every expression is entered in the simplification table using its signature as a key. The signature of an expression is a hashing function itself, with one very important attribute: signatures of trivially equivalent expressions are equal. For example, the signatures of the expressions $a + b + c$ and $c + a + b$ are identical; the signatures of $a * b$ and $b * a$ are also identical. If two expressions' signatures disagree then the expressions cannot be equal at the basic level of simplification.

Searching for an expression in the simplification table is done by:

- simplifying recursively all of its components,

- applying the basic simplification rules, and

- computing its signature and searching for this signature in the table.

If the signature is found then a full comparison is performed (taking into account that additions and multiplications are commutative, etc.) to verify that it is the same expression. If the expression is found, the one in the table is used and the searched one is discarded. A full comparison of expressions has to be performed only when there is a "collision" of signatures.

Since simplified expressions are guaranteed to have a unique occurrence, it is possible to test for equality of simplified expressions using a single pointer comparison. Unique representation of identical expressions is a crucial ingredient to the efficiency of tables, hence also the **remember** option. Also, since the relative order of objects is preserved during garbage collection, this means that sequences of objects can be ordered by machine address. For example, sets in Maple are represented this way. The set operations union, intersection, etc. can be done in linear time by merging sorted sequences. Sorting by machine address is also available to the user with the **sort** command.

The Name Table

The simplest use of hashing in the Maple kernel is the *name table*. This is a symbol table for all global names. Each key is computed from the name's character string and the entry is a pointer to the data structure for the name. The name table is used to locate global names formed by the lexical scanner or by name concatenation. It is also used by functions that perform operations on all global names. These operations include:

1. marking for garbage collection,

2. the saving of a Maple session environment in a file, and

3. the Maple functions **anames** and **unames** which return all assigned and unassigned global names, respectively.

Remember Tables

A remember table is a hash table in which the argument(s) to a procedure call are stored as the table index, and the result of the procedure call is stored as the table value. Because a simplified expression in Maple has a unique instance in memory, the address of the arguments can be used as the hash function. Hence, searching a remember table is very fast.

There are eight kernel functions which use remember tables: **evalf**, **series**, **divide**, **normal**, **expand**, **diff**, **readlib**, and **frontend**. The internal handling of the latter five is straightforward. There are some exceptions with the first three, namely:

- **evalf** and **series** need to store some additional environment information ('**Digits**' for evalf and '**Order**' for series). Consequently, the entries for these are extended with the precision information. If a result is requested with the same or less precision than what is stored in the table, it is retrieved anyway and "rounded". If a result is produced with more precision than what is stored, it is replaced in the table.

- **evalf** only remembers function calls (this includes named constants); it does not remember the results of arithmetic operations.

- If the division succeeded and the divisor was a non-trivial polynomial, the divide function stores the quotient in its remember table. Otherwise nothing is stored in the remember table.

If **option remember** is specified together with **option system**, at garbage collection time the remember table entries which refer to expressions no longer in use elsewhere in the system are removed. This provides a relatively efficient use of remembering that will not waste storage for expressions that have disappeared from the expression space.

Maple Language Arrays and Tables

Arrays and tables are provided as data types in the Maple language via the **array** and **table** functions. An array is a table for which the component indices must be integers lying within specified bounds. Arrays and tables are implemented using Maple's internal hash tables. Because of this, sparse arrays are equally as efficient as dense arrays. A table object consists of

1. index bounds (for arrays only),

2. a hash table of components, and

3. an indexing function.

The components of a table T are accessed using a subscript syntax (e.g., `T[a,b*cos(x)]`). Since a simplified expression is guaranteed to have a unique instance in memory, the address of the simplified index is used as the hash key for a component. If no component exists for a given index, then the indexed expression is returned.

The semantics of indexing into a table are described by its indexing function. Aside from the default, general indexing, some indexing functions are provided by the Maple kernel. Other indexing functions are loaded from the library or are supplied by the user.

Maple Language Rectangular Tables

Rectangular tables (as implemented by the `RTABLE` structure), can use a variety of storage formats. One format, Maple-sparse, is identical to that used in tables and arrays, namely a hash table. There is another sparse format, NAG-sparse, which uses one vector for each dimension to record indices, and a third vector to record the values of the entries. The majority of `RTABLE` storage formats are dense, the simplest being the rectangular. Other dense formats include upper-triangular and band, where storage is allocated only for the upper triangle or a band of elements respectively. To the user, rectangular tables manifest themselves as objects of type `Array`, `Matrix`, `Vector[row]`, and `Vector[column]`. Note that an `Array` is not the same thing as an `array`.

A.4   Portability

The Maple kernel and the textual user interface are not tied to any one operating system or hardware architecture. The Maple kernel was designed to be portable to any system which supports a C compiler, a flat address space, and a 32-bit or 64-bit word size. Some platforms on which Maple is supported are (refer to the installation instructions for currently supported OS versions):

Hardware	Operating System
Intel Pentium Based PC	*Microsoft Windows*
	Linux
Apple Power Macintosh	*Mac OS*
Sun SPARC	*Sun OS/Solaris*
Silicon Graphics Iris	*IRIX*
Hewlett Packard PA − RISC	*HP − UX*
IBM RS/6000	*AIX*
DEC Alpha	*Digital UNIX/Compaq True 64*

The majority of the source code comprising the kernel is the same across all platforms. Extensive use of macros and conditional compilation take care of platform dependencies, such as word size, byte ordering, storage alignment requirements, differences in hardware floating point support, and sometimes, C compiler bugs.

The Maple library is interpreted by the Maple kernel. Therefore, other than issues such as maximum object size, it is completely independent of the underlying architecture.

Maple's graphical user interface is implemented in C and $C++$, and makes use of a platform independent user interface class library to achieve portability. There are only very few pieces of platform-specific source code.

Index